INTRODUCTION
TO
EDUCATIONAL ADMINISTRATION

ALLYN AND BACON, INC.

BOSTON • LONDON • SYDNEY

Introduction
To
Educational Administration

fourth edition

Roald F. Campbell
The Ohio State University

Edwin M. Bridges
The University of Chicago

John E. Corbally, Jr.
University of Illinois

Raphael O. Nystrand
The Ohio State University

John A. Ramseyer

© COPYRIGHT 1971 BY ALLYN AND BACON, INC.

© COPYRIGHT 1958, 1962, 1966 BY ALLYN AND BACON, INC.

Library of Congress Catalog Number: 74–144035

PRINTED IN THE UNITED STATES OF AMERICA

ISBN: 0-205-03153-6

Seventh printing . . . February, 1976

The Fourth Edition of this book is dedicated to JOHN A. RAMSEYER. His contribution and dedication to this work, cut short by his death, has been an inspiration to all of us.

Contents

Preface

For some time, it seemed doubtful that there would be a fourth edition of this book, since our colleague, John A. Ramseyer, died on August 20, 1968. Fortunately, Edwin M. Bridges and Raphael O. Nystrand joined the writing team. Thus, this edition represents the work of five authors. Sections written by Mr. Ramseyer for the third edition have been retained with some revision.

This book has two major purposes. Primarily, we have prepared it to help orient the prospective educational administrator. Such a person should get a view of the field, as well as a view of himself as a possible worker in that field. With this information, we believe that he will be in a better position to decide whether or not such a profession is for him. Should he decide in the affirmative, the book can help him plan his initial preparation for the job and for his continued professional development.

A second purpose of this book is to help teachers understand the role of administrative personnel in the schools and participate more effectively in administration. For those teachers who may be interested in becoming administrators, it will suggest ways of getting into the field.

Certain sections may also be useful to many practicing administrators, since the academic study of some administrators has included little material on the administrative process, administrative behavior, social systems, or policy formation. The book may also be helpful to school board members and interested lay citizens who wish to know more about educational administration. By acquainting such people with the purposes and problems of the field, the book will give them a better understanding of administration in their own schools and school districts. Finally, the book may provide useful information

for those administrators and educators who are working to improve
programs for the selection and training of administrative personnel
for the schools.

We have taken certain positions in this book. We believe that the
field of educational administration is now too comprehensive to be
surveyed adequately; thus a first book should be an *introduction to,*
not a *survey of,* the field. We are convinced that educational administration covers a wide range of positions, of which the school superintendency, although very important, is but one. In order to provide
an adequate concept of educational administration, we deal with the
purpose of educational administration and then present four ways of
viewing the field. In addition to considering the internal operation of
schools, we examine the external forces in society that impinge upon
school operation. Finally, we take the position that competent administrative leadership is crucial to the perpetuation of the democratic way of life in America.

The most complete treatment in the book deals with the actual job
of administration: the tasks that comprise it, the steps in the administrative process, administrative behavior, and administration of the
school as a social system. We then deal with the administrator as an
individual in terms of the demands made on him by the job and the
qualifications necessary to meet these demands. We also suggest
methods of determining one's potential for the job and ways of preparing oneself for an administrative position. Finally, we discuss the
field of educational administration as a whole—its opportunities and
challenges as a profession—and emphasize the role of administrative
leadership in a democratic society.

The book is built upon the conviction that one develops an understanding of educational administration as one examines concepts and
relates them to actual experiences. This posits a partnership between
the campus and the field. Each chapter of the book should be seen as
part of the whole rather than as a separate entity. Thus the reader
will obtain maximum meaning from the book if he sees the content of
these chapters as aspects of a developmental process of concept
building.

How may this book be used? As we see it, the book can be useful
as a text in the beginning course in educational administration. In
many institutions such a course is available to students early in the
graduate program. Actually, the material in the book has been used
with many groups of such graduate students. The questions, concerns,
and reactions of these people have helped shape the book into its
present form. We are grateful for their help.

Changes in schools and society over the past few years suggest that a new edition of this book is desirable. Developments within society itself have been responsible for much of this change. Social issues related to war, race, pollution, and other problems demand attention. Concerns in the larger society inevitably affect the program and operation of the schools. The critical nature of relationships between teachers, both as individuals and as organized groups, and boards of education and administrators has come into sharp focus. While the federal government has a role to play in education, that role has not as yet become a very stable one. All of these and other changes since the appearance of the third edition have been considered as much as is possible in an introductory treatment of educational administration.

We have tried here to give frank expression to our convictions about the book and our aspirations for it. We want it to make a contribution to the growing professionalism of an important calling. We know that the extent to which this proves to be the case now rests in the hands of those who use this book.

R.F.C.
E.M.B.
J.E.C., Jr.
R.O.N.

1

A Preliminary Look
At Administration

What is the function of administration in the modern school? Does it have a counterpart in business, government, the military, and other established organizations? How does educational administration differ from, and in what ways is it similar to, administration in these other organizations? What are the best modern theories and expert opinions with regard to the art or science of administration? What contributions do administrators make to help organizations become more efficient and effective? What should the role and responsibility of the educational administrator be in working with civic and other leaders to solve the many complex problems that confront communities and people in today's rapidly changing, high-pressure, pluralistic society? What are the duties of the principal, the supervisor, and the superintendent of schools? If I were to be employed in one of these positions, what would be expected of me? Could I live up to those expectations? These are a few of the questions asked by those who are anticipating educational administration as a career.

Teachers, too, are concerned about the roles of administrators in the schools in which they work. The beginning teacher, for example, wants to know what the principal of the school "will be like." How much will he help? Will he understand that I may have certain difficulties in getting started? May I go to him with my questions? How much administrative support can I expect if parents and others are somewhat critical of my beginning efforts? Experienced teachers may have similar questions, but they know that teachers have a part in decision-making. They have worked with parent-teacher organizations, and some of them have participated actively with lay groups in educational planning. These teachers are asking for a clarification of their roles, and the roles to be played by others, in the important decisions that are to be made about school matters.

This book is designed to help both the prospective administrator and the teacher answer the basic questions: Why is administration necessary? What is it? How does it affect me? What role do I play in the administration of schools today? The student's problem is to answer these questions and others that come to mind as facts, issues, and propositions are presented in this and following chapters.

Chapter 1 describes some interesting incidents that have occurred in certain schools and school districts.[1] Similar happenings could certainly be cited by the readers. It is suggested that these incidents be read largely for the purpose of identifying the problems that require solution. The reader should attempt to play the role of an administrator of the school or district in which the incident took place and think about the means he would use to solve these problems. The reader should understand that there is probably no "right" solution to the problems presented in the incidents. Even experts in administration and the social sciences have conflicting opinions about how some of these matters should be handled.

SOME INCIDENTS

JIMMY IS PROMOTED

Jimmy was in the eighth grade. He had been a good citizen of the Midland schools since the time he enrolled as a pupil in the fourth grade. Although slow to learn, he was co-operative with his teachers and liked by his classmates. When the boys chose sides to play ball, Jimmy was always among the first selected. His friends admitted that he was "a little dumb, but a nice guy."

When Jimmy transferred to the Midland schools in the fourth grade, his report cards showed that he had received failing marks in reading and arithmetic several times. Because these failures persisted, his teachers thought it best that he repeat the fourth grade. In the two ensuing years his progress was fair; it appeared that he had found about the right level of learning for him. After all, he had an I.Q. of only about 90 and, with considerable help from his teachers, he had managed to pass the fifth and sixth grades. In the seventh grade he failed arithmetic and history. Again he was required to repeat the grade. Now in the spring of the year he was one of six eighth-graders whose promotion was a subject of deep concern among the faculty members.

A faculty meeting was called by Superintendent Jones. The teach-

[1] Names and places cited in these cases are fictitious.

ers of both the elementary and secondary divisions of the school were present, since the business of this meeting seemed to concern both groups. The first item on the agenda, "Promotions," had been discussed many times in the lunch room, the halls, and any place where a few teachers chanced to meet.

"This year, as has been true in years past, we have a number of pupils who, the elementary school teachers think, should be admitted to high school even though their work in the elementary grades has not been too satisfactory. According to board policy these teachers have the authority to promote them, but knowing that some of you would be displeased, I thought that we should discuss the matter together," was Superintendent Jones's opening remark.

Mr. DeMuth, the high school mathematics teacher, asked, "Who are the kids being passed this time?"

Mrs. Wirth, the head teacher for the elementary school, read off the list of names.

"Well, take Jimmy Keith, for example. We all like him and all of that, but from what I've heard of him he just can't do high school work," said DeMuth.

A number of teachers joined in the discussion. Most of the elementary school teachers took the position that these pupils were working almost to the limit of their individual capacities. High school teachers, on the other hand, reflected the feeling that grade school teachers "were not tough enough."

DeMuth, the most outspoken member of the high school staff, said, "I don't suppose that there is anything we can do about it now, but I'm warning you, if he comes into my algebra class, he's a dead duck."

After a few minutes of this kind of talk, Superintendent Jones broke into the conversation with, "Now that Jim has been pointed out as our example, I guess we would have to admit that he might not get as much out of high school as most of our students. Let's keep in mind, though, that he is only one of six pupils that we are talking about."

One of the high school teachers expressed his point of view this way: "It isn't Jim. I like him. But you know what people are saying. 'High school graduation doesn't mean anything any more.' How can we make it mean something if we keep graduating these morons all the time? The elementary teachers don't have to take the rap for this, but we do. I'm against it."

Miss King, a teacher in the elementary school, said, "Isn't the policy on matters of promotion clear? I thought we settled all of this two years ago. Now, here we go again."

Sensing that this was the time to channel the meeting into a more objective course, Superintendent Jones agreed that a policy had been adopted by the board of education two years ago. He then read from the Teacher's Handbook this statement of board policy on promotions:

1. When the work of any child has been below the minimum level of achievement commonly accepted for promotion, the case may, upon recommendation of the grade teacher, be referred to the appropriate faculty to be acted upon in terms of their judgment as to what is best for the child and the school.
2. No child shall be retained in any grade more than one year, or in either the elementary or secondary school more than two years beyond the normal number of years for pupils to complete this work.

"Although I was not superintendent at the time this policy was adopted," he continued, "I would interpret this last statement to mean that when a child has been retained in any grade for one year or in either division of the school for the two years, the faculty has no choice in the matter. Promotion is automat. . . ."

"That's just it. You said it!" shouted DeMuth. "Promotion is automatic. What do the teachers have to say about it? The kids know that. Do you think that makes them respect us any more? They know they'll pass. What should they care. . . ."

Superintendent Jones interrupted to say, "I wasn't finished with my statement, Mr. DeMuth. The policy statement does give the faculty the right to decide at least four times in a pupil's career—twice in the elementary grades and twice in high school—whether or not to promote him.

"I'm not saying that I agree with the policy. I'm merely stating that according to the policies we inherited—those statements in your handbook—the elementary teachers have acted within their rights as nearly as I can determine. The high school teachers have a similar privilege—or responsibility—for the pupils in that division."

Another high school teacher, seemingly resigned to accepting the decision in part, commented, "O.K., we get Jim! But I thought we were going to consider. . . ."

What do you suppose the last teacher had in mind? Is there some alternative to the present policy that might be considered? Whose responsibility is it to mention alternatives? What should the superintendent do now? Given the action of the teachers of the elementary school, the dissatisfaction of the high school teachers, and the board policy, what course of action would you recommend?

NEGOTIATIONS IN BIGTOWN

The Bigtown Board of Education and the teachers' union began negotiations for a new contract. In each of the preceding two years, imminent strikes had been avoided at the eleventh hour when the Bigtown mayor mediated settlements. In each instance, the board of education had granted salary increases that would require an increase in revenues if they were to be met. The first year, a voted increase in the local property tax and action of the state legislature had provided the necessary funds. However, the second year, funds the board had believed it would receive when it had negotiated the contract were not forthcoming. While teachers had received their promised raises, the board had been forced to make severe program cutbacks and had begun the school year anticipating a large deficit. Remembering this experience, several board members resolved not to grant raises in the current negotiations unless the necessary funds were in hand.

The president of the Bigtown Teacher's Union announced that program improvements rather than pay raises would have top priority in the forthcoming negotiations. He specifically mentioned class size, teacher aides, preparation periods for elementary teachers, and in-service training for inner-city teachers as items of importance to the union. He added that some effort would also be made toward raising salaries and called upon the state to make more money available for schools.

On the following day, the chairman of the school board negotiating team announced that the system simply had no money available to meet any of the union proposals. Shortly thereafter the superintendent made public the proposed budget and indicated that the schools might be forced to dismiss six thousand teachers in September unless added revenues were received. The union president responded that the state must help and that the teachers' union and the board should work together to find more money for Bigtown's schools.

By mid-December, union spokesmen were listing salary demands ahead of, rather than after, the educational matters that they had given top billing earlier. The president explained this as response to the fact that police and firemen had just been given raises that would make them better paid than teachers. However, it was also clear that the union leadership was confronted with two differing factions—one that believed higher pay should have top priority and another that stressed educational improvements. By this time, one reporter noted that "neither side seems optimistic about averting a strike" and that some board members were saying they would not seek mediation help from the mayor again.

Also at this time, the union house of representatives resolved that a contract offer would have to be ready for their consideration by January 6. Another source of temporal pressure was the fact that the school budget had to be presented to the City Council in mid-January.

As the month wore on, it became apparent that talks were dead-locked. The union president made statements indicating that strike preparations were underway and speculated about the effectiveness of selective strikes "where teachers don't want to work anymore because they say conditions are intolerable." The chairman of the board negotiating committee responded that such talk was premature and that no strike would be effective because the board lacked money. The union leader replied that the purpose of the strike would not be to get money but to "simply call attention to the plight of the Bigtown school system."

On January 6, a proposed contract, which did not include pro-visions for salary increases, was placed before the union. Although the president recommended acceptance of this contract, claiming it was the best that could be achieved under the circumstances, the union (with less than 15 percent of its members voting) rejected it and authorized a strike. This rejection reportedly came because of feelings that the proposed educational improvements were not "sub-stantial enough" and because some members demanded a cost-of-living salary increase. The union leadership made some effort to obtain a second vote on the proposal through a membership referen-dum but abandoned this when it became evident that the membership would demand a salary increase.

The union then announced that it would present a new contract proposal and called upon the board to re-enter negotiations. The union president referred to the earlier membership vote as a "man-date" to include a salary increase in any proposal he might make. The board of education, however, held fast to its position that no more money was available and that it had already done the best it could. At this point, the mayor stated at a press conference that although he had no plans to mediate the disagreement, his office was "always available to try and resolve questions that confront the community. But unless the people involved want to come in," he said, "I've never been one to force them."

Negotiations resumed on January 10. The union and school board leadership agreed to extend the prior contract for six months without a salary increase and to add a few minor educational improvements to those offered earlier. The union president and his executive board endorsed this proposal "not because it is adequate, or satisfactory, but only because it contains as much as we can get at this time without an immediate strike." The union membership sustained this agreement by a margin of nearly two to one and authorized the president to negotiate on salaries after July 1, when the amount of aid forthcoming from the state legislature would be known.

Now the issue shifted to the state legislature, where both the board and the union had made known their intention to seek more funds. Both sought an increase in the basic state aid formula from $400 to $600 per pupil. The governor proposed a figure of $500 and a group of legislators urged $550, which officials said would provide sufficient funds to meet the Bigtown budget deficit but not to increase teacher salaries as well. Approximately two thousand Bigtown teachers journeyed to the state capital in late April to lobby for the $600 figure. The governor responded by urging them to marshal legislative support for the state income tax he was proposing, and many legislators referred them back to the governor.

According to one news account, "The teachers came back to Bigtown, bitter, frustrated, and inclined to strike." At an early May meeting, the union voted to strike later that month, with the president claiming that the board had reneged on some contract features and had not worked hard enough for the increase in state aid. The strike date was subsequently set for May 22.

Reaction was quickly forthcoming. The board negotiating-committee chairman again said the board had done all it could. The superintendent of schools warned that a strike would "immediately lose support for the schools" and urged that the legislature decide on funding levels soon. The governor referred to the proposed strike as "the most ridiculous action that any group of people has ever taken at any time" and warned that "if . . . [the teachers] walk out, they're going to stay out because I'm not going to give them any help." The union president said this statement was "unfortunate" and referred to the governor as "a very frustrated and excited man."

In a last-ditch effort to avoid a strike, the mayor arranged for both sides to meet in his office on May 21. Nonetheless, preparations for the strike proceeded because, the union president stated, it would not be possible to hold the membership vote needed to call off the strike until the next day at the earliest. The superintendent announced that if the strike were held, the schools would be open to teachers but closed to students. The daylong negotiations did not produce a settlement, and the first teacher's strike in Bigtown history began the next day.

Approximately 85 percent of the teachers participated in this walkout, which lasted two days. Significant opposition to the strike was apparent among a coalition of black teachers who announced that their action had two goals—"to protest the board of education's closing of the schools and its failure to educate black children" and to protest against the union, which "has not addressed itself to the needs of black schools." Negotiations continued under auspices of the mayor. The strike was settled over the weekend when the board of education agreed by a one-vote majority to a contract that met most of the union demands. As in the previous two years, full implementation of the contact would require acquisition of funds (presumably from the state legislature) that the board did not yet have. The union membership voted overwhelmingly in favor of the new contract but stipulated that unless it was fully implemented in September another strike vote would be taken.[2]

This case points up some important questions about the scope of negotiations and about participants in them. What is negotiable? Who decides this? Who should participate in negotiations? What effect does disagreement within the teachers' union or the board of education have upon the negotiating process? Officials of the city and state government were involved in this particular case. What are the implications of such involvement for school administrators?

MOTIVATING STUDENTS IN NORTHTON: A STUDY IN FRUSTRATION

Northton is the capital of an important industrial and agricultural state in the Midwest. The population of the Northton metropolitan area is slightly over 1,000,000 persons. This population is largely middle-class, native-born, and politically conservative. About 4 percent of the core city population of 600,000 persons has recently

[2] This account is based on a paper prepared by Francis Landwermeyer.

immigrated to Northton from the Appalachian area, and about 14 percent is black.

The Northton City School System has a total enrollment of just over 100,000 pupils. There are 9 senior high schools (grades 10–12), 24 junior high schools (grades 7–9), and 132 elementary schools (grades K–6) in the system.

Much of the southeastern section of Northton is comprised of low-value slum or slum clearance dwellings. A large percentage of the city's black, chronically unemployed, and "on-relief" citizens live in this section. Most of the teen-age children living within this part of the city are sent to the four junior high schools and the one high school (Tower Park) which are found in the eight-square-mile area.

A recent survey of the Tower Park enrollment area revealed that most of the homes are either in low-cost public housing projects or in somewhat higher cost (in terms of rent) crowded, semislum apartments. Less than 10 percent of the residents of the area own their own homes.

Over 12 percent of the family units in this area have no male head of family present in the home. A large percentage of the female heads of family are unwed mothers, others have been deserted by their husbands, or the husbands are in prison. Of the family units with male heads of family present, 27 percent of the men are unemployed. In 11 percent of these families, *both* parents are unemployed. Over 40 percent of all family units are dependent upon some form of welfare or unemployment payments. A rough breakdown of the welfare picture is as follows: 24 percent of all family units receive Aid to Dependent Children, 9 percent receive Poor Relief, 7 percent are drawing Unemployment Compensation, and less than 1 percent receive Aid for the Blind and Aged.

No matter what instruments are used for evaluation, there is little question that Tower Park High School and its feeder junior high schools qualify as depressed or underprivileged area schools.

The crux of this case involves the frustrations experienced by Mrs. Beck, a teacher of commercial subjects at Tower Park, as she attempted to help some of her students help themselves to overcome some of the disadvantages and deprivations under which they lived.

Mrs. Beck was in her eighth year as a teacher at Tower Park during the months when the incidents described took place. She invariably had a warm relationship with her students; she was understanding, firm, and fair. Her students recognized that Mrs. Beck was a teacher who respected them, was interested in them, and wanted to help them.

As a result of her experience over the years at Tower Park, Mrs. Beck was convinced that one of her pupils' most important needs was that of "gaining a feeling that they have a chance in life," a feeling that "they are not destined to spend their lives living on the relief rolls as most of their parents have." In short, despite her occasional feelings of hopelessness about the school, she believed that the students needed personal accomplishments and success experiences in order to demonstrate to themselves that there was some opportunity to move out of the environment in which they lived.

Mrs. Beck spent a great deal of her off-duty time trying to find ways to provide these experiences for her pupils. She had learned long ago that success in class work and activities was not enough for these children—this kind of success motivated them for a very short time. The culture from which her students came recognized more tangible gains, such as success in athletics or making money. She could not, of course, do much to help her students become star athletes, so she attempted to provide for achievement through teaching wage-earning skills.

For the past five years Mrs. Beck had been helping students in her advanced typing, bookkeeping, and general office practice courses obtain part-time employment in business offices throughout the city. She had been able to develop many contacts with employers in Northton, most of whom were sympathetic to the problems her students faced. Students recommended by Mrs. Beck were, in almost every case, found to be dependable, honest, and, for their age and experience levels, competent. Thus the relationship between Mrs. Beck, the employers, and the student-workers gradually but steadily improved over the years. Most of the students enrolled at Tower Park were aware of the opportunity to "prove that they could do something" and to "earn some money" which Mrs. Beck tried to provide. Consequently, her classes were always full to capacity, and motivation was high. Mrs. Beck felt that, although her efforts fell far short of solving all the problems of all her students, her work was a promising step in the right direction. During the previous four years, increasing numbers of students had been placed annually in part-time positions. The program seemed to be developing very well; student morale and motivation, while still not high enough, were definitely improving. But far from being content with her efforts, Mrs. Beck's constant concern was to find more jobs—and better jobs, if possible—for more of her students.

On Thursday, November 12, Mrs. Beck was asked to stop in at the principal's office after school. The principal, Mr. Gordon, was aware of and appreciated Mrs. Beck's efforts to help her students. He had offered her constant support and encouragement and had tried to see that she received all the teaching materials and supplies that she requisitioned. Many times Mr. Gordon had helped Mrs. Beck find positions for her students, and he felt a personal concern for the progress of her program. After her last class, Mrs. Beck stepped into Mr. Gordon's office. After they exchanged greetings and some small talk, the following conversation took place:

GORDON: Mrs. Beck, I feel badly about having to tell you, but it looks like we may be in trouble with your job program.

MRS. BECK: Oh, Mr. Gordon, what do you mean! The children are all old enough to work, they all have work permits, their parents approve, and I've had no complaints from any of the employers. Do you mean that the people downtown at the central office don't think that I should be getting jobs for the students?

GORDON: No, that's not it at all. I wish it were that simple. You see, this afternoon I had a call from Mr. Bartholemew of the County Welfare Department. He told me that he had received a complaint from an 'interested citizen' with regard to 'chiseling' by relief recipients. The 'chiselers' involve the families of the children in your program, or so he said.

MRS. BECK: But Mr. Gordon, I don't understand! What have welfare and 'chiseling' to do with the work of my students? What are they trying to do?

GORDON: Well, Bartholemew said that he probably shouldn't have called at all, but he wanted to let us know that because of this complaint he would be *forced* to make an investigation of the incomes of some of the relief recipients who have children in Tower Park. I don't quite understand it myself, but it seems that there is a standard allotment set by the state and county for the monthly amount to which a family receiving Aid to Dependent Children or other welfare funds is entitled. Bartholemew said that if *any* family receiving welfare funds has any income at all from any member, this income *must* be reported to the Welfare Department and it *must be deducted* from the amount of aid to which the family is entitled.

MRS. BECK: Do you mean to tell me that the tiny bit of income that these children make must be reported? The *kids* aren't on relief!

GORDON: That's exactly what I said to him. But his answer was that the law is clear—the income must be reported, and no matter how little it is, or who makes it, it has to be deducted from the sum the family usually gets from the Welfare Department. Bartholemew said that it was a state law and that if anyone pushed the matter further the parties involved could lose their welfare benefits entirely. They could even be prosecuted for fraud.

MRS. BECK: But it's not fair! Isn't there anything we can do? How can I face the children when they find out about this? How can I explain to them why they can't get anything for their work? Think of all the work in school that they've done so that they could get these jobs, and that doesn't include all the work I've done to get this thing going. I don't care if it is the law, how can we be expected to help these children become self-respecting, productive members of the community if this is what the community is going to do to them as soon as they begin to try to help themselves? Actually, it's forcing them *not* to try. What sort of person would do such a thing? Who could have complained?

GORDON: I know how you must feel, I feel the same way. I think it's one of the most unjust situations I've heard of in a long time. Mr. Bartholemew couldn't tell me who lodged the complaint, but from the way he talked I got the impression that it was someone from a family in our area; someone who is envious because his child does not have a job. He didn't say that the kids would have to quit their jobs, only that they would have to declare their earnings so that they could be deducted. I pointed out to him that this was rather a poor way to help these kids—the families' total income would be the same whether the kids worked or not. They would be, in effect, working just for the sake of working. These children aren't stupid. They can see that they will be just as well off to stay home and watch T.V. I'm sure their parents won't be able to see any reason for them to continue working for nothing when they could be home to help around the house. Bartholemew said that he recognized the problem that we face, but that his hands were tied—he must see to it that the law is followed. He pointed out that any students from families not receiving welfare aid would not be affected by the law. I felt like saying, 'Thanks a lot,' but he was only doing what he had to do, and I don't think he likes doing this at all.

MRS. BECK: Well, about one-third of the children we have on jobs will not be affected, but the ones that will be hurt are the very ones who need the jobs and the self-respect that goes with them most. Isn't there anything we can do? I mean, after all, if we can't get any more help and cooperation than this, then what's the use?

GORDON: Well, I've tried to think of what we might do. We can try to talk Bartholemew into looking the other way on this. I'm willing to go with you to speak with him. We know that what we're trying to do for these children is right, but we have to consider what might happen if looking the other way backfires and these families lose all their welfare aid because of us. If this happens the parents are going to blame us, the schools, and their children for the loss of the little money they get—and rightly so, since we have been warned of how the law reads. I don't know if we have the right to risk the parents' much-needed income in spite of the need we see for continuing our program.

MRS. BECK: No, you're right, we can't risk other people's money or take the chance of being the agency that involves them in legal difficulties. But isn't there anything we can do . . . what am I going to say to the children? I've been trying for years to instill in them the belief that effort will pay off for rich man, poor man, white man, or colored man. Now this happens and makes a lie of all that I've said as far as they're concerned.

GORDON: The only other thing that I can think of is to take this problem to the superintendent and to the board of education. Perhaps we can get support from the public if our case is presented to them. The Urban League and the NAACP should be willing to help us. The newspapers may help, but you know how the city is 'down' on relief recipients. The newspapers are continuously crying about 'chiselers' and reliefers who drive in cabs or Cadillacs to pick up their money—some of those reporters should spend a week with us just seeing how these people really live. The problem of explaining to the students is going to be a tough one. I'll try to help you. We're going to have to do some fancy talking to keep this from destroying their morale completely.

In this case, an interpretation of parents' legal rights seems to thwart the efforts of the teacher and principal, who are attempting to help their disadvantaged students. What might have been done to resolve problems resulting from such restrictions? Should the principal take the problem to the superintendent? What might the superintendent do? How far should schools be expected to go in solving this kind of problem? What other community agencies should schools be working with on problems of this kind? How would you explain what had happened to the students involved in this situation? What are some other factors that tend to limit the schools' efforts to help such children?

A NEW COMMUNITY SCHOOL

Port City has been known for many years as a wealthy, provincial, and conservative town. The minority population has been small, and few people have been unemployed or on welfare rolls. The ideology of self-help and independence has been very strong in Port City. It has been paralleled by public skepticism of welfare programs, federal assistance, and centralized planning in any form. Moreover, there has been strong sentiment to keep taxes low and public programs at relatively limited levels. As with many cities, however, recent years have been a time of change in Port City.

During this time a number of national firms established plants in Port City that brought new residents in search of jobs. Many of these newcomers were black, and among them were some relatively outspoken leaders. Other new black leaders came to work for the Port City anti-poverty program and local social agencies. They helped direct attention to school issues in the Port City black community.

Black concern for school issues in Port City during the current year focused upon North Junior High School. This school was located in an old section of the city that had recently become predominantly lower-class and lower-middle-class black in its composition. Approximately 50 per cent of the student body was black. One-fifth of the students at North qualified for assistance under Title I of the Elementary and Secondary Education Act. Average academic achievement at the school was low, and many students posed disciplinary problems.

A number of neighborhood residents were dissatisfied with conditions at the school. Several parents began to meet informally to discuss the situation. They were especially concerned with improving communications between neighborhood residents and the school, and with reports of questionable disciplinary actions by some faculty members.

While these parents were meeting, another local group released a report that showed that the average student achievement level at North was the lowest in the city and far below national norms. These figures and the concerns of the parent group became rallying points which led to formation of the Citizens for Good Schools (CGS) Committee. A series of meetings was held at the North Side Community Center to discuss ways of resolving the problems that had been identified. Leaders of this group included the center director, administrators of other neighborhood agencies, a former teacher at North, and several parents.

The CGS Committee focused its effort on North Junior High School, but it also gave attention to other schools which had a large number of black students in attendance. In addition to holding meetings in the neighborhood, CGS leaders met on several occasions with administrators of neighborhood schools and with central office school officials. They attended and made presentations at board of education meetings and used meetings of the Northside Community Organization and the Northside Community Center as forums for solidifying neighborhood support. Issues raised by the committee at these sessions and before the board of education were reported by the news media and thus introduced to the city at large.

As these meetings continued amid much publicity but little in the way of official response, demands and grievances began to escalate. Some persons even began to suggest that community residents themselves take over North Junior High School. A list of demands regarding the program at North and other schools was gradually formulated out of these discussions.

The committee called for the reduction of pupil-teacher ratios, emphasis on teacher knowledge about the heritage and living conditions of black people, inclusion in the curriculum of minority group contributions to the American way of life, more black teachers, more black counselors, more black administrators, a more effective and efficient system for educating minority group children, more male teachers in elementary schools, priority to minority area schools in assigning quality teachers, evaluation of the administration at a number of schools, a special class in discipline for students and parents, student counseling before suspensions or expulsions, establishment of a community relations department, and the establishment of a laboratory school at North with its own controlling board.

The group took their list of demands directly to the board of education and superintendent of schools at a special meeting. The superintendent told the committee at this meeting that implementation of their demands would require policy revision, which was the responsibility of the board of education.

The CGS Committee then made it clear to the superintendent and board that if action was not begun on their demands within twenty-four hours, they would boycott North Junior High School. When steps were not taken within that time, the boycott began. This carefully planned action included picketing of the school, which received the attention of newspapers and television. Events at North became a topic of citywide discussions; citizens disagreed about the appropriateness of both the goals and tactics of the CGS committee.

Although students returned to school after one day, demonstrations continued until the regularly scheduled board of education meeting the following week. At this very crowded session, members of the committee marched to the front of the room and repeated their demands in forceful terms and dramatic fashion. By the time of this session, however, the committee had compromised their demands on one important point. At an informal meeting with the superintendent and two of his aides, they agreed to substitute the demand of a local advisory board for their original demand of a local controlling board. In effect they were told that the board would not allow a controlling board but probably would agree to an advisory board.

The response of the board of education at this meeting was to appoint a fifteen-member committee to investigate the feasibility of committee demands and to make suggestions for necessary program changes. Membership on this new committee included representatives of the CGS Committee, the local education association, and leaders of other agencies and institutions in the city. Faculty members from a nearby college and university served as staff and helped assess the needs of the North community and suggest possible approaches to local problems.

The work of the committee resulted in a proposal to convert the North Junior High School into a "laboratory school" where the emphasis would be placed upon developing innovative programs. Later, the term "community school" was substituted for laboratory school in order to allay citizen's fears that their children were to be used as guinea pigs. In fact, the term community school was a more accurate definition for the program proposed at North. Three of the most significant features called for an extended school day with adult as well as youth programs, the establishment of a neighborhood advisory board, and the introduction of an ombudsman to the school community.

The board of education accepted the committee report at its next meeting and subsequently agreed to implement those recommendations that it could finance and to submit the remainder in a proposal for support from the federal government. Among the specific steps taken by the board of education were the appointment of an advisory board, authorization of funds to support an ombudsman and two assistants until federal money was made available, the removal of special education students from North, a reduction in class size, and announcement that any teacher who did not wish to teach at North could transfer to another building. The principal at North accepted an offer to become principal at another school in the district. Several members of the CGS Committee were appointed to the North Community School Advisory Board with the result that the CGS Committee was formally disbanded. Community residents, school officials, and board of education members agreed that the North Community School would not have been started without the efforts of the CGS Committee.

This case raises questions about community participation in school policy development. Is this an example of "community control"? Why or why not? Why do you believe the board of education responded as it did to the CGS? What does this case suggest about the need for political skills and understandings on the part of administrators? What responsibility does an administrator have to work with groups such as CGS as well as with his staff, superiors, and the board of education?

SHUTDOWN AT LINCOLN JUNIOR HIGH SCHOOL

Lincoln Junior High School was attended by nearly nine hundred students who resided in an urban ghetto. Almost all of these students were black, as was approximately half the faculty. Less than ten years earlier, the neighborhood was predominantly white and lower middle class. Now it was nearly all black and had been declared a "target area" in the "war on poverty." Almost one-third of neighborhood families had an annual income of less than $3000. Fifteen hundred of the neighborhood's five thousand housing units had been declared substandard, and there were six hundred welfare cases in the area. The Wilson County Community Action Agency maintained a neighborhood center to serve residents of the area.

Early in October Marty Phillips, a youth worker from the neighborhood Community Action office, appeared at the school to speak with the principal, Mr. Owens. Phillips expressed concern about youngsters in the community who were potential dropouts and stated his desire to work with a small number of these students. The principal agreed to have the school guidance counselor identify some of these youngsters and to provide the youth worker access to records of the students he would be working with. He also made a room near the school office available to him for talking with these students on the assumption that he would arrange to interview them out of school. No official agreements were made regarding the limits of Mr. Phillips' activities or the duration of his stay.

The principal later commented that he had assumed that Mr. Phillips would need only a few days to collect his information and that he then would leave. However, Phillips remained in the school for approximately three weeks, during which time the original group of twelve students with whom he worked expanded considerably. At this point, Owens, with the backing of his central officer superiors, asked Phillips to bring his work at school to a close and leave the building. The principal explained that Phillips had begun to counsel students in school and maintained that he had no authority to allow persons other than certificated employees of the board of education to do this. Some persons also took exception to some of Phillips' methods. For example, criticism was offered of an incident in which Phillips and some students sat and talked in an office which was dark except for a candle burning on a table.

Phillips maintained, on the other hand, that he was simply using different situations to establish communication with the youngsters and that he did not consider this to be counseling. At least some of the students he worked with believed him to be effective. They said that Phillips knew how to talk with them and that they would rather meet with him than "sit up in some dumb class." He also received support from some adults in the community. The local black newspaper referred to him as a "counselor who cracked the wall of hopelessness for some students" and quoted one parent as saying, "He used the candle in a dark room as a way to get through to kids; he used innovative methods and helped raise one boy's grade from F to B in a short time. The issue of Marty brought to light the fact that a different type of counseling is necessary."

Phillips was asked to finish up his work on a Wednesday, and he did not return to the school after that day. By the end of the week some of the students he had been working with began circulating petitions protesting his removal. On the following Monday, the principal met with officials from the Community Action office and Marty Phillips. The outcome of their discussion was that the school would maintain its position and continue to disallow Phillips the use of school facilities to work with youngsters. Reports of these events spread through the community. On Tuesday, school staff members began to sense tension as indicated by unusual amount of lateness to class, disrespect to teachers, and horseplay in the halls.

On Wednesday morning a group of approximately thirty parents and leaders from community groups arrived at the school to discuss the developing unrest. This meeting lasted for quite some time. Many students were aware of the fact that it was taking place and began milling around in the halls in anticipation of what they thought was to be some kind of decision about the status of Marty Phillips. As the number of youngsters who gathered around the room where the meeting was taking place continued to increase, the meeting was moved to the auditorium so more people could hear what was happening. However, as news spread, an estimated two hundred students filled the halls and refused to go to class.

Student tension heightened further when a neighborhood resident reported to the police that there was trouble at Lincoln, with the result that six police cruisers were dispatched to the scene. Although no acts of violence had actually occurred inside the school (there were reports of thrown erasers and chanting in the halls), the principal felt that the situation endangered the safety of students. He therefore asked for and received permission from the central office to dismiss school for the remainder of the day. Students left the school without serious incident shortly after noon. The school was also closed early on the following day when a number of students refused to return to class after an assembly.

While school remained in session all day Friday, it too was tension-filled. Police patrolled the halls, and one teacher was reported by the press to have said that teachers feared their safety without such protection. The principal reportedly told his teachers at a Thursday evening meeting that they must take a stand against outside agitators and that the student demonstrators were being directed by leaders of various social agencies. Approximately 150 students boycotted Friday classes following a Thursday evening meeting of parents. (Some parents said they kept children home for their safety rather than in support of the boycott.) At the meeting, parents called for curriculum changes, improved counseling services, parent and student involvement in decision-making, amnesty for student demonstrators, review of discipline procedures, and evaluation of teachers.

The director of the Community Action agency took a middle ground position. He agreed that his staff member should not be counseling students at Lincoln ("That's what school counselors are for.") but that he could work with them at the center. This, however, was not the real issue. In his view, "What the parents really are saying is that they are concerned about the quality of education their children are getting. This was a chance to get a foot in the door. Now they are going to speak."[3]

Might this incident have been anticipated? What is the responsibility of the building administrator in the face of student unrest? How would you respond to the student boycott and the demands set forth by the parent group? What guidelines would you suggest for working with the police when disruptive incidents occur? What do you think of the implication in the CAP director's comments that student activism provides adults with a "foot in the door" to change schools?

---

[3] This account is based upon a paper prepared by Charles E. Taylor.

SOME UNDERSTANDINGS

All administrative situations have a past history. Even when an entirely new district has been formed and new schools are built, there remain from the former districts certain perceptions of what schools should do and how they should be operated. Often there remain, also, certain habits or ways of making decisions that are characteristic of the people who live there. Some of the teachers who are selected for the new school have built their expectations of an administrator out of past experiences. However much the administrator would like to start anew, these remnants of past situations are real and must be reckoned with. Even the administrator is a product of his past experience and cannot escape some influence from it. So the usual administrative problem is to "move from where we are," not to "start from scratch."

PROBLEM-MAKER OR PROBLEM-SOLVER

Each of the administrative incidents described above has been lifted from context. There are additional factors and circumstances affecting all of them. It could scarcely be said that these factors are unrelated to other circumstances of the same situation. Undoubtedly the causes for incidents such as these are more complex than they appear on the surface. Occurrences of this kind represent problem situations that require solutions. To ignore them is an abdication of leadership responsibility which often allows an already serious problem in school affairs to grow worse.

It would be naïve of any administrator to expect to find a position devoid of problems. But situations do differ in the kinds of problems they present. Often problems differ in complexity and ease of solution. The questions of concern here are: What are the causes for problems that arise? Are these causes inherent in the situation itself? Is a climate being created which is conducive to problem-making or to problem-solving?

WHAT LABEL IS APPROPRIATE?

The manner in which problems are solved often determines the label with which people characterize the administrator of their schools. Pupils might call him a *dictator* because of their perception of his rigidity in solving problems that concern them. Yet the same behavior might cause parents to speak of this administrator as a *good disciplinarian.*

Sometimes teachers refer to the principal or the superintendent as *the boss.* The term may connote a feeling of warmth and kindliness toward a person whom they fondly call the boss, or it may be a sign of disrespect for one who treats his teachers as underlings rather than as professional equals. Usually the latter interpretation results from the feeling on the part of teachers that the administrator does not consider their opinions, that he tells them what to do and does not seek their co-operation. He has to have the final answer, regardless of the time and energy which the teachers have given to the solution of the problem.

A *good manager* is a label that often goes along with efficiency. An administrator who is economical in the use of funds, who organizes his time wisely, or who manages to have appropriate facilities ready and handy is said to solve management problems effectively. Good equipment, clean school buildings, well-organized services, accounts in good condition, buses running on time and in good order, funds available when needed, and smoothly running schedules represent some of the more apparent evidence of effective management.

The *co-ordinator* is one who sees relationships and organizes events so that they appear to work in harmony. He is contrasted with the person who solves each problem as though it were unrelated to any others, for whom activity is a series of separate acts. Management problems are solved without reference to their relation to program development; public relations is the strategy employed for passing bond issues or special levies. The co-ordinator, however, relates these activities so that all administrative tasks are linked together in a meaningful chain of events that promote the instruction of boys and girls. Activity interrelated in a meaningful way is his objective.

Two abilities, at least, characterize *the leader.* He has a goal for the future and a plan for achieving it. In addition to this, he understands that effective planning for the achievement of goals involves the people who are affected by those goals. The leader marshals the intelligence of these people to get a job done. The leader is expected to furnish ideas. He in turn expects to receive ideas from his associates. He inspires people to cooperate in dealing with these ideas, so that the purposes of education are served.

In all problem situations, administrators face the decision of when to suggest, when to urge, and when to require people to act. A leader must make up his mind about who should help make a decision—the lay public, the board of education, the teachers, the pupils. What will the circumstances permit in this case? Is this the appropriate time? What are we waiting for? How will this decision affect the educational program? Will this answer make it easier or more difficult to answer questions or solve problems in the future?

Pondering such questions may render some people inactive altogether. These people are not the administrative type. An administrator must act with the full knowledge that the manner in which he acts, the way in which he involves other people in action, and the way people perceive the results of the action will determine the label that people place upon him.

Developing a Concept of Administration

To look at administration in terms of the problems that arise and the manner in which the administrator goes about the solution of problems, as we have done in this chapter, is just one of many ways of beginning to think about the subject. Certainly administration has a problem-solving dimension. For some people this may be the most challenging aspect of administration as a profession. Others may find it tiresome to be forever facing the prospect of solving problems created by people and the circumstances that surround them. Can administration be defined as the process of solving problems such as those presented in the incidents above? Or is it more than that? Perhaps a consideration of the following questions will be helpful in building a concept of administration.

What is the purpose of administration? Nations, states, and municipalities have their executive officers and branches of government. The armed forces, business, the church, and social, governmental, and professional organizations, like schools, have some administrative arrangement with an executive officer at the head. The duties and functions of an administrative officer and the staff that assists him must be determined by the organization to be served. A major task before the prospective administrator is that of determining how to serve the functions for which the group is organized in the way in which the group intended. This question is treated in some detail in Chapter 4.

What is educational administration? In recent years we have become increasingly conscious of the problems of human relations in all sorts of organizations. There is also a burgeoning science and technology of administration which cuts across many fields. Public administration, business administration, church administration, social welfare administration, and educational administration have many common elements. Some studies have been made of military organization, procedure, and strategy in the search for clues to improve administrative behavior in other areas. Undoubtedly there is much to be learned by a transfer of knowledge from one field of administration to another. But in an attempt to get help from research in a related field, one could make a grave error by incorporating practices designed to accomplish a mission different from that of the public schools.

Big business deals in production of goods. It is prompted by the profit motive. Although it is the aim of our country and others to limit war to a protective measure to permit freedom to flourish, this is not the usual military motive. In waging war a nation must be prepared to kill and destroy if necessary. Education, on the other hand, promotes the enrichment of living. The strategies employed for the accomplishment of these various objectives may be quite different. Later we shall consider the elements which educational administration may have in common with other kinds of administration. It is sufficient for our purposes at this time to point out that in some respects educational administration is unique.

What do people expect of the educational administrator? Research findings indicate that expectations differ. Studies have shown that the board of education, the faculty, and the citizens of a town differ in what they expect of their school administrators. Differences of opinion exist even within each group. Sometimes individuals hold two or more expectations, which are opposed and cannot be fulfilled, as a realization of one would deny the achievement of the other. The problem of the administrator is to determine how to deal with various expectations, however different or similar they may be.

Do I have an adequate concept of the job? Probably not. Most prospective administrators in education come to the job through teaching. They view the administrator's job from the viewpoint of the teacher; their sympathies are with the teacher. In many respects this is good, because administrators may often be accused of failure to appreciate the teacher's point of view. But that is only one of the points of view to be considered. The pupils, the parents, the board of education, other patrons of the school, the state as a whole, and even the nation have a stake in the school. Administrative decisions must be made with due consideration for all parties concerned. To broaden one's own outlook to encompass all viewpoints, and yet not lose the vividness of each, is indeed a task of high order.

How can I gain a more adequate understanding of educational administration? This book is the beginning. It is designed, first, to provide the student with some *perspective* from which to view administration. In this chapter, one's own experience furnished the setting in which to think about problem situations similar to those encountered in many public schools.

It is our intention that as students build their own concepts of educational administration, moving progressively from one consideration to the next, they will continue to draw upon their own experience, the experience of their associates, and that of other writers in this field. Hence, at the close of each chapter, the suggested activities and selected readings provide guides for obtaining greater depth and breadth of meaning. Our purpose will have been served if this book alerts the student to the need for a more critical analysis of the nature of administration, the competencies required for it, and the professional obligations and challenges which it provides, and if it helps him make his own decisions about administration as a career.

SUGGESTED ACTIVITIES

1. For one of the incidents reported in this chapter:
   a. Identify the problem or problems confronted by the administrator.
   b. List the facts in the case which might be useful in solving the problems.
   c. State the unknowns in the incident that complicate the solution to the problem.
   d. State your idea of some next steps to be taken. Upon what do you base your projected solution?
2. Write an incident that occurred in a school in which you were a member of the professional staff. Give your analysis of the problem presented in the incident and the procedure you would employ in its solution.
3. Read one of the cases presented in Sargent and Belisle or in Culbertson, *et al.* (see Selected Readings). How does this case differ from the incidents presented in this chapter? Identify the administrative problems in the case you selected.
4. Attend a meeting of a board of education. Briefly describe what happens at the meeting. List your criteria for the effectiveness of such a meeting, and evaluate this meeting in terms of them.

SELECTED READINGS

CORBALLY, JOHN E., JR., JENSEN, T. J., and STAUB, W. FREDERICK. *Edcational Administration: The Secondary School,* 2nd ed. (Boston: Allyn and Bacon, 1965), Chap. I.

CULBERTSON, JACK A., JACOBSON, PAUL B., and RELLER, THEODORE L. *Administrative Relationships: A Casebook.* (Englewood Cliffs, N.J.: Prentice-Hall, 1960), Chap. I.

HACK, WALTER G., RAMSEYER, JOHN A., GEPHART, WILLIAM J., and HECK, JAMES B. *Educational Administration: Selected Readings,* 2nd ed. (Boston: Allyn and Bacon, 1970), Chap. I.

HODGKINSON, HAROLD L. *Educational Decisions: A Casebook.* (Englewood Cliffs, N.J.: Prentice-Hall, 1963).

JENSON, T. J., and CLARK, D. L. *Educational Administration.* (New York: The Center for Applied Research in Education, 1964), Chap. I–III.

MILLER, VAN. *The Public Administration of American School Systems.* (New York: The Macmillan Co., 1965), Chap. III.

MORPHET, EDGAR L., JOHNS, ROE L., and RELLER, THEODORE L. *Educational Organization and Administration,* 2nd ed. (Englewood Cliffs, N.J.: Prentice-Hall, 1967), Part I.

SARGENT, CYRIL G., and BELISLE, EUGENE L. *Educational Administration: Cases and Concepts.* (Boston: Houghton Mifflin, 1955).

2

The Evolving
American School System

It is important for every school administrator to realize that he is the appointed leader of a segment of America's school system, a system in a constant state of growth and change. The present chapter is designed to acquaint the administrator with the broad dimensions of this evolutionary process. Contemporary controversy about "community control" notwithstanding, it has often been said that what makes American schools different from other educational systems is the extent of local autonomy in their operation. Perhaps it is this same characteristic of American education that accounts for what many critics call "lack of system." But on one point protagonists and antagonists of American schools agree: These schools have a quality of uniqueness that distinguishes them from schools in countries with a national system of education. Americans generally believe that this quality is something to be maintained.

While the dynamics of the evolutionary process tend to push for better organization and a more effective system of education, the American people would be reluctant to give up a large measure of the local control of education which they have cherished so long. Yet the interdependence of our several communities and states is irrevocable, and the mobility of our population is a trend that is seemingly irreversible. Not only is this interdependence evident among our communities and states, but it increasingly permeates international relationships as well. Although educational planning and school operation restricted to local school districts have their place, they are not adequate for our day or for the future.

School districts throughout the nation are now in the position of having to face up to several questions: What can and should they do alone? What can and should they do in co-operation with other districts? What must they do as parts of a larger educational unit—

that is, the state and the nation? The fact that in recent times the number of basic school districts has been greatly reduced suggests that people find that the school districts which were in existence in the first half of the twentieth century are no longer adequate for the educational program needed in the second half of the century. At the same time, it is clear that people sometimes believe their school districts are too large. This concern has led to the decentralization of some city school systems.

To gain perspective for the leadership task ahead, let us briefly review some of the steps through which the American school system has passed. Notice that throughout much of the development of American education, the lay people, through town councils, directors, and boards of education, along with much state legislation and litigation over various disputes, provided the basic control for the American system of education. This tremendous expression of lay interest in education is without precedent anywhere else in the world. It is incumbent upon the school administrator to build upon this lay interest and to supply the element of professional guidance necessary to wise decision-making in the future.

GROWTH OF EDUCATION IN AMERICA

DECISIONS MADE IN COLONIAL AMERICA

Even while the early American settlers, lacking the conveniences of the homes and towns from which they came, struggled for existence amidst the hardships of remaking a wilderness into a fit place to live and raise their children, their faith in education was manifested by the steps which they took to develop an educational system as an essential part of their program of living. When we remember that the Boston Latin Grammar School, the first secondary school in America, was established in 1635, and that Harvard University was founded in 1636, we realize that education was recognized as important to the future development of the country, even at that early date in American history.

The New England common school. Attitudes toward education differed throughout the colonies. In New England people began to teach their children in the home. At the elementary level the objective of this instruction was to help children understand and participate in religious ceremonies at home and at church. This proved to be inadequate, however, and by 1642 Massachusetts passed a law requiring all children to be taught to read and write and to know the principles of religion.[1]

This was the beginning of compulsory education in America. The law did not require that children attend a school, but it did place pressure on each town or community to see that parents provided for instruction in the home. Enforcement was difficult because of different interpretations of the meaning and effect of the law. A notable consequence, however, seemed to be that, although the law did not require instruction *other than* by parents, there was an increase in the amount of teaching done by masters of apprentices, by private tutors, and by town school masters. Latin grammar schools were established in the larger towns to prepare boys for colleges. This educational plan, of course, was dominated by the church. In the law of 1642, the people of the Massachusetts Colony had merely recognized the state as servant of the church. In this case, the civic body became the legislative and enforcement agency of the church. Thus, the New England educational pattern began as part of the program of the religious state—a pattern much like that of England.

Colonial America, however, was not entirely like the mother country. Colonial towns and communities were made up of people who had to carve out their own way of life in a land where precedents were lacking. Ideas about many things, including education and schools, differed. By 1647, the enforcement of compulsory education in the home had proved to be inadequate; but faith in education persisted, and a new law was written in Massachusetts ordering:

1. That every town having fifty householders should at once appoint a teacher of reading and writing, and provide for wages in such manner as the town might determine; and
2. That every town having one hundred householders must provide a grammar school to fit youths for the university, under a penalty of five pounds (afterward increased to twenty pounds) for failure to do so.[2]

While these laws did not enforce attendance, they clearly established the precedent for compulsory schools. The Massachusetts Colony, by passing the laws of 1642 and 1647, had pioneered the common-school concept in America.

[1] Ellwood P. Cubberley, *The History of Education* (Boston: Houghton Mifflin, 1920), p. 363.

[2] *Ibid.*, p. 365.

Parochial school concept. In the middle colonies, particularly New York, Pennsylvania, and Maryland, where Baptists, Catholics, German Lutherans, German Reformed, Mennonites, Moravians, Presbyterians, Quakers, and other religious denominations were represented, the concept of the parochial school developed. In these colonies each church wanted to teach the children of its denomination according to its own beliefs and doctrines. Instruction carried on in the homes was under the direction of clergymen. Private schools, which developed in the larger centers of population, were church schools, supported by church funds and by the tuition paid by families who could afford the cost of this kind of education.

Even though such a program of education obviously favored families of means, the churches stubbornly resisted any move toward the establishment of a state system of education. They wanted to preserve at all costs the right of each church to educate its children and youth. Representing many different denominations, the churches of these colonies supported each other in this position and thus established the private school. Even today these schools are recognized as essential elements of our total educational system.

This is not to say, of course, that the right of attendance at private schools has never been questioned. In 1922, the people of the state of Oregon passed an initiative measure that, in effect, required that children attend the public schools. The law was to become effective in 1926, but two private corporations—the Sisters of the Holy Names of Jesus and Mary, and the Hill Military Academy—sought a restraining injunction against the enforcement of the law and received favorable action from the District Court. In 1925, the state of Oregon appealed to the Supreme Court of the United States, which ruled in favor of the two corporations. The *Oregon Case* stated in part:

> We think it entirely plain that the Act of 1922 unreasonably interferes with the liberty of parents and guardians to direct the upbringing and education of children under their control. . . . The fundamental theory of liberty upon which all governments of this Union repose excludes any general power of the state to standardize its children by forcing them to accept instruction from public teachers only. The child is not the mere creature of the State; those who nurture him and direct his destiny have the right, coupled with the high duty, to recognize and prepare him for additional obligations.[3]

[3] *Pierce v. Society of Sisters of the Holy Names of Jesus and Mary* (and *Pierce v. Hill Military Academy*), 268 U.S. 510, 45 Sup. Ct. 571 (1925).

This seems to make it clear that parents have the right to educate their children in private schools as long as these schools meet the state's educational requirements.

The pauper school. One of the problems that disturbed the consciences of people who developed these early concepts of education was that of making adequate provision for orphans and children of the poorer classes. This problem plagued the people of the middle colonies more than it did their neighbors to the north, due partly to the fact that the private-school pattern established in the middle colonies definitely favored people of some means. Then too, the poorer classes immigrated in greater numbers to the middle colonies than to the New England colonies.

The Southern colonies had an even larger number of poor immigrants. While the church and state made some provisions for schooling the paupers and orphans, these were temporary measures. People of means resisted proposals to extend such provisions into some kind of permanent remedy for the lack of educational opportunity for all. Some historians believe that the need to extend education to the many who were being denied the opportunity during colonial days was a powerful force in promoting legislation leading to the tax-supported educational program now existing in all of the states.

A dual program emerges. To students of American education it is quite apparent that by the time the colonies were ready to declare their independence, two patterns of education had emerged—*public schools,* having their beginnings in Massachusetts and the other New England colonies, and *private schools,* still largely under the direction of church groups.

Throughout our history as a nation we have witnessed the separation of church and state. From the laws which have been enacted and the court decisions that have been made in reference to this principle as it affects education, it appears that the people have reserved the right to educate their children in either a public or a private school, but that they have conceded to the state the right to enforce a minimum standard in private and in public schools. The Oregon Case, to which reference has just been made, and the Hawaiian Cases, which established the right of parents to send children to foreign-language schools,[4] give ample evidence that the courts agree

[4] *Farrington v. Tokushige,* 273 U.S. 284, 47 Sup. Ct. 406 (1927) and *Stainback v. Mo Hock Lok Po,* 336 U.S. 368, 69 Sup. Ct. 606 (1949).

that the interest of the state in an education for all children can be served in both private and public schools.

EDUCATION AS A STATE RESPONSIBILITY

The time between the Declaration of Independence and the War of 1812 is generally regarded as a period in which American education deteriorated. As a matter of fact, because of the impoverished condition of the nation at that time, schools and colleges did suffer severe setbacks. People could not afford the advantages of private education and they were reluctant to increase their tax burdens to support public education. Nevertheless, this period is important in the development of our schools because it was the time when the first state constitutions were written.

State responsibility grew out of colonial action. By 1800, sixteen states had joined the new Union. Of these, seven had incorporated in their state constitutions certain provisions concerning the state's responsibility for education. The New England states, having gone through a long colonial period during which state responsibility for education was being developed, incorporated in their constitutions the most comprehensive provisions for public education. The middle states, which had espoused the parochial-school concept, were less emphatic in placing state responsibility. The Southern colonies and the new states of Kentucky and Tennessee ignored the matter entirely.

Federal recognition of state control. By the time the ordinance for the organization of the Northwest Territory had been adopted (1787), the theory of education as a state function had been quite generally accepted. Article 3 of the Ordinance of 1787 is significant in this regard as it provides that:

> Religion, morality, and knowledge being necessary to good government and the happiness of mankind, schools and the means of education shall be forever encouraged (in the states to be formed from this territory).[5]

When Ohio was admitted to the Union, Congress gave the new state land to establish and maintain a state system of schools, a practice continued by the federal government as states were admitted

[5] Quoted in Ellwood P. Cubberley, *Public Education in the United States* (Boston: Houghton Mifflin, 1934), p. 92.

to the Union. General state school laws began to be adopted by the older states in the Union. In 1784 the University of the State of New York, an administrative organization similar to present-day state departments of education, was formed to supervise secondary and higher education in New York.

No provision was made in the Constitution of the United States for federal support or control of education. Article X of the Bill of Rights, passed by Congress in 1789 and ratified by three-fourths of the states in 1791, stated that "The powers not delegated to the United States by the Constitution, nor prohibited by it to the States, are reserved to the States respectively, or to the people." This clause clearly indicated that the growth of state control of education was entirely acceptable to the founders of our federal government.

Article X is often cited by advocates of a "states rights" point of view in federal-state relations. Paradoxically, those who would like to see the federal government take a more active role in certain affairs that have traditionally been the responsibility of the states use the same Article to defend their position. Those who advocate increasing federal responsibility point to the last four words of the clause—the "or to the people" phrase—as a Constitutional justification for federal intervention *if* such intervention is the will of the people.

General acceptance of state regulation. Many of the early state laws on education were permissive. Such laws provided that people had a right to establish schools in their own communities if they so desired. The people were also permitted to tax themselves for school purposes if they wished. The fact that legislation was permissive left many communities without adequate provision for education, and it can be readily understood that in time of stress the school program deteriorated. Gradually, however, permissive legislation gave way to mandatory provisions. The adoption of state financial aid for public schools completed a series of actions and regulations which now made it mandatory that the powers of the state be defined. Thus, in each state we witness the adoption of a *school code* that provides a framework by which the school districts of the state are regulated.

All state constitutions now have sections devoted to education. It should be noted that the states reserve to themselves the authority and power over education. The school district is a subordinate creation of the state and is established for purposes of local administration. The districts—towns, townships, villages, cities, or counties—derive their powers from the state legislature. Thus, the people of the state, acting through their state legislature and not in small competing groups representing individual communities, have given their sanction to such a system. The courts have upheld this action and have repeatedly ruled that the state may establish standards below which the district programs of education may not fall.

Delegation to local districts. An examination of the educational programs of the several states reveals, however, that much power is delegated by the state to the local district. In the beginning, such a practice was necessary just to get schools started, and all of the states find it necessary for efficient administration of the schools. The states differ, however, in the degree of delegation of powers and in the size and number of districts to which such power is delegated. The tendency in recent years has been to provide a greater amount of state aid, to enforce minimum standards more rigidly, and to increase the size of school districts.

The current movement to reduce the number of administrative units has been encouraged by state governments not only to take better advantage of the taxable wealth, but also to provide an educational program to meet more adequately the needs of children growing up in our expanding communities. Some people have interpreted this movement as a gradual revocation of delegated powers. They would argue that there is not only an increasing amount of state control, but also a tendency toward centralization of administration of schools at the district level; and these schools are becoming more and more remote from the people. Even so, the school district reorganization movement has gained momentum in recent years. In New York the number of school districts has been reduced from 9,500 in 1925 to 1,932 in 1955. In Illinois the major reorganization took place in a period of 10 years, 1945 to 1955, and reduced the number of school districts from approximately 12,000 to 2,349. In the United States the number of districts reached a peak of about 127,000 in the 1930's, was reduced to approximately 80,000 by 1950, and by 1970 the number of operating districts was only about 20,000.

During the 1960's substantial interest developed in two other types of reorganization: The first was the establishment of special purpose or supplementary service districts which serve a number of local school districts. In some instances, this involved the creation of new units to administer programs in areas such as vocational education. In other states, the movement has been one of restructuring the boundaries and functions of existing intermediate school districts. The second type of reorganization which has achieved recent popularity is the decentralization of large city school systems into semi-independent operating districts. The best known example is New York City where the city-wide board of education retained jurisdiction over some functions (e.g., establishing teacher salaries) and other operating responsibilities (e.g., assignment of personnel) were given to thirty-one local boards of education. Public pressure for decentralization also has been apparent in other cities including Chicago, Detroit, Los Angeles, and Philadelphia.

These developments underscore the continuing validity of a statement in the 1954 Yearbook of the Department of Rural Education.

> The size of the administrative unit best suited to provide all the educational services which would be included in a comprehensive prógram has not yet been determined. . . . Distance, topography, climate, density of population, patterns of communication, occupational diversity, social responsiveness, and social unity are among the factors which influence the operation of an educational program.[6]

Thus, the size of the school and of the school district, which at one time was the major criterion in determining the number of schools and districts, is now just one of many criteria that need to be considered in organizing our schools to meet the needs of children who are growing up in rapidly changing communities.

BASIC PRINCIPLES AFFECTING THE EVOLUTION OF OUR SCHOOL SYSTEM

As we review the evolution of the American school system, it is apparent that certain basic principles are emerging to guide us in the further development of our schools. Some of these principles have withstood and continue to withstand severe tests of both public and legal opinion. All educational leaders have the obligation to acquaint themselves with the manner in which these principles have been established, to weigh the evidence for or against them, and to provide leadership to help the people of the school district in which they work to establish for themselves sound principles of action and the means of implementing those principles. With this in mind, let us turn our attention to eight principles that seem to have become firmly established by the American people as guides for the continuing development of our schools.

---

[6] Department of Rural Education, *The Community School and the Intermediate Unit* (Washington: National Education Association, 1954), p. 15.

Universal education is essential. One of the basic struggles in the history of America has been the determination of whether or not education should be universal. That is, should it be required of all? Is education basic to our way of life? America's answer to these questions has been an emphatic *Yes!* Sometimes we wonder if the American people have always been aware of the responsibility that has devolved upon them as they have given their answer.

The early settlers of America had great faith in education. They proceeded earnestly and quickly to provide educational opportunity. Although at first the purpose was largely to create understanding of religious doctrine, secular concerns and interests soon modified this purpose. The fact that some educational provisions were made for paupers and orphans suggests a feeling that all children had a right to receive some education. The unwillingness to develop an adequate tax base to help make education generally available may suggest, on the other hand, that education did not receive top priority on the colonists' list of essentials. Or it may suggest that the purposes of education differed so much from community to community, church to church, and colony to colony that no uniform practice could be developed.

Later, however, these purposes did become clearer. Some of the founders of America eloquently expressed their belief that ignorance and freedom are incompatible. Thomas Jefferson expressed it well when he said, "If a nation expects to be ignorant and free, in a state of civilization, it expects what never was and never will be." To develop a nation of free people—free to think, to express their thoughts, to remold these thoughts in the melting pot of ideas, and finally to put them to work for the betterment of society—that was the purpose of the founders of America and the purpose for which we struggle today.

The elimination of the pauper school was a big step in the movement to provide education for all because of the prospect which it holds for the betterment of society. The chief battle was waged in Pennsylvania and New Jersey, two of the states in which the idea of the pauper school had developed. Political statesmen approved the new plan for free schools on the principle that "all men are created equal, and endowed by their Creator with certain inalienable rights." People caught the spirit of this concept and saw the obvious implication: The continuation of private schools for those able to pay, and of public schools at state expense for the poor, could lead only to the development of class distinction, a condition unacceptable to our democratic way of life.

The separation of the population into upper and lower classes was to have no place in American education. The Pennsylvania Free School Act of 1834, together with subsequent legislation in that state and in New Jersey, eliminated the pauper school from the Northern states. The West had never tolerated it. Although the idea lingered somewhat longer in a number of the middle and Southern states, it was almost entirely eliminated in the reorganization that took place in these states following the Civil War.

With the decision that schools are a responsibility of the state and that class distinction should be eliminated from the educational program, much of the battle for universal education had been won. However, education was still considered a privilege, not an obligation. It was not until 1852 that the first compulsory school-attendance law was passed. Here again, it was the state of Massachusetts that led the way. More than 200 years had elapsed since the passage in Massachusetts of the school law of 1647.

We know, of course, that prior to this time some of the states could not have supported an educational program that would have been adequate to meet the requirements of compulsory school-attendance laws. This is one of the reasons why such laws appeared so late in our educational development. Without doubt, the reluctance to force education upon those who did not wish it was also a deterring factor. Here was a problem of democracy that required some real thinking. In a freedom-loving country, do we have the right to force people to do something against their will? Or, in reality, is the education of all essential to the freedom that people desire to achieve and maintain? The history of legislation from 1852 to the present time indicates that the American people have answered the latter question in the affirmative because, by 1918, all forty-eight states had enacted some form of compulsory education law. Alaska and Hawaii have, of course, enacted like statutory provisions.

Current compulsory education laws vary considerably. The most common practice is to require children to attend school between the ages of seven and sixteen years. In some states the age range is eight to sixteen years and in others eight to eighteen. Most of the states have regulations that deal both with school attendance and with employment of children between the ages of fourteen and sixteen, or fourteen and eighteen. Under these regulations, permission to accept employment may be granted a pupil when it is believed that the child can profit more from employment than from attendance at school.

Parents are held responsible for the attendance of their children in school during the age range for compulsory education adopted by the state in which they live. The recent tendency, however, has been to place some responsibility on the school for meeting the wider range of needs of the children and youth as growing numbers of them crowd our schools. Increased provisions for vocational education, education for children with special problems, programs to meet individual differences of the so-called normal children, cooperative work and school arrangements, and many pupil personnel services are incorporated into our educational program to meet this obligation.

Education should be free. Despite the many reforms made in the educational system throughout the first half of the nineteenth century, many states were unable to raise sufficient money to support the system. Thus was prolonged the undesirable practice, held over from colonial days, of adjusting costs above those paid by taxation on a pro rata basis according to the number of children per family. This so-called *rate-bill* had an effect similar to that created by the pauper school. Wealthy districts voted local taxes, which together with state funds were sufficient to provide free schools for their children. Poor districts, unable to do so, struggled along with shorter school terms and inferior programs of education.

By the middle of the century, however, the fight for free schools was being waged. Cities led in the battle by securing legislation to form school systems operated apart from city governments under the administration of local boards of education. Boards of education were given power to levy taxes at the local level for educational purposes. Pennsylvania was the first of the Northern states to eliminate the rate-bill (1834).

After a stormy battle and much agitation over this subject in New York State, the legislature, in 1849, submitted the problem to the people who overwhelmingly voted in favor of "making the property of the state educate the children of the state." Immediately, opponents of the action organized in sufficient strength to convince the legislature to turn again to the people for their voice in the matter. The action of the previous year was sustained, and the battle for free schools in this state was won. Indiana, Ohio, and Illinois passed similar legislation in the years immediately following that in which New York made its decision. Other Northern states were going through similar struggles at about the same time; in a five-year period they too had won the battle for free schools. In the Southern states free education was provided in the reorganization that took place following the Civil War.

The story just related is a very brief description of the struggles which the people of America have undergone to provide free schools. This statement should not be mistaken to mean that we now have free education. The problem that remains with us is, how much education should be free? For the most part, we seem agreed that it should include the elementary and the secondary school, with college education at nominal cost. Kindergarten and junior colleges represent extensions in public educational opportunity provided in some parts of the country.

How much instructional material is to be included in "free" education? Should laboratory fees be charged? What special services are to be provided? Do the schools that are free to the children provide them equal educational opportunity? Should schools attempt to provide extensive vocational-technical training, perhaps including thirteenth and fourteenth years for pupils who do not intend to work for a college degree? Should college or a part of it be free? Might the schools provide free programs for school drop-outs who wish to resume their education? Should free education be provided for adults who are unemployed or underemployed simply because their particular skills are no longer needed in our highly automated society? Is free education for adult avocational and leisure time activity a proper function of the schools? Finally, should the schools provide free preschool programs for three- or four-year-old children? Inferior programs, programs inadequate to the special needs of some children, and the hidden costs imposed by activities sponsored by the school are just a few of the problems that remain to be solved in providing free education.

The state has the responsibility. The obvious consequence of the actions related so far has been to place the state in control of education. The process of extending education to all children and youth, and providing public funds to support an adequate educational system required that the issue of state versus local control be settled over and over again throughout the entire nation. The previous discussion indicates that many problems remained unsolved until state legislation was provided.

Authority for education, then, was left to the people of the several states when our national Constitution was formed. The people, in turn, in attempting to solve their problems, found the state to be the logical agency for the final resolution of issues. Along with this recognition of the authority of the state came its obligation to control the educational program. Towns, cities, villages, and rural areas were organized into school districts and were asked to meet state requirements in providing schools. In the early days this problem was even greater than it is today.

One way to meet the problem was to appoint a state officer to supervise the schools of the state. New York was the first state to create such a position, and in 1812 it enacted legislation providing for the appointment of the first State Superintendent of the Common Schools. Gideon Hawley, the first superintendent, apparently was so vigorous in his enforcement of state law that local pressures on the legislators caused the position to be abolished for a period of time. However, the secretary of state acted ex officio in this capacity for some time. Some states, fearing that they might have similar difficulties with a chief state school officer, used the ex officio arrangement as a temporary solution to their problem.

Another means of exercising state control was through the formation of a state board of education, with a secretary who performed the same functions as a state superintendent of schools. Horace Mann, as secretary of the Massachusetts Board of Education, became a vigorous leader in school organization. Mann and Henry Barnard, secretary of the Connecticut State Board of Commissioners for the Common School, and later State Commissioner of Public Schools in Rhode Island, became the nation's outstanding campaigners for educational reform. They were not merely officers who controlled schools through the enforcement of legislation. These were men of vision who helped the people define their problems, visualize new prospects for their schools, and develop new interest and enthusiasm for public education and its support.

Now all states in the United States have chief state school officers, and virtually all of them have state boards of education in each of which the chief state school officer is the executive officer of the board. State control is not always as enlightened as was that exemplified by Horace Mann and Henry Barnard. Nevertheless, all states recognize an obligation to enforce state school regulations and have state departments of public instruction with extensive staffs consisting of personnel who carry out specialized regulatory, research, or leadership functions to improve schools throughout the state. Adjustments are constantly being made concerning the relative amount of state and local tax funds to be used for school purposes. The functions of state departments of education are redefined periodically. What state control exists and how it functions changes from time to time and from state to state. It is significant that the people, through their representatives in the legislatures, exercise their authority and responsibility for regulating education at the state level.

There seems to be little controversy over the states' right to fix minimum standards for the schools. Questions do arise concerning the nature of the standards and the means that shall be used for enforcing them. Likewise, the use of public monies for schools is a privilege of the state which has general acceptance, but considerable controversy ensues when these monies are used for purposes of regulation. School administrators and local boards of education usually display an active interest in these matters and often are responsible for the initiation of legislation that will determine what the state does toward improving education at the local district level.

It is generally agreed that the state is most successful in assuming its obligation for school improvement when it emphasizes a leadership rather than a regulatory function. What the state department of education can accomplish through state-wide planning and co-ordination, and through advice, assistance, and encouragement to local districts far outweighs the results obtained from mere enforcement of regulations. Unless a large percentage of the schools can exceed the minimum standards which the state can enforce, public education is not meeting the challenge of our time. Dynamic, forward-looking school programs thrive under the stimulation of appropriate leadership, as was demonstrated by Mann and Barnard. The need is equally great today.

Local districts operate the schools. The recognition that the state has an obligation for the education of its children and youth by no means implies that the state is the appropriate agency to administer the schools. In fact, the history of the reorganization of school districts within states indicates that the people hold very zealously to their local schools and to their right as citizens to participate in decisions about what the schools shall do.

In the United States the development of the school system has never been from the top down. State governments, early in our history, accepted from the people the obligation to regulate the formation, support, and standards of the school program so as to equalize educational opportunity. These are still the functions which the people exercise through their state governments. It seems probable that the people will never permit the regulatory framework that is established by the state to become so rigid that some local initiative in educational program development is eliminated.

The number, size, and types of school districts vary from state to state. In some states the town or township is the basic unit. For twelve states the basic unit is the county. One state (Hawaii) is organized as a single statewide district. In most states, whatever the classification of basic units may be, there are exceptions by which certain towns or cities have been constituted as independent or separate districts. The movement for district reorganization has been an effort on the part of the states to perform their function of improving local schools and equalizing educational opportunity for all of the children of the state.

For purposes of operation, the state delegates most of its powers to the local district. A district board of education is elected by the people of the district to represent their wishes in formulating the policy by which their local school is to operate within the framework established by the state. Sometimes members of these boards of education find themselves in a quandary because they are officers of the state and at the same time elected officials of the local district. Where local interests conflict with state regulations, the course of action to follow may become complicated. If the regulation in question is a state law, the most common course of action is to submit to it. But, as we have seen from the previous discussion, there may be times when state regulations should be challenged. Many court actions have actually clarified the regulatory powers of the state, because someone had the courage to test the interpretation of a regulation as it was being enforced.

The main reason that it seems appropriate to keep the operation of schools at the local level is that this is the way they remain the people's schools. The rank and file of the citizenry should give regular attention to the kind of education that is required to promote the way of life in which we believe. When the operation of the school becomes so remote that few people have an opportunity to participate in decision-making as to its nature, interest in education withers and the co-operative relationship between the school and other educating agencies of the community diminishes.

Several of our larger cities have been concerned with this problem for some time. New York and Chicago, for instance, developed at least the first stage of regional administrative areas under the jurisdiction of the general administrative organization of the city school system by the middle 1960's. Public demand for citizen participation has intensified since that time and led to more extensive decentralization in some cities, notably New York and Detroit.

We find ourselves at a stage in our history where we are seeking an optimum size of local operating school districts. Undoubtedly the size will vary with many conditions; but we can be fairly certain that the principle of local initiative has been so firmly established in the minds of both the educator and the layman that more adequate means will be found to make it effective in determining the role of the school in the community.

Federal participation is desirable. An issue of current importance to people throughout the nation is to what extent the federal government should support the public schools. Most advocates of additional support for schools base their case essentially on two arguments: (1) that there is great need for equalization of educational opportunity among the states; and (2) that since about two-thirds of the tax dollar now goes into the federal coffers, there is little chance that an appropriate part of our total wealth will be spent for educational purposes unless this source of revenue is used.

Compared with a few years ago, relatively few persons now argue against federal aid to schools. However, the traditional arguments have been that federal control would be the inevitable result and that the states can meet their school needs if they so desire. Some of the opponents of federal support have claimed that a recognition of the possibility of federal control was the reason why the framers of the Constitution made no mention of education, and also the reason for the Tenth Amendment, which reserves to the states and to the people all powers not expressly delegated to the United States. It is difficult, of course, to document the motives that prompted the founders of our government to leave education to the states and to the people. Whatever the reasons may have been at that time, the Congress representing the people of the United States has not interpreted the Tenth Amendment to mean that the federal government cannot participate in the improvement of educational opportunity.

As mentioned earlier, the people, referred to in the Tenth Amendment, have many ways of making decisions in this country. At the neighborhood level, these decisions may be made quite informally. At the village, town, city, state, and national levels we have duly constituted legal procedure. Nevertheless, these are the processes through which *the people* act. Hence, in matters of education the people may act through their district organization, their state government, or even their federal government.

As a matter of fact, the people have been using all of the levels of government for the support of their schools for a long time. The participation of the federal government began immediately after the ratification of the Tenth Amendment, when the government made land grants to aid the states in the establishment of public schools and colleges. Additional ways in which the educational program of the country has been assisted by the federal government include: grants for special education, particularly in the field of vocational education; maintenance of certain types of schools for special purposes, notably the military schools and military programs in our colleges and universities; financial support of schools in the District of Columbia, in the territories, and for the Indians; authorization and maintenance of welfare programs having certain educational benefits, such as the Civilian Conservation Corps, the National Youth Administration, and the Works Progress Administration; aid to school districts affected by war-incurred federal activities; support for the education of veterans of World War II and of the Korean War; support for special programs thought to be in the interest of national defense under the National Defense Education Act; support of the United States Office of Education; the Vocational Education Act of 1963; the Economic Opportunity Act of 1964; and the Elementary and Secondary Education Act of 1965. Generally speaking these aids have been "categorical" in that they have been available to support only those activities designated by the legislation.[7]

In all of these instances, it seems fair to say that the fear of undue federal coercion has not been borne out by the facts. The great bulk of the activity that affects the program of general education has been carried on with a minimum of federal control and with much of the responsibility delegated to the states. The most prominent philosophical question now surrounding federal aid is not whether it should be provided but in what form. Some persons who are skeptical of federal intentions or strong supporters of state and local initiative advocate federal "block grants" to the states. The states, in turn, would allocate these funds to whatever educational purposes they might specify instead of administering "categorical" requirements. Despite the appeal of the "block grant" approach in some quarters, we believe that its adoption on a large scale is unlikely. It does not seem reasonable to expect the federal government to appropriate funds "to promote the general welfare" without providing some direction for its achievement. Moreover, we would expect that states supplying the great amount of wealth to make increased federal support of education possible would insist that legislation contain provisions for the appropriate use of these funds. Neither is it likely that the wealthier states will be completely altruistic in this matter. When such legislation is

---

[7] For discussion of the federal role in school affairs, see Roald F. Campbell, *et al., The Organization and Control of American Schools,* second edition, (Columbus, Ohio: Charles A. Merrill Publishing Co., 1970).

passed, the problem that our legislators in Washington will need to solve is not how to eliminate federal control, but how to provide that federal control which insures to each of the states its fair share of federal funds while treating problems of national concern.

The mobility of our population being what it is, inequities in educational opportunity become increasingly apparent. Economists tell us that the trend toward the collection of the large bulk of our taxes at the national level will not be reversed. If schools are to receive a greater portion of the tax dollar, and if these monies are to be used to provide our children and youth with comparable opportunities for education, it seems imperative that we move toward even greater federal participation in education, especially in the form of financial support.

The school system should be extended. The recent trend toward continuing education beyond the high school raises once again the old question of how far the public school program should go. Many school districts now provide for kindergarten and pre-school programs. Some people have raised the question of whether or not there should be any limiting age. Adult education is serving a useful purpose and will be more and more necessary. Many school systems have realized this and provide extensive adult offerings on credit and noncredit bases. Should the state make some provision for education at all age levels?

The answer lies squarely within our system of values. How much do we value education and where do we place it on our scale of wants? While it is impossible to compare meaningfully the relative expenditure for education in Russia and the United States, we do know that, by edict from the Kremlin, Russia can spend for education that portion of its national income that its leaders deem necessary to meet the desired ends. In the United States, on the other hand, the decision to increase expenditures for education depends in large part upon the intelligence, the insight, and the understanding of need on the part of the citizenry. Only history can tell how far we shall go in extending and improving our educational program. If the behavior exhibited by the American people in the past is to be taken as a clue to what will happen in the future, with effective leadership we shall continue to extend our effort to meet adequately the challenges which face us.

The common school, our first division of publicly supported education, provided the rudiments of the 3 R's. The extension of this school into the primary age brackets permitted extensions of the curriculum. The next problem to be faced was the addition of high schools. Up to about 1850, most of what we now call high school education was taught in the Latin Grammar School. Later, the academy, a semi-private school depending largely upon tuition and grants of money from churches and other benevolent organizations and groups, became the popular "high" school.

The academy was not simply a college preparatory school like the Latin Grammar School. It was open to both girls and boys, and its curriculum contained a variety of subjects not unlike those found in many of our secondary schools today. Although the Boston Latin Grammar School admitted boys at the secondary school level, its single aim of college preparation rules it out as the real forerunner of the modern secondary school. Perhaps the Massachusetts Law of 1827 really marks the beginning of the high school movement as we know it.

The Latin Grammar School movement was not widespread. Very few schools were established, and most of them died out when the academy grew in popularity. This new kind of secondary school spread throughout the eastern half of the United States and reached its peak of popularity about 1850. Its decline in number after 1850, however, was almost as spectacular as its rise in the preceding fifty years.

Massachusetts and New York were leaders in the development of the high schools as an upward extension of the common school system. Legislation permitting districts to tax themselves for this purpose was passed in a number of states, but progress came slowly because many schools had to be supported solely by local taxation.

The enactment of permissive legislation is an illustration of a device that has been used by the states over and over again, one which gives the people a chance to try out the idea. Where the legislation is seriously questioned, it is tested in the courts. The famous Kalamazoo Case,[8] in which the Supreme Court of the state of Michigan upheld the right of the state to enact such legislation, is an illustration of the impetus given by such legislation to extend public education to include the secondary school. The speed with which the states incorporated the high school as a part of the common school system was greatly accelerated after the settlement of this case.

The Vocational Education Act of 1963 (Public Law 88–210) is an example of permissive legislation which may serve to extend the public school system beyond the traditional twelve-year program of

---

[8] *Stuart v. School District No. 1 of Kalamazoo* (1874) 30, Mich. 69.

instruction. Authorizations for federal grants to the states under this Act were intended, among other things, to allow the extension of vocational programs of the public schools beyond the twelfth-grade level. One of the purposes of the Act is:

> To provide instruction so that persons of *all* ages in *all* communities will have *ready access* to vocational training or retraining which is of high quality, realistic in relation to employment, and suited to the needs, interests, and ability of the persons concerned. Such persons were identified: (a) those in high school, (b) those who have completed or discontinued formal education and are preparing to enter the labor market, (c) those who have already entered the labor market and who need to upgrade their skills or learn new ones, and (d) those with educational handicaps.[9]

The growth of the state university is still another chapter in the history of the upward extension of our school system. The earlier colleges and universities were private institutions, supported by tuition, church, and endowment funds. By 1800 there were about two dozen of these institutions, with not over a hundred professors and no more than two thousand students in all. By 1860, the total number of colleges and universities had grown to 246, of which 17 were state universities. In this case, as well as at the lower levels of the school program, great effort was made to change church-dominated colleges into state schools. The idea did not work out in practice, but the movement to establish state universities persisted. Weak at first because of inadequate state support, state universities have grown in strength and have now become the institutions of higher learning in which the great majority of our youth receive their college education. The basic theory upon which this gradual development is founded is that the welfare of the democratic society can best be achieved by raising the educational level of the people.

Religion and the public schools. There can be little doubt that religion played a large part in the early development of American education. In New England, it was the concept of the Calvinistic religious state, the state as servant of the church, which gave the state the power to regulate the schools. All churches throughout the several colonies continued many of their European habits, one of which was education for the furtherance of the church. They could not break

---

[9] M. D. Mobley and M. L. Barlow, "Impact of Federal Legislation and Policies Upon Vocational Education," Chapter VIII in *Vocational Education,* 64th Yearbook of the National Society of the Study of Education, Part I (Chicago: University of Chicago Press, 1965), p. 200.

away from this idea, even though a strong motive for many of the early settlers to come to America had been to break away from religious oppression.

When we recall that, in the beginning, schools were controlled by the church and maintained largely to promote religious purposes, we recognize how much the public schools as we know them now have changed. History supports the conclusion that this change has not been easy, but that people gradually have come to recognize the wisdom of the principle of separation of church and state. Religious instruction became a private concern and a right which the state has always protected on that basis.

The parochial school of the middle colonies has withstood the test of time and has established itself along with the public school as a recognized agency in which children and youth may receive the education prescribed by the state. Many of the court cases cited below indicate that the principle of separation of church and state gets much of its support from church groups. Hence, even today, the protection of the minority from religious domination and the right of different denominations to provide religious instruction as they see fit influences the kind, the place, the time, and the responsibility for instruction in the community.

The public school, however, became an educational agency that reached many different church groups; hence the parochial interests of each could not be protected. Public monies, collected as they were by different forms of taxation and paid by individuals and groups with vastly different concepts of religion, could not be spent in such manner that each of these interests was appropriately served. Cubberley points out two factors that he says served to bring about the secularization of the public schools. They were:

1. The conviction that the life of the Republic demanded an educated and intelligent citizenship, and hence the general education of all in common schools controlled by the State; and
2. The great diversity of religious beliefs among the people, which forced tolerance and religious freedom through a consideration of the rights of minorities.[10]

Not only did this principle of secularization of the public schools serve to shift the control from the church to the state, it also eliminated the practice of using state funds to support church and other private schools. There was a bitter battle in most of the Eastern states

[10] Cubberley, *The History of Education,* p. 692.

because such a principle required almost a complete reversal in policy and practice. Horace Mann was a leader in the struggle in Massachusetts while he served as secretary of the Board of Education. Pennsylvania, New Jersey, and New York were the states where the problem seemed to be unusually difficult to solve. New Hampshire, as early as 1792, was the first state to settle the issue by a constitutional amendment. The matter was resolved generally throughout the country by the adoption of constitutional amendments forbidding a division or a diversion of public funds for the support of parochial or private schools. Most of the states joining the Union after 1850 had this provision in the original constitutions. Butts reminds us that

> from 1876 onward all new states added to the Union were required by Congress to include in their basic laws an irrevocable ordinance guaranteeing religious freedom in line with the principles of the First Amendment. . . .[11]

and that

> the principle of separation of church and state in education was almost completely accepted through the United States by 1900.[12]

There is still another aspect of the problem that plagues us. This is the use of the school for religious instruction. "Released time" programs of religious education, a practice whereby a portion of the school day is set aside for religious instruction, have been ruled by the courts to be unconstitutional. The case of *McCollum v. Board of Education of School District No. 71, Champaign, Illinois*[13] is just one example of many such cases where released time was seen as a violation of the principle of separation of the church and state. In this case, the interpretation of the court was that the use of school buildings for religious instruction resulted in making the school "an establishment of religion." Thus, the practice of providing religious instruction within the school building, even on time released from public school responsibilities, was ruled illegal.

On the other hand, in 1952, the Supreme Court of the United States in *Zorach v. Clauson*,[14] upheld the school board of the city of

---

[11] R. Freeman Butts, *The American Tradition in Religion and Education* (Boston: Beacon Press, 1950), pp. 103–104.

[12] *Ibid.*, pp. 137–138.

[13] *McCollum v. Board of Education*, 333 U.S. 203, 68 Sup. Ct. 461 (1948).

[14] *Zorach v. Clauson*, 343 U.S. 306, 72 Sup. Ct. 679 (1952).

New York in providing that children may be released from school for religious instruction off the school premises.[15] The combined effect of these two actions seems to be that children may be excused from regular classroom activities for religious instruction that is conducted off the school premises. It would appear from the comments of the judges that in such cases the released time would need to be kept to a minimum, and administration on the part of the school would be improper. Presumably, a case could arise to test the extent of time, money, and effort that could go into such an enterprise without jeopardizing the public school function.

It is interesting to note in this connection that in 1961 when federal participation in the financial support of public education was proposed by President Kennedy, the religious issue again reached a peak in the intensity of heat generated. The President saw public support of non-public schools as unconstitutional, a violation of our time-honored principle of the separation of church and state. One of the arguments used in the defeat of his program for federal financial aid to the public schools was that aid to the public schools without aid to private schools was in violation of the principle of equal educational opportunity for all.

In 1963 the United States Supreme Court disposed of two cases in a single opinion expressed by Justice Clark. These cases, *Abington Township v. Schempp*[16] and *Murray v. Curlett*,[17] are considered of major significance because they appear to indicate a basic shift in the Court's interpretation of the First Amendment. While previous decisions of the Court placed great stress on the concept of the "wall of separation between church and state" the *Abington* decision set forth a "neutrality" concept. This concept means that the state (and the schools) must be neutral in its impact upon religion. In effect, the opinion makes the "wall of separation" illegal, for if the schools erect a wall they are not being neutral in their impact upon religion.

The Court has not dealt with every issue that may arise or every public school practice involving religion. The school administrator still has a responsibility for guiding the development of local policies and practices.[18]

---

[15] Clark Spurlock, *Education and the Supreme Court* (Urbana, Ill.: University of Illinois Press, 1955), pp. 126–133.

[16] *Abington Township v. Schempp,* 374 U.S. 203 (1963).

[17] *Murray v. Curlett,* 374 U.S. 203 (1963).

[18] Help in guiding policy development is offered by the many suggestions to be found in American Association of School Administrators, *Religion in the Public Schools* (Washington, D.C.: The Association, 1964).

The chief administrative problem in communities where the issue of religious instruction is raised is to help people understand that the principle of separation or of neutrality is intended not to prohibit religious instruction in the community by a church or private enterprise, but to protect the right of all by restricting the use of public school funds and property to that which is a public and not a private concern.

In fact, this issue caused the Congress much concern as they were debating the enactment of the *Elementary and Secondary Education Act of 1965* (Public Law 89–10).

> Title II proposes a five-year program to assist states in the purchase of books for school libraries and for student use, including instructional materials and textbooks, to be made available to children in public and private nonprofit elementary and secondary schools.
>
> Title III proposes a five-year program to provide supplementary educational centers and services within the community and to develop exemplary elementary and secondary school programs to serve as models for regular school programs.
>
> . . . .
>
> Children attending nonpublic, as well as public schools, and out-of-school youth and adults would be able to receive services and participate in these educational and cultural activities.[19]

Despite the assistance provided nonpublic schools through the Elementary and Secondary Education Act of 1965, many of these schools face serious financial problems. The number of nonpublic schools and the number of students in them decreased somewhat during the late 1960's because of this factor. The financial plight of nonpublic schools has led to considerable pressure for providing state financial aid to them. Legislation to provide such assistance has been introduced in many states and passed in some including Ohio, Connecticut, New Jersey, and Pennsylvania. Moreover, the list of functions for which such aid is requested is growing. The principle of state support for benefits which go directly to children rather than schools (e.g., textbooks and transportation) has been well-established.[20] More questionable are the demands heard recently in some states that public funds be allocated for teacher salaries (either lay teachers or teachers of non-sectarian subjects) in nonpublic schools.

[19] Elementary and Secondary Education Act of 1965 (Public Law 89–10).
[20] *Cochran, et al., v. Louisiana State Board of Education, et al.,* 281 U.S. 370 (1930).

The debate over such legislation has been heated at times and court tests in this area are imminent.

Another proposal which would aid nonpublic schools and have important consequences for public schools would be the widespread implementation of a "voucher system." A number of plans of this type have been suggested. In general, they would provide government aid in the form of vouchers to be given directly to students and their parents rather than the schools. The students would then be able to cash their vouchers in return for education at a school of their choice. If adopted, such plans would have the effect of putting the schools, public and private, in competition with each other.

The melting-pot influence. In a very real sense, the growth of public education in America reflects the development of a pattern of values which we like to think of as distinctively American. Gunnar Myrdal, a Swedish student of the American way of life, has observed that "America, compared to every other country in Western Civilization, large or small, has the *most explicitly expressed* [italics in original] system of general values in reference to human relationships." He goes on to say that "this body of ideals is more widely understood and appreciated than similar ideals are anywhere else."[21] He refers, of course, not only to the Bill of Rights and other formal documents in which these ideals have been expressed, but also to the struggles through which we have gone as a nation to realize them.

While the majority of the people who first settled America were of Anglo-Saxon origin, coming from England, Wales, and Scotland, these settlers were soon joined by Dutch, Swedish, French, Spanish, Irish, and German nationals and people of other races and nationalities. By and large, these were common people—people of the middle or lower classes. The Beards tell us "it seems probable that at least one-half the immigrants into America before the Revolution, certainly outside New England, were either indentured servants or Negro slaves."[22] Religious and political dissenters, a few English adventurers and French aristocrats, some people who sought wealth and power, others who withstood the misery of illness and poverty to be free, carved out their fortunes together. To them, coming to America meant the hardships of frontier life; but it also meant freedom to shape their way of life as they saw fit.

[21] Gunnar Myrdal, *An American Dilemma* (New York: Harper & Brothers, 1944). Vol. 1, p. 3.

[22] Charles A. Beard and Mary R. Beard, *The Rise of American Civilization* (New York: The Macmillan Company, 1927), Vol. 1, p. 103.

These were the people who settled America—different in beliefs, values, customs, stations in life, homeland, and culture. It is largely people like them who have continued to come to America. Counts describes them as the "common people" of the world, but common people who "were beyond or outside the ordinary in some way."[23] In an extraordinary sense, these people have built a new kind of common school—a school to which all children may go, and a school through which children may, by their own efforts, rise above their own stations in life.

The equality of all men, the worth and dignity of the individual, the faith that problems can be solved and society advanced through the application of intelligent thinking ("the method of intelligence"), and a belief in the co-operative process of decision-making are ideals and values that urge us constantly to re-examine our practices. So it is even in the last half of the twentieth century. The careful student of American history realizes that the decision of the United States Supreme Court on May 17, 1954, though truly a memorable event, was not a precipitous one.[24] It marked the climax of a long series of events and decisions through which the American people have been developing a workable plan of racial equality and relationships.

Throughout this entire chapter, we have described the struggle that was necessary to solve problems similar in kind to the problem of desegregation of the races in the public schools. The elimination of the pauper school and the events leading up to the achievement of free common schools were battles against forms of discrimination among people. The persistence of our democratic values, the insistence on the rights of the minority, and a faith that the people can work out their differences are all reflected in the many decisions, from early Colonial days to the present, that make our school system what it is today.

The summer riots in Northern cities during the late 1960's and controversies over *de facto* segregation remind us that the problems of discrimination against minority groups, including racial segregation in the schools, are not confined to one section of our country. They are more dramatically illustrated, perhaps, in the Southern states because of the long history of segregated education and the delay on the part of a number of these states in enforcing the Supreme Court ruling.

---

[23] George S. Counts, *Education and American Civilization* (New York: Teachers College, Bureau of Publications, 1952), Chap. 5.

[24] *Brown, et al., v. Board of Education of Topeka,* 347 U.S. 483.

Introduced to this country as a mere chattel, the American Negro has won many freedoms but has, nevertheless, endured a long and bitter struggle to achieve the rights and privileges of citizenship. The Thirteenth, Fourteenth, and Fifteenth Amendments to the Constitution of the United States specify the privileges and status afforded him as a result of the Civil War. At the beginning, blacks did not have many educational privileges. In the Northern states some of them attended the pauper schools of Colonial times. As free schools were provided, blacks were gradually accepted in them. But in the South black education began to be accepted much later. Philanthropic interests and agencies assisted in its development until the separate public schools were established.

After the Civil War, the principle of *separate but equal* was established to meet the standards for racial relationships which had been set forth by the newer amendments to the Constitution. Although the principle was contested in the courts, the case of *Plessy v. Ferguson* in 1896, in which the Supreme Court ruled that "separation did not necessarily mean inferiority,"[25] gave it support sufficient to establish the principle as the legal basis for the development of a dual school system in the South. It was not until the mid-thirties of the present century that this principle was challenged successfully. At this time there were a number of court cases in which blacks were granted the privilege of attending graduate schools in certain Southern colleges and universities.

The following excerpts from the Supreme Court decision of 1954 clarify, for our purposes, the position of the court:

> The doctrine of "separate but equal" did not make its appearance in this Court until 1896 in the case of *Plessy v. Ferguson, supra,* involving not education but transportation. American courts have since labored with the doctrine for over half a century. In this Court, there have been six cases involving the "separate but equal" doctrine in the field of public education. In *Cumming v. County Board of Education,* 175 US 528, and *Gong Lum v. Rice,* 275 US 78, the validity of the doctrine itself was not challenged. In more recent cases, all on the graduate-school level, inequality was found in that specific benefits enjoyed by white students were denied to Negro students of the same educational qualifications. *Missouri ex rel. Gaines v. Canada,* 305 US 337; *Sipuel v. Oklahoma,* 332 US 631; *Sweatt v. Painter,* 339 US 629; *McLaurin v. Oklahoma State Regents,* 339 US 637. In none of these cases was it necessary to re-examine the doctrine to grant relief to the Negro plaintiff. . . .

[25] *Plessy v. Ferguson,* 163 U.S. 537 (1896).

Segregation of white and colored children in public schools has a detrimental effect upon the colored children. The impact is greater when it has the sanction of the law; for the policy of separating the races is usually interpreted as denoting the inferiority of the Negro group. A sense of inferiority affects the motivation of a child to learn. . . .

We conclude that in the field of public education the doctrine of "separate but equal" has no place. Separate educational facilities are inherently unequal.[26]

Despite a number of advocates (black and white) who state otherwise, we continue to believe that racial segregation should be eliminated from our schools. The unresolved issue, however, centers about the urgency and means of enforcement which in some areas is looked upon as either unfortunate and unnecessary or demographically impossible. The Supreme Court decision, coming at a time when progress was being made toward giving blacks equal treatment with regard to voting privileges, jury duty, eligibility for employment, and equivalent pay for equivalent work, as well as when a real effort was being made to provide black schools equal in quality to those for whites, has led some of the people of the South to conclude that these honest efforts to improve the status of the black have not been appreciated.

A number of attempts have been made to set aside or to ignore the decision of the Supreme Court. Probably the most notable among these was the incident in Little Rock, Arkansas, in which the state government opposed the federal government in the desegregation of the public high schools on the basis that public education is a state, not a federal, function. Nevertheless, the basic rights of all people of the nation, the principle upon which the Supreme Court decision was rendered, have held firm. Desegregation of the schools is far from universal, but states are gradually moving toward compliance with Supreme Court decisions in this area. In October, 1969, the Supreme Court provided a strong prod in this direction by holding that time for "deliberate speed" toward desegregation of dual school systems had passed and ordering that thirty-three Mississippi school districts desegregate immediately.[27] As the states proceed toward the implementation of desegregation in the schools, we can hope that they will consider their actions in terms of the system of values to which we ascribe.

[26] *Brown, et al., v. Board of Education of Topeka, op. cit.*

[27] *Alexander, et al., v. Holmes County Board of Education, et al.,* 396 U.S. 1218 (1969).

The segregation that exists in the South is essentially de jure segregation; schools in the North are experiencing difficulties because of de facto segregation. A first step in understanding the factors contributing to this form of segregation is to note what has been happening in the past two decades to black-white relationships in the North.

One significant change that has implications for the schools is the massive migration of southern blacks into northern cities. The black population in some of these cities has more than doubled as the result of this migration. The influx of blacks into the near central core of the northern cities has precipitated an out-migration of many whites to the suburbs. The net result of this in- and out-migration has been to create a stable or even an increasing amount of residential segregation for blacks, while other ethnic groups have continued a pattern of desegregation. In addition, national economic growth has outpaced the blacks' economic advance. High unemployment among blacks, particularly the black youth, has aggravated the problems associated with inability to provide for one's economic needs.

These factors have led to de facto segregation in a number of school districts in the North. Such districts usually have schools in which the enrollment is largely, if not totally, black, while in the same districts there are schools in which the enrollment is largely, or totally, white. Indeed, the population shifts which have created Northern ghettos are probably the principal reason that more black students attended segregated schools in 1965 than in 1954.[28] While the schools may be innocent victims of larger social problems and conditions which have created segregation, the adverse effects and racial antagonisms are no different than those encountered in de jure segregation.

Debate over the importance of school desegregation and means of achieving it has intensified in recent years both academically and in the streets. Evidence that school desegregation could help improve education for lower-class and minority group children was presented by Coleman[29] in a widely discussed report commissioned by the U.S. Office of Education. A subsequent report of the United States Commission on Civil Rights[30] extended the Coleman findings and sug-

[28] U.S. Commission on Civil Rights, *Racial Isolation in the Public Schools* (Washington, D.C.: U.S. Government Printing Office, 1967), Vol. 1, pp. 2–10.

[29] James S. Coleman, *et al., Equality of Educational Opportunity* (Washington, D.C.: U.S. Government Printing Office, 1966).

[30] U.S. Commission on Civil Rights, *op. cit.*

gested means to achieve desegregation. These reports have been subjected to powerful criticism. For example, Henry Levin[31] asserted that the methodological bias of the Coleman study underestimated the importance of school factors and gave undue prominence to contextual variables such as social class in predicting student achievement. More disturbing yet to advocates of desegregation was the work of Arthur Jensen,[32] which revitalized the argument that achievement differences between black and white students can be explained genetically.

While scholars have explored the ramifications of these and other studies, administrators faced with the task of desegregating school systems have encountered strong public feelings.[33] Demonstrators who charge school officials with reluctance, if not ill will, toward desegregation have registered protests in school systems across the nation. On the other hand, when school officials have taken steps to desegregate, they often have met counter-protestors whose militance equals that of civil rights advocates. During the late 1960's the pressure for school desegregation slackened. It was replaced, however, by strong demands that minority groups and communities be given more control over schools in their neighborhoods including the right to make decisions about curriculum and to employ and dismiss teachers and administrators according to their sensitivity and dedication to neighborhood children and objectives.

It presently appears that the melting-pot tradition in American education is being threatened by public insistence upon neighborhood schools at a time when neighborhoods are increasingly homogeneous. Schools continue to face the perplexing problems of providing equal opportunity for persons who are unequal in many ways. Moreover, they have the task of helping individuals to understand and accept others who are unlike themselves. The dilemma posed by the continuing need to work for an integrated society based upon shared values on the one hand and the likelihood of growing separation among citizens in ideological and geographical terms on the other must be of concern to contemporary educators.

[31] Henry Levin, "Do Schools Make a Difference?" *Saturday Review* (January 20, 1968), 57–58 and 66–67.

[32] Arthur R. Jensen, "How Much Can We Boost IQ and Scholastic Achievement?" *Harvard Educational Review*, 29 (Winter, 1969), 1–123.

[33] For a series of cases which illustrate and analyze this problem, see Robert L. Crain, *The Politics of School Desegregation*. (Chicago: Aldine Publishing Co., 1968).

OTHER INFLUENCES ON THE EVOLUTION OF OUR SCHOOL SYSTEM

The struggles through which the American people have gone, and in which they are yet engaged to establish the American school system, represent democracy in action. Despite our borrowing from other countries and cultures, the school system that has evolved in the United States has been greatly influenced by a number of factors which may be characterized as truly American.

THE FREEDOM MOTIVE

Historians tell us that great migrations seldom involve people who are satisfied with their stations in life. There is no need to re-emphasize here the need to be free which our immigrants felt, for the historical documentation of this point is clear. The freedom motive is equally evident in the development of the schools. The tenacity of the American people to decide for themselves is reflected in the overthrow of church domination, the struggle to make schools free to everyone, and the enforcement of equal educational opportunity to all.

Moreover, the schools have been called upon to keep the freedom motive alive. To learn what America stands for is one of the accepted objectives of our schools. It has been said in many ways that people must be informed to be free. Does the struggle for freedom that has been characteristic of America make us better able than other nations to understand the nature of freedom and pass this understanding on to later generations? It seems to the American people that this is true, and they express the hope and faith that through education this freedom can be kept alive in the world.

CIVIC AND OCCUPATIONAL RESPONSIBILITIES AND NEEDS

The needs to make a living and to participate intelligently in decision-making at all government levels have always had their influence on the schools. Even though in early days the major purpose for the instruction of the children was to make it possible for them to participate in the affairs of the church, it was not long before these other needs also had to be served.

It is not uncommon to hear adults inquire of children in school, "What are you studying?" From their common experiences with the question, children know that it has reference to their future occupation and that a correct answer is "Oh, I'm going to be a nurse," "a doctor," "a lawyer," "an engineer," "a teacher," or "a bricklayer." Going to school to develop the competence required for a job has become an important objective of the school.

Civic competence, meaning the knowledge, interest, and understanding needed to vote and participate intelligently in community, state, national, and international affairs, has broadened in significance throughout the years. In Colonial times it often referred to a special kind of occupational competence, such as preparation to become a local official in the town meeting, a lawyer, a mayor, or a higher government official. Today it is even more important for all citizens to participate in civic affairs. It has become a duty of the schools to play a major role in helping to make people competent for this responsibility. These civic and occupational influences have been important factors in the secularization of the schools.

GROWTH IN PROFESSIONALISM

The first institution in America that provided some instruction for prospective teachers was established in Concord, Vermont, in 1823 by Reverend Samuel R. Hall. This was a three-year program including instruction in the common-school subjects and a series of lectures during the latter part of the third year on the "Art of Teaching." In 1839 Horace Mann established the first state normal school in the United States at Lexington, Massachusetts. The normal school had a much more complete teacher education program than that started by Hall. By 1870, the state normal school had grown greatly in popularity. Today the teachers college, often a part of a state university, is an essential portion of the educational system

With the coming of the normal school there was a renewed emphasis on influences from the European schools. In addition to the ideas that continued to come from England, the thinking of such educators as Pestalozzi, Froebel, Rousseau, and Herbart began to have an effect upon practices in American schools. A new profession seemed to be in the making and, with its development, there grew up a great body of educational literature.

Professional knowledge about teaching and learning. The rise of the normal school and the teachers college brought about a great interest in investigating the nature of the learning process and, hence, the determining of appropriate methods of teaching. Soon American educators were carrying on their own investigations and adding to the professional literature contributions that were equally as important to teaching as the knowledge which they had gained from their colleagues in other parts of the world.

During the latter part of the nineteenth century, G. Stanley Hall led a movement which became identified as Child Study. As a part of this movement, educators sought to ascertain how the personality of the child develops. Children were observed, weighed, and measured to determine aspects of physical growth. Detailed records were kept on these phases of growth and on achievement in school. By the turn of the century, the scientific movement, so important in the development of our technology, had begun to have a real impact on the field of education. Thus were developed such courses as "The Physical Development of the Child," "Educational Psychology," "Intelligence Testing," "General Methods of Teaching," and "Special Methods" (for the teaching of special subjects). Thorndike and Terman are familiar to students of education as men who made tremendous contributions to testing and measurement.

Such studies led investigators into further examination of teaching procedures, the grade placement of children, promotions, individual differences, the social development of the child, curriculum reorganization, the methods of adjusting to individual differences, and many other such topics. One need but glance at a recent volume of the *Encyclopedia of Educational Research* to be impressed by the great body of knowledge about education and the educative process that is accumulating year by year.[34]

The interest in the social development of the child has caused the educator to realize that education is perhaps both an art and a science. Hence, in recent years considerable attention has been given to a combination of these approaches. Philosophical considerations have made it necessary to raise again the question of purposes. New knowledge about child development and evaluation of the "total growth" of the child has led to a consideration of new procedures, new methods of classifying pupils, new curricular interests, and new concepts of the role of the school in modern society.

Articulation of purposes. Throughout the development of the schools, the American people have shown a profound faith in knowl-

---

[34] Robert L. Ebel, ed., *Encyclopedia of Educational Research,* 4th ed. (New York: The Macmillan Company, 1969).

edge. A prime responsibility of the school was to pass on to each generation the heritage of the past. Fact-gathering was essential. The acquisition of course content in the several subject-matter fields became very important.

The disciplinary concept of learning, now discredited because it was based upon a faulty psychological theory, had a tremendous influence on our schools. According to this concept, the training of the mind, which disciplined the child in the learning process, was a major value to be derived from schooling. Proponents of the concept believed that mastery of the more difficult subjects had a greater disciplinary effect than that of learning the content of easy subjects.

In recent years, the schools have been guided in a further clarification of their role by a careful examination of the unique function of the school in a democratic society. In 1918, the Commission on the Reorganization of Secondary Education emphasized the fact that in a democracy education "should develop in each individual the knowledge, interests, ideals, habits, and powers whereby he will find his place and use that place to shape both himself and society toward nobler ideals." The Commission then went on to name the major objectives of education in a democracy, the seven "cardinal principles" of secondary education, which, in brief, are:

1. Health knowledge and habits.
2. Command of the fundamental processes.
3. Worthy home membership.
4. Education for a vocation.
5. Education for citizenship.
6. Worthy use of leisure time.
7. Ethical character.[35]

Practically all basic textbooks in elementary and secondary education, as well as those on the special aspects of these programs, summarize professional thinking about the purposes of education. Usually such statements point out the unique purposes of education in a democracy, especially as we view them in America. Among the statements of purposes that have made a deep impression upon school people were those issued by the Educational Policies Commission.

In 1938, this Commission grouped the objectives of American

[35] Quoted in Ellwood P. Cubberley, *An Introduction to the Study of Education and Teaching* (Boston: Houghton Mifflin, 1925), p. 160.

education under the four headings, Self-Realization, Human Relationship, Economic Efficiency, and Civic Responsibility.[36] Two more recent reports, *Education for All American Children*[37] and *Education for All American Youth,*[38] outlined ways in which elementary and secondary school programs can be extended to reach the basic "needs" of *all* children and youth. In 1959, the Commission, on behalf of the profession, took up the challenge of lay critics and issued *An Essay on Quality in Public Education* in which many of the aspects of program, organization, administration, and commitment to education are spelled out for the American people.[39] This same Commission, in 1961, issued a statement on *The Central Purpose of American Education*. In this publication, the "freedom of the mind" achieved by the development of one's "rational powers," or ability to think, was conceived as being central to the accomplishment of the full range of objectives that had been stated previously. Thus these professional spokesmen reiterate in succinct and forceful language the overarching purpose of American education. Their concluding statement presents the challenge in these words:

> Man has before him the possibility of a new level of greatness, a new realization of human dignity and effectiveness. The instrument which will realize this possibility is that kind of education which frees the mind and enables it to contribute to a full and worthy life. To achieve this goal is the high hope of the nation and the central challenge to its schools.[40]

Professional organizations. From the preceding discussion it is obvious that professional organizations tend to become the official representatives of the school workers. The National Education Association, with its many departments, serves as a clearning house for the expression of ideas about education which come from its large membership throughout the country. State and local teachers' associations, too, are organizations created to give expression to the

[36] Educational Policies Commission, *The Purposes of Education in American Democracy* (Washington, D.C.: National Education Association, 1938).

[37] Educational Policies Commission, *Education for All American Children* (Washington, D.C.: National Education Association, 1948).

[38] Educational Policies Commission, *Education for All American Youth: A Forward Look* (Washington, D.C.: National Education Association, 1952).

[39] Educational Policies Commission, *An Essay on Quality in Public Education* (Washington, D.C.: National Education Association, 1959).

[40] Educational Policies Commission, *The Central Purpose of American Education* (Washington, D.C.: National Education Association, 1961), p. 21.

leadership that is growing up among members of the emerging teaching profession. The American Federation of Teachers, a teachers' union affiliated with the A.F.L.-C.I.O., has been active particularly in improving the welfare of the teacher.

The three major professional organizations for school administrators are the Department of Elementary School Principals, The National Association of Secondary School Principals, and the American Association of School Administrators. These organizations have auxiliaries at the state level in most states.

Administrators' professional organizations, especially the A.A.S.A., have been active in attempting to upgrade their standards for admission and continued membership. This, of course, tends to upgrade the standards for admission and membership in the profession itself. These organizations set standards not only to create minimum qualifications for entry into the organization, but also to provide rules for ethical behavior of their membership. Many educators see control of entry into and regulation of standards for continued membership in professional education organizations as an important step toward the total professionalization of all educators. For education cannot become a "true" profession until its members are able to control both the minimum qualifications for entry into the profession and minimum standards of competency and ethical behavior for continued membership.

In 1968 the AASA took what many persons view as another important step toward upgrading the profession. The association formed the National Academy for School Executives as a means for providing in-service education on a continuing basis for interested superintendents.

CHARACTERISTICS OF OUR SCHOOL SYSTEM

Throughout our discussion of the development of American education we have attempted to document the fact that, although the American people have, at times, borrowed from European countries, they have built a school system that is essentially American. Certain characteristics of this system set it apart from that of any other country in the world. The administrator is introduced to them at this point so that he may reflect upon them and their implications for his behavior as he learns more about his job, himself, and the challenges of his profession.

SCHOOLS BELONG TO THE PEOPLE

Nowhere in the world do the rank and file of the citizenry have as much to say about their schools as in this country. While the state is regarded as the legally responsible agency for the development of the school system, the people, through their representatives in government or through the courts, have always limited, and continue to limit, this authority according to their will.

Furthermore, the people actively participate in school matters at the level of the school district. Any administrator who has worked on a school bond issue knows and respects the power of the citizens. Even the tenure of an educational administrator is often dependent upon the development of an educational program that is satisfactory to the people. The power of community forces is in fact so strong that there is little hope of building an adequate educational program without their support. Thus the ability to lead in community thinking about education is one of the competencies which the prospective school administrator must acquire.

OPPORTUNITY FOR ALL

Although the goal is still unachieved, America is moving toward having children of all classes attend equal schools. Rich or poor, laborer or professional, Protestant, Catholic, or Jew, white or black, the children receive essentially the same general education. They often attend these schools together to learn, in common, the democratic values for which their country stands.

Free universal public education is one of the powerful forces that hold class distinction in check. No matter how low a child's station in life may be, his chances of rising above it can be enhanced if he has an educational opportunity equal to that of the children of families in more fortunate circumstances. This is the ideal toward which we strive. Through our schools, we attempt to diminish class distinctions, while in many parts of the world schools perpetuate them.

To realize this ideal, however, we must achieve greater equalization of educational opportunity among communities and among states. More must be done to provide opportunities for those who have ability but lack financial resources to extend their education beyond high school. Better facilities will need to be developed to accommodate children and youth whose educational needs are out of the ordinary.

PROGRAMS ARE ADJUSTED TO NEEDS

The horizontal extension of the schools—that is, widening the range of curricular offerings and the services provided by the school to minister to the needs of pupils—has been tremendous. As the school system has developed, the purposes of education have broadened, the number of pupils has greatly increased, and the range of abilities, interests, and needs of children has been extended.

Many new programs and innovations have been introduced into the schools to meet the variety of needs of our children. Among them are computer-assisted instruction and information retrieval systems; team-teaching programs; individualized reading programs; increased use of instructional television and other audio-visual devices; introduction of mechanical teaching aids, such as teaching machines and language laboratories; provision of guidance and counseling services in secondary schools and in some elementary schools; increased attention to vocational education and preparation; and advanced placement programs for college-bound students. Many more changes could be mentioned, all of them a part of the continuous efforts of our schools to meet the needs of all children.

Adjustment to these changes constitutes a major problem in education today. The need to expand the program is increasing so rapidly that we have neither the educational facilities nor the personnel to cope adequately with the problem. Yet here again the United States leads other countries in efforts in this direction.

PUPILS LEARN A DEMOCRATIC WAY OF LIFE

Foreign visitors to American schools express great surprise at the freedom with which school children go about their educational tasks. They show concern over the wide range in achievement that can be recognized among children in the same grade. They are amazed and bewildered on the one hand at the seeming lack of discipline and, on the other hand, at the initiative of children to see a task through to completion.

As our schools have developed, we have come to realize that responsible action, such as that required of each individual in a democracy, with a minimum of compulsion from external authority, is something to be learned. So children must learn how to be democratic, what it means to be responsible, and what the consequences of irresponsible behavior are, just as they must learn the knowledge and skills necessary for the vocation they choose to follow. The successful induction of children into a democratic society is a difficult task. No doubt the schools have made many mistakes in the attempt thus far. However, we believe the effort is characterized by the following, in varying degrees:

1. A democratic organization in which there is a recognized place for participation in planning and developing the school life by children, teachers, parents, and administrators.
2. Sufficient respect for individual differences so that administrators, boards of education, parents, laymen, and teachers are making an effort to vary the learning experiences of children to meet individual needs; and so that differences of opinion, beliefs, values, and customs, both in school and out, are given freedom of expression in making decisions.
3. Sufficient faith in the method of intelligence, so that decisions (of any consequence to those concerned) are made after appropriate processes of collecting, analyzing, and seriously reviewing and interpreting appropriate data necessary to the decision.
4. Freedom to examine the issues that are controversial in the school, community, and nation, with a view toward gaining a deeper understanding of the differences among people and of the need to perpetuate or diminish these differences.
5. The disposition to withhold judgment until it can be formulated on the basis of a reasonable amount of available data.
6. Encouragement of individual and original expression, giving proper place to initiative, but at the same time recognizing that all must play by a common set of "rules for the game."

Hence the school tends more and more to get outside the four walls, to engage in community affairs as part of the learning experiences of children and youth, and to take its place along with other agencies in assuming responsibility for the induction of students into responsible community life.

THE SCHOOL HAS A UNIQUE ROLE

As the purposes of the school have encompassed the total development of the child, an increasing number of duties and responsibilities have devolved upon it. Not only has the curriculum been broadened to teach children the many skills they need to take their places in society, but services too have increased both in number and kind. The major function of services to pupils has been to create those conditions under which learning takes place best.

Some people believe there is danger that the school may, in its zealousness to serve the people, actually take over functions that rightfully belong to other community agencies. The fact that the school has to bear the brunt of the criticism for the delinquency of youth indicates that people have assumed the school to be the agency of greatest influence in the child's life. In some instances this may be true. By and large, however, children and youth are educated by the experiences that are provided throughout the communities in which they grow up. The home, the church, the Y.M.C.A. and Y.W.C.A., the settlement house, the 4-H Clubs, the Future Farmers of America, and many other formal and informal groups, as well as the school, are educating the child.

In developing a community-wide educational program, it must be remembered that the school has a responsibility for *all* the young people of the community. No other single institution or agency has this responsibility. As a public trust, and with an equal responsibility to each of its pupils, the school is the agency upon which the American people have depended for examination, assessment, and interpretation of the many community influences on the life of its young people.

THE CHANGING CHARACTER OF EDUCATIONAL ADMINISTRATION

In the early years of our national history, schooling was a relatively simple enterprise. Children walked to school—first, to learn to read the Bible, and, later, to learn the 3 R's for broader secular purposes. The school buildings they attended were not elaborate structures. Furnishings were meager. Permissive rather than mandatory legislation was largely the governing role of the state. Local autonomy permitted people to have good schools or poor ones.

Probably the little red schoolhouse, which has only recently passed from the American scene, is the most characteristic symbol of the local school operation that was so jealously guarded. There was little need here for administration in the sense that we know it today. The teacher taught the children of grades one through eight, made out the attendance records, took care of his own discipline, made the fires and did other janitorial work, all as a part of the day's activities. A local board of laymen hired the teacher and made a record of the financial affairs of the district. Usually the local board "opened the school" in the fall of the year. It was the responsibility of the board to see that the school house was cleaned and painted, that the roof was repaired, that the stove was in order, that the floors were oiled, that the seats and desks were repaired and varnished, and that the coal and other supplies needed for the year were purchased. The teacher assumed the responsibility for the children while in school. The board of directors—school committee or otherwise designated local board of education—managed the business affairs. When the office of county superintendent was created in the nineteenth century, the county superintendent became the arm of the state through which local schools were regulated.

In the cities, however, the development of administration took place somewhat differently. Here, school buildings were needed to house more pupils than could be handled by a single teacher. Thus in the multiple-teacher school, someone, usually the teacher of the highest grade, became the "head teacher" or the "principal teacher." Early Latin Grammar schools of sufficient size to require more than one teacher, and later the academies, often referred to the head teacher as the "head master," a name still used commonly in private schools. Head teachers, head masters, or principals "had charge of the building," usually kept all records, and had general responsibility for the discipline of the pupils. Before the establishment of the superintendency, these building heads were responsible to the local school committee, or some other similarly named body, which had legal responsibility for the schools and performed any necessary administrative functions.

As schools took on more complex responsibilities, and as the population of the nation congregated in the urban centers, a greater number of managerial tasks needed to be performed. The sheer weight of these responsibilities caused lay boards of education to see the wisdom of employing an administrative officer to assume such obligations. Throughout the growth of this American school system, then, there has developed an increasing awareness of the need for professional leadership and administration. This chapter has provided some of the historical setting for the educational challenges to present and future school administrators. The following chapter describes the contemporary setting in which he functions.

SUGGESTED ACTIVITIES

1. List a few important decisions which the American people should be making about the public schools and show how these decisions would affect the schools in which you work.

2. Select one school problem about which decisions need to be made at the present time. In solving the problem, what decisions should be made at the district level? The state level? The national level? Why?
3. As an administrator, what part do you think you should play in the decision to be made in 2 above?
4. Read Chapter V, "A Country of Common People," in Counts' *Education and American Civilization*. What is the implication for the development of education in America?
5. What are the implications of the pattern of American values described by Passow (see bibliography below) for the elimination of discrimination among groups in the schools in which you work?

SELECTED READINGS

American Association of School Administrators, *Religion in the Public Schools*. (Washington, D.C.: The Association, 1964).

BRICKMAN, WILLIAM W. and LEHRER, STANLEY. *Religion, Government, and Education* (New York: Society for the Advancement of Education, 1962).

CAMPBELL, ROALD F., *et al. The Organization and Control of American Schools*, 2nd ed. (Columbus, Ohio: Charles E. Merrill Books, 1970).

COUNTS, G. S. *Education and American Civilization*. (New York: Bureau of Publications, Teachers College, Columbia University, 1952).

CREMIN, LAWRENCE A., *The Transformation of the School*. (New York: Alfred A. Knopf, 1964).

Educational Policies Commission, *The Central Purpose of American Education*. (Washington, D.C.: National Education Association, 1961).

————. *The Unique Role of the Superintendent of Schools*. (Washington, D.C.: National Education Association, 1965).

EDWARDS, N., and RICHEY, H. G. *The School in the American Social Order*. (Boston: Houghton Mifflin, 1963).

PASSOW, A. HARRY, ed., *Education in Depressed Areas*. (New York: Teachers College, Columbia University, 1963).

SUFRIN, SIDNEY C. *Issues in Federal Aid to Education*. (Syracuse, N.Y.: Syracuse University Press, 1962).

THAYER, V. T. *The Role of the School in American Society*. (New York: Dodd, Mead, 1960).

3

The Current Setting

Our intention in this chapter is to describe some characteristics of the setting in which the contemporary administrator works. What happens within schools is often influenced by conditions and events which are not subject to the direct control of the administrator. Policy decisions are not a product of the people of the local school community alone, but often reflect the desires of the people of the school district, the state, and in some sense the world beyond. In like manner, program decisions are not made by the professionals of a single school in isolation. The administrator is sometimes constrained and advantaged by outside factors as he works toward objectives. The successful administrator will be aware of such factors and their particular implications for his assignment. In this chapter, we will consider some general background factors, the place of education in national development, and the contest to shape educational policy at the local level.

BACKGROUND FACTORS

Four general characteristics of American society which have implications for schools are urbanization, economic growth, socioeconomic diversity, and tension regarding national issues. The expectations which citizens have for schools and their willingness and ability to support them are associated with these factors.

URBANIZATION

The United States is increasingly a nation of cities and suburbs. The percentage of the American population residing in urban areas increased from 45.7 in 1910 to 56.2 in 1930 to 69.9 in 1960. Most of these people are concentrated in large metropolitan areas. Approximately 63 percent of the total population resided in 212 Standard Metropolitan Statistical Areas in 1960. By 1968, more than 127 million of the nearly 200 million United States citizens lived in these same areas. Moreover, Hauser and Taitel have estimated that approximately 95 percent of the 47.3 million population increase projected for the nation by 1980 will be in metropolitan areas.[1]

The growth of metropolitan populations has not been uniform. Suburbs have grown at a much faster rate than central cities which in many instances have actually declined in population. Seventy of the 257 cities which were centers of the 212 Standard Metropolitan Statistical Areas in 1960 declined in population from 1950–1960.[2] Hauser and Taitel project a continuation of this trend and estimate that 100 million of the projected 170 million metropolitan area residents of 1980 will live in suburbs.[3]

Population shifts from rural to urban areas have had important consequences for schools and educators. Most obviously, they have brought about a redistribution of schools and students on the American landscape. The one-room rural schoolhouse which occupies a prominent spot in the history and hearts of many Americans, is fast disappearing. Less than 2 percent of American students are enrolled in school districts of less than three hundred pupils, and nearly two-thirds of them attend schools in districts of more than five thousand pupils.[4] Approximately 9 percent of the American public school enrollment was registered in fifteen large city school districts in 1968–1969.[5] The shift in student population has been so great in some cities that lack of classroom space has forced schools to operate two half-day sessions. Many cities have mounted large-scale building programs to keep pace with expanding enrollments. The Columbus, Ohio, public schools, for example, opened a new classroom on the average of every three and one-half days between 1950 and 1968.

As most knowledgeable persons are aware, the impact of urbanization upon schools goes considerably beyond the need to provide

---

[1] Philip M. Hauser and Martin Taitel, "Population Trends—Prologue to Educational Programs." In Edgar L. Morphet and Charles O. Ryan, eds., *Designing Education for the Future, No. 1: Prospective Changes in Society by 1980* (New York: Citation Press, 1967), p. 37.

[2] *Ibid.,* p. 34.

[3] *Ibid.,* p. 36.

[4] U.S. Office of Education, *Education Directory, 1968–1969, Part 2: Public School Systems* OE-20005-69 (Washington, D.C.: U.S. Government Printing Office, 1969).

[5] Richard H. Barr and Betty J. Foster, *Fall 1968 Statistics of Public Elementary and Secondary Schools* OE-20007-68 (Washington, D.C.: U.S. Government Printing Office, March, 1969), p. 6.

classrooms. The popular as well as professional literature has discussed such problems as teaching large numbers of students who have serious educational deficiencies, fiscal inequities related to city schools, the impersonality of large school bureaucracies, and the lack of co-ordination among schools and other public service agencies. While most acute and obvious in largest cities, such problems often exist in smaller school systems as well. Many educators and national policy makers believe the amelioration of urban educational problems should have top priority in American education.

It is important to note that urbanization also affects the task of schools which are not in urban areas. This is true because urbanization is a style of life as well as a clustering of people.[6] The central feature of urban life is the interdependence of individuals and institutions. Rural as well as city residents are affected by this life style in our predominantly urban society. As the institutions charged with preparing young people for life in an urban society, schools must teach the skills and values essential to urban living.

ECONOMIC GROWTH

The United States is a wealthy nation. Since 1929, the gross national product has increased more than eightfold to an estimated $860.7 billion in 1968.[7] Some of this gain was due to inflation. When standardized on a 1958 price base, the gain was from $203.6 billion in 1929 to $706.9 billion in 1968. On the same basis, personal consumer expenditure increased from $139.6 billion to an estimated $450.7 billion, federal purchases from $3.5 billion to an estimated $79.3 billion, and state and local government purchases from $18.5 billion to an estimated $69.9 billion. Also on the basis of 1958 prices, per capita disposable personal income rose from $1236 in 1929 to an estimated $2373 in 1968. We can summarize these data by saying that although prices have increased over the last forty years, the real levels of government services and personal consumption also have increased.

For the most part, the economy has expanded at such a rate that the availability of jobs has kept pace with population growth. The rate of unemployment in relation to the total civilian labor force has not often exceeded 5 percent since 1942. Economic growth has

---

[6] Urbanization is analyzed in this context by Scott Greer, *The Emerging City* (New York: The Free Press of Glencoe, 1964).

[7] Figures in this paragraph are from *Economic Report of the President* (Washington, D.C.: U.S. Government Printing Office, 1969).

provided the resources necessary to finance the new schools and expanded programs required by the growing population. To be sure, few school systems are financed at the level which their strongest supporters advocate. Nevertheless, it can be said with confidence that the expansion of American education has depended upon economic development.

It should be noted, however, that economic growth is not a steady and all-encompassing process. It is often accompanied by serious dislocations for particular regions or occupational groups. For example, the decision of a large corporation to close a plant in a particular town cannot only leave its own employees without work, but will simultaneously reduce the income potential of merchants and professional persons in that community. Such a community is unlikely to feel it can afford an increase in school tax rates until the local economy is revitalized. Similarly, inflation can be a deterrent to increased levels of school support, particularly when citizens believe that taxes are already high.

There is at least one other aspect of this subject worth noting here. Continued economic development depends upon educational development. Industrialization and technology have revamped the American occupational structure. We are no longer a nation of farmers and factory workers. The number of white collar workers has grown steadily larger than the number of blue collar employees in the nation since 1956.[8] Many jobs which were common a decade or two ago (locomotive fireman, streetcar conductor) no longer exist and a host of new positions (key punchers, computer operators, air-conditioning and televison repairmen) have emerged. A large percentage of young people now in school will work at jobs that are not yet existent. This changing nature of the occupational structure means that schools should provide students with the background needed to adapt to changing vocational opportunities.

SOCIOECONOMIC DIVERSITY

Our comments about economic development notwithstanding, a large part of the American population is not prosperous. The Council of Economic Advisors reported that, in 1966, 29.7 million people (15.4 percent of the total population) lived in poverty.[9] Although

---

[8] Joseph W. Garbarino, "The Industrial Relations System." In Edgar L. Morphet and Charles O. Ryan, eds., *op. cit.*, p. 162.

[9] *Economic Report of the President* (Washington D.C.: U.S. Government Printing Office, 1968), p. 130.

rural poverty has continued to be a problem in some areas, notably the South, most of the poor are concentrated in central cities. The same report noted that the incidence of poverty is greatest among nonwhites, the aged, and households headed by women. At the other end of the spectrum, the President reported that, in 1967, more than 14 million families enjoyed incomes of more than $10,000.

As noted in Chapter 2, it has been traditional to refer to the public school as a "melting pot," where children of varying ethnicity and socioeconomic status come together for common education. Indeed much of the argument in favor of neighborhood schools derives from the presumed benefits of such intergroup experiences. Today the neighborhood school is less likely to provide such experiences. Neighborhoods, particularly those in large metropolitan areas, have become progressively more segregated in terms of ethnic and socioeconomic characteristics. Continued adherence to neighborhood school policies has meant that schools are segregated as well. Race is not the only variable by which urban residents have segregated themselves. The newcomer to most metropolitan areas quickly learns which neighborhoods are high-income suburbs; which are working-class communities; and which are predominantly Polish, Irish, Jewish, etc.

The reality of a pluralistic society living in relatively homogenous neighborhoods affects school administrators in several ways. If his school is in a particularly high or very low income area, it is unlikely that either he or members of his staff will have the first-hand sensitivity to local concerns which comes from experiencing them. Whether he lives in the community or not, he and his staff will need to give careful thought to ways in which the school can help its clients become more knowledgeable about and understanding of the broader society. Finally, many of the concerns and decisions which come to the attention of administrators will depend upon the neighborhood in which their school is located. We would expect the demands upon an elementary school principal in a very wealthy suburb to differ in many respects from those of his counterpart in a school which draws all of its students from a public housing project.

A TIME OF TENSIONS

Because America is a pluralistic and democratic society in which freedom of expression is a fundamental value, disagreement among citizens has been commonplace in our history. At times the issues have been so fundamental and the feelings so intense that the very fabric of society has been threatened. The classic examples, of course, center around the periods of the Revolutionary and Civil wars. Schools were not ignored during these conflicts, as citizens sought education for their children which was consistent with their own beliefs. The same has been true at other times in history, although the issues have been less dramatic. For example, many citizens in the middle decades of this century divided over the nature of steps which schools should take to indoctrinate students against Communism. Divisiveness regarding the appropriateness of sex education in the schools has been apparent more recently.

Although contemporary administrators need to be aware of tensions surrounding the anti-Communist and sex-education issues, two other conflicts in American society seem even more basic to school operation: The first deals with the role of youth in society; the second is race relations.

Student unrest became a national concern in the late 1960's.[10] Although the movement began at colleges and universities, it spread to the point that more than two thousand elementary and secondary schools experienced some form of unrest during 1968. These protests were violent in some instances. Students demanded and sometimes won a variety of changes in school policies and procedures ranging from dress codes, to criteria for selecting principals and assigning teachers, to expanded curricula. This series of protests raised fundamental questions about the role of students in their own education. Educators and laymen alike have diverse views on this subject, and often hold these views very strongly. Meanwhile many youths continue to challenge not only school procedures but also other institutions in society.

Despite the challenges posed by youth to older generations, the basic tensions in American society continue to be racial. Following the disastrous riots during the summer of 1967, the National Advisory Commission on Civil Disorders issued a report which declared "Our Nation is moving toward two societies, one black, one white— separate and unequal.[11] The commission's allegation that "white racism" was fundamentally responsible for the disadvantaged status of black Americans became a topic for heated debate. A national

---

[10] For more discussion of this subject, see Kenneth L. Fish, *Conflict and Dissent in the High Schools* (New York: The Bruce Publishing Co., 1970) and Jerome A. Skolnick, *The Politics of Protest: Violent Aspects of Protest and Confrontation.* A staff report to the National Commission on the Causes and Prevention of Violence (Washington, D.C.: U.S. Government Printing Office, 1969), pp. 63–69.

[11] Report of the National Advisory Commission on Civil Disorders. (New York: Bantam Books, 1968), p. 1.

survey in July, 1968, by CBS News gave some indication of public attitudes toward this conclusion. Seventy-four percent of blacks but only 31 percent of whites agreed with the statement "white racism is essentially responsible for the conditions in which Negroes live in American cities."[12]

A detailed examination of the implications of racial issues for schools is not in order here. Suffice it to say that schools have been confronted with many demands to improve educational opportunities for minority group students. Both the presentation of such demands and efforts to respond to them have frequently generated tension in school communities. It seems likely that such tension will continue not only until equality is achieved in the broader society but also until persons in the majority accept this condition.

EDUCATION AND NATIONAL DEVELOPMENT

We noted in Chapter 2 that the state has responsibility for education and that operating decisions are generally made at the local level. However, there are many developments which make it clear that the public has a stake in education at the national level and that some decisions and activities have nationwide implications.

EDUCATION AS PUBLIC INVESTMENT

Economists[13] have suggested that expenditures for education can be viewed in either or both of two ways. From one perspective, they can be treated as personal consumption in which individuals or governments spend their money for education instead of other goods or services because they enjoy the result. On the other hand, Theodore W. Schultz[14] and others have argued that expenditures for

---

[12] CBS News, *White and Negro Attitudes Towards Race Related Issues and Activities* (Princeton, N.J.: Opinion Research Corp., 1968), p. 5.

[13] For review of research on the economics of education, see John Vaizey, *The Economics of Education* (London: Faber and Faber, 1962) and Maureen Woodhall, "The Economics of Education." In *Review of Education Research* 34: (October, 1967), pp. 387–398.

[14] "Education and Economic Growth" in Nelson B. Henry, ed., The Sixtieth Yearbook of the National Society for the Study of Education, Part 2, *Social Forces Influencing American Education* (Chicago: University of Chicago Press, 1961). Also see Frederick Harbison and Charles A. Myers, *Education, Manpower and Economic Growth* (New York: McGraw Hill, 1964).

education can be considered investments in human capital. Conventional wisdom has acknowledged this view for individuals for some time. Thus many parents have advised their children to attend school to increase their earning power. However, it has also been shown that national levels of education are associated with gross national product and other indicators of economic health. Therefore, it is argued that investment in public education can enhance prosperity on national as well as individual bases.

We believe that the interest which many federal policy makers have shown in extending vocational education as well as improving other opportunities for schooling can be attributed at least partially to acceptance of this "investment perspective." During the middle 1960's, the extent of poverty in an affluent nation was documented by researchers and deplored by the American public. Passage of the Economic Opportunity Act of 1964 and the Elementary and Secondary Education Act of 1965 was achieved in this atmosphere.

Increasing federal appropriations for education are just one indication that expenditures for education are being seen as investments in human capital rather than simply as another form of personal consumption. Other signs include the efforts of organizations such as the Urban Coalition and the National Alliance of Businessmen to expand job opportunities.

There are also local examples of private citizens and agencies investing in education. The Association of Huntsville Area Companies (AHAC) was formed in Huntsville, Alabama, for the initial purpose of assuring compliance with civil rights measures by providing equal job opportunities. The organization soon learned that expanded educational opportunities were needed to qualify persons for jobs. As a result, AHAC became involved in support of several educational projects ranging from preschool programs to remedial programs for adults. In Philadelphia, the Reverend Leon Sullivan began a job preparation program in the black community which has been widely publicized and which represents investment in human capital. More generally, the notion of "Black Capitalism," which achieved considerable support during the late 1960's, applies the concept of investment in human capital as a means of building strength in the black community. Education in traditional as well as nontraditional forms (the tutoring of new merchants in accounting procedures by established businessmen) is essential to the Black Capitalism movement.

THE PUBLIC AND ITS SCHOOLS

More than one-fourth of the American population is directly involved with the schools in some way. There were in 1968 an estimated 45 million students enrolled in public elementary and secondary schools. Nearly two million teachers were employed in these schools and their efforts were supplemented by approximately 120,000 administrators. These persons worked in nearly 100,000 different schools located in approximately 20,000 different school districts.[15]

Approximately six million other students attended nonpublic elementary and secondary schools during the same year. These schools were staffed by approximately 240,000 teachers and an additional 20,000 administrators. There were close to 20,000 nonpublic schools operating at this time.

Public and nonpublic school expenditures for current operation and capital outlay were nearly $36 billion in 1968. Public school expenditures alone were approximately $32 billion. Only national defense accounted for a greater proportion of government expenditure.

The above figures do not reflect the large and growing number of persons and amount of resources related to the schools in a supportive or supplementary way. Business and industry have shown interest in relating to schools in a variety of ways. The traditional relationship has been profit-oriented. Schools have long depended upon private firms to provide the books, furniture, and materials which they need. Few would deny that business has had substantial impact upon school curricula in the design, production, and supply of these materials.

During the 1960's, several large firms made known their interest in developing new and improved materials for schools and also in providing services heretofore not available from commerical sources. Among the early leaders in this area were General Learning Corporation (a new firm formed by Time-Life and General Electric) and subsidiaries of other major corporations such as IBM, Westinghouse, and Litton Industries. While the exact nature of the contribution

---

[15] Most of the data in these paragraphs are drawn from U.S. Bureau of the Census, *Statistical Abstract of the United States, 1969,* 40th ed. (Washington, D.C.: U.S. Government Printing Office), pp. 100–124.

which these and similar firms can make to education remains undetermined, the extent of their interest establishes the fact that education is big business in the United States.

There also appears to be another side to the new business interest in education which is less directly related to profits. Many firms have demonstrated a desire to help remedy social problems such as poverty and unemployment through education. For example, Michigan Bell and the Chrysler Corporation have "adopted" two high schools in Detroit. The businesses provide the schools with special equipment, technical personnel, and other resources. Other examples of similar business efforts include support of the Urban League Street Academies in New York City, the Parkway School in Philadephia (in which high school students can take a variety of courses offered by different businesses), and a number of joint employment-education arrangements throughout the country.

NATIONALIZING TENDENCIES

Campbell and others[16] studied nationalizing influences upon education during 1961 and 1962. In particular, they examined the impact of the National Science Foundation, the National Merit Scholarship Program, the National Defense Act of 1958, and The College Entrance Examinations Board (CEEB) upon secondary schools. They reported nine general findings:

1. National programs have changed substantially the courses offered in science, mathematics, and foreign languages in our high schools.
2. National programs have altered the guidance programs of our high schools.
3. National programs have created a vast external testing program for our high schools.
4. National programs have changed college admissions procedures.
5. National programs have established a new pattern for the inservice education of teachers.
6. National programs have altered school plant planning and construction.
7. There has been differential use of national programs. . . . Rural schools appeared to be the low users of the most programs. Suburban users were high users of NSF and the College Board and most NDEA programs.

---

[16] Roald F. Campbell and Robert A. Bunnell, eds. *Nationalizing Influences in Secondary Education* (Chicago: Midwest Administration Center, 1963).

8. National programs have given the public a new measuring stick with which to evaluate schools.

9. Apparently many people do not recognize or will not acknowledge the impact of the national programs on the schools.

The programs which Campbell and his colleagues studied have expanded considerably since they viewed them. For example, more than three million tests were administered by the College Entrance Examinations Board (CEEB) in 1966–1967 whereas an estimated 750,000 students took such tests in 1960. During the same period, the number of colleges and universities which were members of the CEEB climbed from 427 to more than 600. It is also likely that both rural and city schools participate more actively in these programs than they did in 1961–1962, and that the American public is more aware of them now than at that time.

In addition, there have been other developments since the early 1960's which have augmented the nationalizing influences already discussed. Funds from the United States Office of Education and some private sources have made it possible to expand the curriculum development projects originally supported by the National Science Foundation. Some of the research and development centers and regional educational laboratories supported by the U.S. Office of Education have been important in this regard.

The activities of national foundations have also been a nationalizing influence. Much of the national interest in improving urban schools by strengthening their relationships with citizens and community agencies can be attributed to the efforts of the Ford Foundation. First through support of the "Grey Areas Projects" and later by their involvement in plans to decentralize the New York City schools, the foundation provided stimuli in this direction. Similarly, the Carnegie Corporation supported the studies of James B. Conant, which most thoughtful observers believe have had enormous influence on educational practice throughout the nation. Carnegie has also sponsored the national assessment program, which is in an early stage but has considerable potential for planning educational programs on a national basis. More recently, the Kettering Foundation has become an active supporter of educational projects.

Nationalizing tendencies were enhanced during the 1960's by what we might term the "multiplier factor of public interest." Citizens more than ever before believe that schools are important and seek expanded educational opportunities for their children. At the same time the national media have made more knowledge about educational developments available to the population. Thus citizens can often read stories in national magazines and see television programs about foreign language in elementary schools, individualized instruction, community control, or other developments. They often become a source of support to introduce similar programs in their own locale. This tendency is strengthened by the fact that approximately 20 percent of the population moves annually and brings expectations for schools which are based upon experiences in their earlier community.

The federal government has been a consistent and significant influence upon educational development in the nation. The notion that federal influence is relatively new in education is widely held but inaccurate. As noted in Chapter 2, federal participation dates back to the earliest days of the nation. It is also true, however, that the federal government has become much more active in recent years, particularly through the Office of Education. For example, Allen reported in 1950 that the annual federal expenditure for education was more than $3 billion and that less than 1 percent of these funds was allocated by the Office of Education.[17] By 1968, estimated federal expenditures for education had increased to more than $11 billion, of which nearly one-third was expended through the Office of Education.[18]

The cornerstone of current federal aid to education is the Elementary and Secondary Education Act of 1965 (ESEA). Although the primary focus of this measure is upon improving educational opportunities for children from low-income families, most local school districts qualify for aid under its provisions. The core of ESEA, in terms of both Congressional intent and the proportion of funds allocated to it, is Title I. More than $1 billion annually has been authorized by this Title for educational programs to benefit children from families with poverty-level incomes.

Title II authorized federal assistance to school districts for the purchase of textbooks and other instructional materials. Title III authorized the creation of supplementary educational centers which would engage nonpublic as well as public schools in collaborative programs with other educative agencies. A variety of remedial and supplementary services has been provided through such centers. Proposals for Title III projects were originally reviewed at the federal

[17] Hollis P. Allen, *The Federal Government in Education*. (New York: McGraw-Hill, 1950).

[18] *Digest of Educational Statistics 1967* (Washington, D.C.: U.S. Government Printing Office, 1967), p. 165.

level, but control over Title III funds was subsequently transferred to state departments of education. Title IV of ESEA authorized additional funds for the cooperative research program as well as the establishment of research and development centers and regional educational laboratories. Title V authorized funds to strengthen state departments of education.

The impact of ESEA is not entirely clear at this point. Certainly, passage of the act helped to focus national attention upon educational priorities, and a wide variety of programs has been implemented with the funds it has provided. These funds have no doubt furnished much of the incentive for the large number of new businesses concerned with education. Although the timing of the federal disbursement process and other matters of coordination have created some administrative problems, it seems fair to say that the general experience of schoolmen with ESEA has whetted their appetite for additional federal assistance. It is unfortunate that shifting national priorities have not allowed the funding of ESEA at the level authorized by Congress, much less made possible its expansion to higher levels. However, experience with ESEA and other federal measures (e.g., the Education Professions Development Act) has increased the political sophistication of educators. Tangible evidence of this was seen in creation of the Emergency Committee for Full Funding of Education Legislation in 1969. This group, comprised of representatives of major educational organizations, lobbied with some success in the Congress.

It may be that the fact that available money has been spread so thin accounts substantially for the lack of strong evidence supporting the effectiveness of Title I programs. One early study concluded that Title I "does indeed succeed in channeling federal government funds to the low-income regions of the country to a very substantial degree."[19] However, few evaluations of the many compensatory programs established with Title I funds have shown much evidence of effectiveness in terms of educational gain.[20]

A 1969 study by the NAACP Legal Defense and Education Fund and the Washington Research Project of the Southern Center for Studies in Public Policy concluded that "Millions of dollars appropriated by the Congress to help educationally deprived children have

---

[19] Murray L. Weidenbaum and Norman P. Swenson, "Federal Aid to Education and Low Income Areas," *Educational Administration Quarterly* II: 232–33 (Autumn, 1966).

[20] Some of these studies are reviewed in U.S. Commission on Civil Rights, *Racial Isolation in the Public Schools, Vol. I* (Washington, D.C.: U.S. Government Printing Office, 1966).

been wasted, diverted, or otherwise misused by state and local school authorities."[21] The report, which was based upon a review of federal audits and other data gathered from selected school districts, state departments of education, and parents, stated that Title I

- has not reached eligible children in many instances
- has not been concentrated on those most in need, so there is reasonable promise of success
- has purchased hardware at the expense of instructional programs
- has not been used to meet the most serious educational needs of school children, and
- has not been used in a manner that involves parents and communities in carrying out Title I projects.[22]

Of importance to schoolmen is the fact that both the Congress and segments of the general public are calling for more direct evidence that federal investment in educational programs is worthwhile.

Federal influence upon local school districts is not limited to legislative approval of various assistance programs. Both the executive and judicial branches exert considerable influence. The participation of the executive branch is evident in several ways. Government administrators are often influential in shaping the nature of legislation which is enacted. For example, this was true in the case of the Elementary and Secondary Education Act.[23] Once legislation is passed, government officials draw up the guidelines for their administration and hold delegate agencies such as school districts responsible for compliance. In this way, government officials may serve as a source of appeal for citizens who believe that federal programs are not being administered appropriately at the local level. Moreover, administrators of federal agencies other than the Office of Education sometimes call upon school officials to assure compliance with particular guidelines and coordination with other federal programs. For example, the Department of Justice has sued school systems for noncompliance with civil rights laws. Local schoolmen have also been called upon to coordinate some of their programs with certain model cities and Office of Economic Opportunity efforts.

[21] Title I of the Elementary and Secondary Education Act of 1965, *Is It Helping Poor Children?* A report of the Washington Research Project of the Southern Conference for Studies in Public Policy, and NAACP Legal Defense and Educational Fund, New York, 1969), pp. 1–2.

[22] *Ibid.*

[23] C. Philip Kearney, "The 1964 Presidential Task Force on Education and the Elementary and Secondary Education Act of 1965" (Unpublished doctoral dissertation, Department of Education, University of Chicago, 1967).

The federal courts have had significant influence upon local school districts through a number of decisions. Some of these decisions have involved interpreting parts of the Bill of Rights such as freedom of speech or religion as they apply to public education. Many other decisions have been based upon interpreting the due process and equal protection clauses of the Fourteenth Amendment. Most of the desegregation cases have involved interpretation of the Fourteenth Amendment.

Areas in which federal courts have made decisions of great impact upon local public school practice include desegregation, relationships with nonpublic schools, and religious observances. Some of the most important cases in these areas were discussed in Chapter 2. Another area in which recent decisions of importance were made is that of student rights. Following its tradition of upholding civil liberties, the Warren Court held in 1967 that rights of due process must be observed in dealing with students charged with delinquency.[24] In a subsequent case, *Tinker et al. v. Des Moines Independent Community School District et al.,* the Court upheld the right of students to wear black armbands to school in peaceful protest of the Vietnam War. The Court stated:

> First Amendment rights, applied in light of the special characteristics of the school environment are available to teachers and students. It can hardly be argued that either students or teachers shed their constitutional rights to freedom of speech or expression at the schoolhouse gate. . . . School officials do not possess absolute authority over their students. Students in school as well as out of school are "persons" under our Constitution. They are possessed of fundamental rights which the State must respect, just as they themselves must respect their obligations to the State.[25]

THE CONTEST TO SHAPE LOCAL EDUCATIONAL POLICY

Thus far in this chapter, we have identified a number of background factors and developments at the national level of which administrators should be cognizant. Our theme has been that such factors influence decisions made at the local school or school district level. We shall now deal a bit more specifically with local issues. It appears that policymaking for local schools has become more controversial in

---

[24] *In the Matter of Gault,* 387 U.S. 1 (1967).
[25] *Tinker v. Des Moines Independent Community School District,* 390 U.S. 942 (1968).

recent years, as a wide range of parties has become involved in decisions. Our approach here will be to identify parties who are often involved in such decisions and then to examine some issues of contemporary importance at this level.

PARTICIPANTS IN LOCAL POLICY MAKING

A logical place to begin the consideration of parties involved in local school policy making is with boards of education, sometimes called school committees or school commissions. Such bodies have legal responsibility for establishing local school policy within the guidelines established by the state constitution and school codes. As noted in Chapter 2, board of education members are state officials and must carry out state laws. The board has legal status only as an entity (individual members cannot act for the board), and enjoys only those powers expressly or implicitly delegated to it by the state constitution or statutes. However, boards of education enjoy considerable "discretionary authority" (although exact conditions vary from state to state) because the wording of state codes is often permissive rather than mandatory and quite general in many areas. To cite only a few examples, boards of education generally make formal decisions to hire and dismiss particular employees; determine salaries and other budgetary allocations; and establish when, where, and in what style new schools will be constructed. Even where boards are guided in such areas by state requirements (personnel certification requirements and salary minimums), they can exercise a wide range of alternatives.

Boards of education should exercise their discretionary powers in the best interests of the citizens they represent. Most board members are elected at large in nonpartisan elections. However, in some locales, they are appointed by the mayor, the city council, or other public official often upon the nomination of another body such as a "blue-ribbon" citizens committee. Regardless of how they achieve office, most board members do not acknowledge indebtedness to a particular local constituency. The general view is that each member represents "all of the people." McCarty and Ramsey[26] have noted that exceptions to this view do exist. In a study of fifty-one school districts, they found that some board members serve as representa-

[26] Donald J. McCarty and Charles E. Ramsey, *The School Managers: Power and Conflict in American Public Education* (Westport, Conn.: Greenwood Publishing Corp., 1970).

tives of special interests and for self-oriented motives, and that such motivations affect the behavior of their respective superintendents.

Middle-class businessmen and professional persons have been traditionally over-represented on boards of education.[27] Similarly, board membership is most widely held by persons who tend to be in middle or upper-middle social strata according to such indicators as education and income. Neither the poor nor the extremely rich serve very often as board of education members. Similarly, representatives of minority groups have generally been under-represented on school boards in the past. There are indications that the latter circumstance may be changing, particularly in large cities where a growing number of blacks have achieved election or appointment to these positions. Similarly, there is some evidence that recent events, particularly the civil rights movement and the concomitant increase in the visibility of school affairs, have associated some board members with particular racial, ethnic, or neighborhood constituencies.

Some scholars[28] have suggested that the actual influence of boards of education upon school decisions is somewhat less than their formal responsibility would indicate. Pointing out that board membership is a part-time and avocational activity, they note that members must rely heavily upon information and recommendations from professional administrators. On the other hand, Crain[29] found that boards of education in eight Northern cities tended to remove the decision of how to respond to civil rights demands from administrators, and that the attitudes of board members were important determinants of these responses.

Minar[30] studied the decision-making relationships between boards of education and superintendents in suburban communities. He found that boards of education comprised of persons who are experienced managers and directors in professional life tend to give administrators more latitude in making operating decisions about the schools than

[27] Cf. George S. Counts, *The Social Composition of Boards of Education* (Chicago: University of Chicago Press, 1927) and Alpheus L. White, *Local School Boards: Organizations and Practices* (Washington, D.C.: U.S. Government Printing Office, 1962).

[28] For example, see Norman D. Kerr, "The School Board as an Agency of Legitimation," *Sociology of Education* 38 (Fall, 1964), pp. 34–59.

[29] Robert L. Crain, *The Politics of School Desegregation* (Chicago: Aldine Publishing Co., 1968).

[30] David W. Minar, *Educational Decision-Making in Suburban Communities* (Washington, D.C.: U.S. Office of Education, Cooperative Research Project No. 2440, 1966) and *Idem.* "The Community Basis of Conflict in School System Politics," *American Sociological Review.* Vol. 31, No. 6, December, 1966, pp. 822–835.

do boards with less managerial expertise among their members. He also reported that such variations in style were associated with community factors. School boards are more likely to give administrators wide decision-making latitude in communities where there is relatively little conflict in school affairs (defined as the percent of negative vote in school board and school tax elections).

The research summarized above points out the importance of the relationship between the school board and the superintendent in policy making. It suggests that the popular notion whereby the school board makes policy and the superintendent carries it out is an oversimplification. Both parties make contributions to this process and they function most effectively when a sense of mutual trust and responsibility exists among them. In exercising their respective legal authority and professional judgment, the successful board and superintendent must show respect for each other and sensitivity to community interests.

The school board-superintendent relationship is the focal point for local policy development. However, many other groups and individuals attempt to influence decisions made at this level. Several years ago, Gross[31] asked superintendents and board of education members from approximately half the school districts in Massachusetts who exerted pressure upon them. The responses to this question are summarized in Table 3.1. Table 3.2 summarizes the kinds of pressures to which these persons said they were exposed.

The data reported by Gross are fairly old, and the nature of local issues has probably changed some in recent years. Nevertheless, his research illustrates the wide range of groups and individuals who attempt to influence school decision-making. In our judgment, current pressures are at least as diverse in origin as they were when Gross did his study. Moreover, it is clear that the intensity with which some groups advocate their views has increased appreciably in the last decade. Many of what the persons interviewed by Gross reported as pressures were no doubt requests, opinions, or demands made quietly by individuals. To be sure, these expressions frequently were not devoid of sanctions, as Gross makes clear.[32] At the present time the quiet demands of individuals are often augmented or opposed by public demands and sophisticated tactics of organized groups.

Certainly the most visible and probably the most powerful of such

[31] Neal Gross, *Who Runs Our Schools?* (New York: Wiley, 1958).

[32] Gross defines pressure as "a request, demand, or expressed opinion behind which lies a threat for failure to conform to the request, demand, or opinion, whether this threat is intended or unintended, implicit or explicit." *op. cit.,* pp. 47–48.

TABLE 3.1   Percentage of Superintendents and School Board Members Who Said They Were Exposed to Pressures from the Specified Individuals and Groups

INDIVIDUALS OR GROUPS WHO EXERT PRESSURE	SUPERINTENDENTS (N = 105)	SCHOOL BOARD MEMBERS (N = 508)
1. Parents or PTA	92	74
2. Individual school board members	75	51
3. Teachers	65	44
4. Taxpayers' association	49	31
5. Town finance committee or city council	48	38
6. Politicians	46	29
7. Business or commercial organizations	45	19
8. Individuals influential for economic reasons	44	25
9. Personal friends	37	37
10. The press	36	19
11. Old-line families	30	26
12. Church or religious groups	28	18
13. Veterans' organizations	27	10
14. Labor unions	27	5
15. Chamber of Commerce	23	5
16. Service clubs	20	11
17. Fraternal organizations	13	9
18. Farm organizations	12	4
19. Welfare organizations	3	1

Source: Neal Gross, *Who Runs Our Schools?* (New York: John Wiley & Sons, 1958). p. 50.

groups are the teacher organizations. The National Education Association and the American Federation of Teachers emerged as strong advocates of teacher interests during the 1960's. Both groups predate this decade, however. The National Education Association was formed in 1857 as the National Teachers Association, a confederation of ten state teachers' associations. The name of the organization was changed in 1879, and it has grown to the point that in 1969 it had more than one million members. These members are served through a large bureaucracy including fifty-three state and 8,827 local affiliated organizations; four departments; twenty-nine national affiliates and associated organizations; and twenty-five commissions, committees, and councils.[33] Although the Department of Classroom

[33] *NEA Handbook, 1969–1970* (Washington, D.C.: National Education Association, 1969), p. 16.

TABLE 3.2 **Percentage of Superintendents and School Board Members Exposed to Specified Pressures**

PRESSURE	SUPERINTENDENTS (N = 105)	SCHOOL BOARD MEMBERS (N = 508)
1. Demands that the schools should place more emphasis on the three R's	59	53
2. Demands that the schools should teach more courses and subjects	64	47
3. Protests about the use of particular textbooks	19	19
4. Protests about the views expressed by teachers	49	41
5. Demands that teachers should express certain views	13	12
6. Protesting school tax increases or bond proposals	73	70
7. Demanding more money for the general school program	66	52
8. Protesting the introduction of new services (in addition to academic instruction) for pupils	39	35
9. Demanding the introduction of new services (in addition to academic instruction) for pupils	63	49
10. Demands that school contracts be given to certain firms	46	24
11. Demands that teachers be appointed or dismissed for reasons other than competence	46	24
12. Demanding the introduction of new teaching methods	29	35
13. Protesting the introduction of new teaching methods	43	28
14. Demanding that greater emphasis be placed on the athletic program	58	52
15. Demanding that less emphasis be placed on the athletic program	40	38

Source: Neal Gross, *Who Runs Our Schools?* (New York: John Wiley & Sons, 1958). p. 49.

Teachers has been the largest division of the association since it was formed in 1942, its internal influence has been exceeded until recent years by other departments, notably those which have represented administrators. At least until recently, the NEA showed more concern for the establishment of national goals and standards through bodies such as the Educational Policies Commission, advocacy of increased state and federal aid to education, and dissemination of research and statistics than it did for direct teacher benefits and expanded teacher participation in policy-making.[34]

The American Federation of Teachers was founded in 1916 as an affiliate of the American Federation of Labor. This organization, which now has approximately 135,000 members in twenty-five state federations and 560 local affiliates, has emphasized teacher rights and welfare since its origin. As Rosenthal[35] points out, the relative significance of the two organizations is belied by simple comparison of membership figures. The Federation has strong support in large cities, and there is little doubt that its activities have prodded the NEA and its affiliates into a more militant position than they formerly held.

What many observers note as the most significant turning points to increased teacher militancy took place in New York City during 1960–1962.[36] In November of 1960, the United Federation of Teachers (an AFT local) held a one-day strike to back its demand that the board of education designate a collective bargaining agent for teachers. The UFT won the subsequent election held to select such an agent, and struck again for a day in April, 1962, to back contract demands that were settled after Mayor Robert Wagner and Governor Nelson Rockefeller intervened in the negotiations. More than 20,000 teachers participated in the second strike, which served notice to the NEA and the nation at large that substantial teacher benefits could be won through collective bargaining. The same event was the first to demonstrate that the New York State law and others like it, which call for heavy penalties such as dismissal for public employees who strike, are virtually unenforceable in the face of large-scale walkouts.

The UFT victory in New York encouraged AFT leaders in other cities to press for representative bargaining status or negotiated contracts in their own locales. In response, the NEA at its 1962 convention adopted resolutions which employed the terms "professional negotiation" and "professional sanctions" for the first time. Lieberman and Moscow note that these acts by the NEA were significant, but considered them less so than the speech by the NEA

---

[34] Alan Rosenthal, *Pedagogues and Power: Teacher Groups in School Politics* (Syracuse, N.Y.: Syracuse University Press, 1969), p. 5.

[35] *Ibid.,* p. 23.

[36] For a review of these events, see Myron Lieberman and Michael H. Moskow, *Collective Negotiations for Teachers* (Chicago: Rand McNally, 1966), pp. 35–47.

executive secretary at the same convention. He "identified unionization as a threat to education and the NEA" . . . [and] "went on to
explain that the newly established Urban Project would direct the
NEA fight against unionization of teachers."[37]

The competition between the two organizations continued
throughout the decade. There were noteworthy differences between
the groups at the outset of this period. The most prominent of these
was the AFT perspective and affiliation which identified teachers with
"labor" in opposition to "management." This contrasted with the
NEA claim to "professional" status and affiliation with administrators in a common organization. A second difference has been AFT
support of strikes, continued negotiation, and mediation in the event
of bargaining impasses. In contrast, the NEA has spoken of professional sanctions (ranging from public notice of an undesirable teaching situation to urging teachers not to seek employment in a particular
school district until such conditions are remedied) and has advocated
written agreement upon procedures for resolving impasses preferably
through educational rather than labor channels.[38]

These differences have led to considerable variation in the rhetoric
employed by organizational leaders. A structural difference which has
been reflected in the membership dues of the two groups has been the
greater emphasis by the NEA upon activities of the state and national
levels. The NEA and its state affiliates have continued to provide
numerous publications, to hold conferences, and to work actively for
legislation. For the most part, the AFT has concentrated on supporting local affiliates in quest of local benefits.

Differences between the organizations apparently have lessened as
their competition has increased. The most noticeable trend in this
direction has been the increasingly militant pursuit of welfare objectives by NEA affiliates. Early steps in this direction were the imposi-
tion of statewide sanctions in Utah and Oklahoma in 1964 and 1965.
More recently, NEA affiliates have moved away from their earlier
aversion to strikes or other forms of work stoppages. The Kentucky
Education Association held a one-day "professional study day" in
1966, and the Florida Education Association staged a three-week
walkout to support salary demands in 1968. Some persons might
consider it surprising that a total number of 114 teacher strikes
occurred during the 1967–1968 school year and that seventy of these

[37] *Ibid.*, p. 45.
[38] *Ibid.*, pp. 319–320.

were waged by NEA affiliates (two others were joint union-NEA affiliate actions).[39] Another difference between the two organizations has been obviated in some states (Ohio and Michigan), where the state associations of administrators have established their independence of the state education association. Against the backdrop of these developments, the president of the AFT, David Selden, has called for a merger of his group and the NEA. Teachers in at least one local school district (Flint, Michigan) did achieve such a merger before the decade ended.

As we enter the 1970's, it is apparent that teacher organizations have become a formidable force in local policy making. The most obvious evidence has been their ability to win substantial salary gains from local school boards. Indeed, they have sometimes won contracts (as in the Bigtown case described in Chapter 1) which call for more revenue for salaries than is available to the local board, and require additional funds from state sources. But teacher power has also been effective on issues other than salaries. A long and bitterly contested strike by the UFT in New York City had substantial effect upon the "community control" debate there.[40]

Further evidence that teachers are a force to be reckoned with in local policy making is the growing formalization of negotiating procedures. Several states have enacted legislation which acknowledges the legitimacy of or specifically requires school boards to negotiate with teacher organizations. Moreover, the range of items subject to negotiation is expanding beyond salaries and working conditions. A 1968 NEA publication[41] which summarized provisions contained in 1,540 negotiations agreements indicated that various aspects of the instructional program were often negotiated. Included were such items as class size, selection and use of instructional materials, parent conferences, and pupil discipline. An item subject to negotiation in at least one state (Michigan), which can further strengthen teacher groups, is the "agency shop." In effect, an agency-shop provision "requires all employees in the negotiating unit who do not become members of the representative organization to pay service charges or

---

[39] "Teacher Strikes in Perspective," *NEA Research Bulletin* 46 (December, 1968), pp. 113–116.

[40] See Martin Mayer, *The Teacher's Strike: New York, 1968* (New York: Harper & Row, 1969) and Marilyn Gittell and Maurice Berube, *Confrontation at Ocean Hill-Brownsville* (New York: Praeger, 1969).

[41] "What's Negotiable?" *NEA Research Bulletin* 46 (May, 1968), pp. 42–43.

the equivalent of membership dues as a condition of continued employment."[42]

Finally, and perhaps most indicative of teachers' enhanced bargaining status, there is the position of the National School Boards Association. This group, which strenuously opposed collective negotiations for some time and which continues to oppose strikes, boycotts, and sanctions, now states as a matter of policy:

> In determining general policies relating to the operation of the schools, handling of personnel problems, and the general welfare of all professional personnel, each local school board should set up satisfactory procedures for communication with all professional [personnel]. Such procedures should recognize that the function of the professional practice of teaching requires that individual teachers have and exercise full freedom of association, expression, organization, and designation of representatives of their own choosing for the purpose of conferring with school boards concerning the terms and conditions of their employment.[43]

The emergence of militant teacher organizations has forced superintendents to reexamine their roles vis-à-vis the board of education and teachers in their district. Several roles have been suggested for them in the negotiations setting—including negotiator for the board, negotiator for the teachers, and impartial advisor to both parties. According to our judgment, the effect of events in most districts has been to identify the superintendent as management and on the side of the school board in negotiations. This does not necessarily mean that he, himself, should be negotiator for the board. This is often a time-consuming and technical responsibility which can be delegated to someone with special preparation for it.

Negotiated agreements with teachers have also limited administrative prerogatives in some areas. For example, where contracts specify that class sizes must be kept below a certain figure, constraints are placed upon the way classrooms are organized. Similarly, contracts which specify that teachers need not remain at school for more than a short time after students are dismissed can limit administrative plans to hold faculty meetings.

Teachers have not been the only group to organize in order to have

---

[42] "Teachers and the Agency Shop," *NEA Research Bulletin* 47 (December, 1969), p. 110.

[43] "Beliefs and Policies of the National Association of School Boards." In *New Dimensions in Leadership,* Proceedings of the 1968 Convention (Evanston, Ill.: The Association, 1968), pp. 88–89.

an impact upon school affairs in recent years. Parent and neighborhood groups have often done likewise.[44] Demands associated with
school desegregation, improved education for minority group children, and, later, "community control" appeared to be the most
frequent stimuli to such activity in the 1960's. Protestors were
sometimes associated with civil rights groups such as the NAACP or
CORE and were sometimes organized independently. Protests have
also been mounted by urban whites in opposition to black demands,
and by suburbanites or small town residents, over various questions
dealing with curriculum, school finance, and other subjects. For
example, a group of parents in one city recently protested and
attempted court action in opposition to a school board decision not to
allow a high school band to march in an out-of-town holiday parade.

In some instances, teacher and citizen groups have been on
opposite sides of issues. A well-known case was the Ocean Hill-
Brownsville controversy (Brooklyn, N.Y.). However, there have
been similar but less visible instances in other cities; and the growing
interest in community control among some Americans suggests that
further confrontations may be in the offing. Citizen groups have often
employed tactics similar to those of militant teacher organizations in
dealing with school officials. These include insisting upon "negotiations" (sometimes to the point of written agreements) and threatening or sometimes bringing about "work stoppages" in the form of
school boycotts, demonstrations, and other disruptions of normal
activities.

One other point should be noted about participation in local policy
making. The demands of militant teacher and citizen groups have
sometimes been so threatening to the established order or so far
beyond the capacity of school officials to respond, that school authorities have turned to other levels of government for assistance. Several
examples can be cited. One is disruptive activity by adult or student
protestors for which schoolmen seek police assistance. Another is the
example of teacher negotiations discussed in Chapter 1, in which
school officials sought additional funds to meet teacher demands
through the mayor and the state legislature. Another was the Ocean
Hill-Brownsville dispute, in which New York officials sought help in
resolving their crisis from the state commissioner of education and
other officials.

In addition, aggrieved citizens who feel they are making little

---

[44] See Luvern L. Cunningham and Raphael O. Nystrand, *Citizen Participation in School Affairs* (Washington, D.C.: The Urban Coalition, 1969).

headway in direct negotiation with school officials sometimes petition other governments to intervene. Thus some white Chicagoans, who objected to school system desegregation plans, appealed to state Congressmen from their districts who in turn threatened to oppose Chicago school requests for more funds from the Illinois legislature if these plans were not altered. Desegregation advocates in many locales have petitioned state and federal courts and executives to withhold funds from their school districts until greater desegregation can be achieved.

The point of the preceding examples is that power to establish educational policy is diffuse and can be checked or augmented by numerous actors in a variety of ways. Moreover, there are signs that the involvement of noneducation officials in school matters is increasing. A recent survey of mayors of big cities revealed that 60 percent of them believed their participation in educational affairs would increase in the future.[45] School administrators work in a very pluralistic setting and must act frequently as brokers who encourage coalitions among diverse groups including citizens, teachers, and sometimes politicians in support of particular policies and programs.

CONTEMPORARY ISSUES

An indication of the wide range of issues which face schoolmen was presented in Table 3.2. A more recent accounting was provided by Goldhammer, who interviewed a number of superintendents across the nation. He categorized many of their problems as follows:

1. *Educational change* . . . Superintendents feel that many of their problems arise from shifting expectations for the schools within the community as well as from the interventions of agencies outside of the school. They are equally concerned with the fact that there are pressures for change within the organization itself.

2. *Teacher Militancy* . . . These problems [dealing with teacher groups] change the nature of the school organization and create new definitions of the limitations and potentialities of public school programs.

3. *Instruction* . . . [The superintendent] is deeply involved in and concerned with problems of curriculum, instructional services of all sorts, evaluation, adaptation, and learning outcomes.

[45] Richard W. Saxe, "Mayors and Schools," *Urban Education* 4 (October, 1969) 243–251.

4. *Administrative Leadership* . . . The times require changes in the nature of the leadership functions of the superintendency and new demands on his competency. He seems to be forced to consider not only these issues and their impacts upon the schools, but also the major role he is required to play within the community and the school organization because of these issues.

5. *Critical Social Issues* . . . The issues of church and state, of desegregation, of the more equitable distribution of economic resources, of the reduction of social distance among cultural and racial groups—all involve the schools and create new demands not only upon the programs of the schools but also upon the nature of the decisions which have to be made in the maintenance and operation of the schools.

6. *Finance* . . . The traditional role of the administrator as the procurer of resources for the school organization has not been greatly changed . . . financial worries still plague the superintendent and are a primary problem for him.[46]

The problems identified by Goldhammer have not been resolved since he reported his research. Indeed, they have probably intensified in at least some areas. They are also interrelated. At the present time, we judge there are at least four general issues which crosscut these problems. Each of them calls for the kind of administrative leadership Goldhammer mentions in response to social change.

The first issue is the one discussed in the preceding section of this chapter: Who should participate in school decision-making? As already noted, the changing roles of teachers seem particularly important in their implications for administrators.

A second and related issue which became quite controversial in the late 1960's deals with the nature of local control. In a series of encounters which began in New York City, citizens in minority group communities have challenged the representativeness of city boards of education. Frustrated by what they see as the failure of school systems to educate their children to the extent they wish, these citizens have demanded that city boards of education surrender their jurisdiction to a number of neighborhood or community governing boards.

Community control proposals have come from and are attractive to citizens who believe the schools have not served them well and who feel they cannot achieve redress of their grievances through exist-

---

[46] Keith Goldhammer, *et al., Issues and Problems in Contemporary Educational Administration* (Eugene, Ore.: Center for the Advanced Study of Educational Administration, University of Oregon, 1967).

ing structures. Through community control, many persons seek a means of holding school personnel accountable for educational outcomes.

The focus on accountability makes it clear that community control proposals challenge more than the traditional prerogatives of school boards. Also under fire are the ability of teacher organizations to negotiate system-wide contracts, administrative procedures for making many kinds of operating decisions including the assignment of personnel and the selection of instructional materials, and procedures for evaluating personnel and programs.

A third contemporary issue deals with what the schools should teach. This question has been controversial for centuries, and there is no reason to predict its final resolution. The specifics of the issue change rather frequently. Prominent at the present time are questions about whether or not the schools should make special efforts to teach the culture and history of minority groups and, if so, to whom and how. Another controversial issue, mentioned above, is what—if anything—the schools should do about teaching sex education. In a more general sense, there has been considerable disagreement about the role of the school in combating social problems. The most visible controversy has been related to desegregation proposals. However, matters such as free lunches or dental examinations, placement of special remedial programs in some schools but not others, and even matters related to the dress and grooming of students have touched off public debates of major proportion.

A fourth issue deals with how schools should be financed. There are two general dimensions to the problem. One is determining how the funds available to schools should be allocated. If X dollars are available to a school system in a given year, what part should be allocated to teacher salaries, introduction of new programs, instructional materials, and other items? This dimension clearly overlaps the issues discussed above inasmuch as controversies about who should make what decisions at what levels about what programs can be defined operationally as questions of resource allocation. As discussed here, these are questions about allocations within particular schools or school districts.

There appears also to be a trend among some school districts to contract with private firms for the provision of particular educational services including the teaching of reading and other subjects. It may be that decisions about allocating funds will increasingly reflect judgments about what the local staff should do and what should be subcontracted to business firms.

The second dimension of the finance problem relates to the sources of revenue available to individual school districts and consequent inequalities of expenditure among them. Levels of expenditure vary widely among school districts. For example, in 1968, the state of Illinois contained "adjoining school districts" where the per pupil expenditure was $382 in one and $1084 in the other.[47] In a recent statewide study of Michigan schools, Thomas[48] demonstrated that the level of financial support available to school districts influences the range of educational opportunities available to students in the respective districts. As seen in Table 3.3, for example, 72 percent of

TABLE 3.3 **Percent and Number of Michigan Junior High Schools by Level of Expenditure Per Pupil Offering Various Special Classes (1966–67)**

| | EXPENDITURE LEVEL | | |
| | MORE THAN | | LESS THAN |
SPECIAL PROGRAM	$510	$440–$509	$440
Classes for verbally talented	72% (143)	44% (89)	30% (50)
Classes for quantitatively talented	65% (128)	37% (74)	32% (52)
School mathematic study group	44% (87)	20% (39)	15% (24)
Modern math at all levels	88% (176)	73% (147)	63% (105)
Curricular provision for below average pupils not qualified for special education	81% (161)	65% (131)	48% (80)
Team teaching	45% (88)	27% (53)	20% (32)

Source: J. Alan Thomas, *School Finance in Michigan* (Lansing: State Department of Education, 1968), Figure 2.3.

school districts which spent more than $510 per pupil provided special classes for verbally talented students whereas only 30 percent of districts spending less than $440 offered such classes.

Public schools depend upon local, state, and federal governments as sources of revenue. Although federal aid has increased and wide variation exists in the levels at which the respective states aid local

[47] Charles A. Daly, ed., *The Quality of Inequality: Urban and Suburban Schools* (Chicago: The University of Chicago Center for Policy Study, 1968), p. 5.

[48] J. Alan Thomas, *School Finance in Michigan* (Lansing, Mich.: State Department of Education, 1968).

schools, schools in most states have depended primarily upon local revenues in the past. Table 3.4 shows there has been little change in this situation during the past two decades.

TABLE 3.4   **Percent of Total School Revenues Received Annually from Various Government Sources**

	GOVERNMENT LEVEL		
YEAR	FEDERAL (%)	STATE (%)	LOCAL (%)
1940	1.8	30.3	68.0
1950	2.9	39.8	57.3
1960	4.4	39.1	56.5
1966	7.9	39.1	53.0

Source: U.S. Bureau of the Census. *Statistical Abstract of the United States* (Washington, D.C.: U.S. Government Printing Office, 1969), 40th ed., p. 115.

The primary source of local school revenues is the property tax. In 1967, 98.6 percent of local revenues collected by fiscally independent school districts was property tax collections.[49] Much of the variation among local district expeditures therefore can be attributed to differences in the amount of taxable property per pupil in given school districts and the level of tax rates, respectively. Table 3.5 presents these data for four Ohio school districts.

Lockland, which has a large industrial tax base and relatively few

TABLE 3.5   **Selected Financial Statistics for Four Ohio School Districts (1969)**

DISTRICT	TAX VALUATION PER PUPIL ($)	TOTAL SCHOOL TAX ($)	LOCAL TAX REVENUES PER PUPIL ($)
Bay Village	12,631	49.40	624
Grandview Heights	35,236	18.50	651
Lockland	75,774	16.84	1,341
Shaker Heights	26,478	38.00	1,006

Source: Ohio Education Association. *Basic Financial Data of Ohio School Districts, 1969.* (OEA Research Report, March 1969), Vol. 23, pp. 10–12.

[49] "Property Taxes: Revenue for Schools and State-Local Governments," *NEA Research Bulletin* 47 (May, 1969), p. 55.

students, raises more local school revenue than the other districts despite its lower tax rate. Grandview Heights, which has a slightly higher tax rate than Lockland, raises less than half as much per pupil than Lockland but more than Bay Village where taxes are more than twice as high. Shaker Heights, which has less tax base than Grandview Heights but considerably more than Bay Village, levies a tax somewhat higher than the state average ($29.40) and comes closer than either of these districts to the Lockland revenue figure.

Support from the state helps to equalize expenditures among these districts but does not do this completely. In 1969 Lockland received no state aid per pupil and Bay Village, Grandview Heights, and Shaker Heights received $196, $118, and $119, respectively.[50] In Ohio, as in most states, state support to local districts is figured according to a formula which not only tries to help equalize expenditures but also rewards local districts for taxing themselves.

The most visible reason why financial questions are at issue is due to a seemingly growing public reluctance to approve local property tax increases for schools. Schools must have more money to provide for growing numbers of students, to add needed programs, and to keep pace with inflation. Yet experiences in California during 1968 and 1969 probably reflect the temperament of the nation on this matter. A report of the California Teachers Association revealed that 48.9 percent of tax elections and 64.3 percent of bond elections held in the state failed.[51]

Present means of financing schools are also criticized because it is argued that reliance upon local property taxes produces financial inequities which impair equality of educational opportunity among districts of varying wealth.[52] Proposals to redress this situation generally look to increased support for education from state and federal governments which (1) have greater access to public wealth, (2) do not rely so heavily upon property taxes, and (3) can distribute funds over a broader geographical region. Some persons have suggested that state and/or federal aid be directed to individual students in the form of vouchers or credits redeemable at schools of their choice rather than to local school districts.[53] Such an approach

[50] Ohio Education Association, *Basic Financial Data of Ohio School Districts, 1969,* OEA Research Report, XXIII (March 1969), 10–12.

[51] As reported in *Phi Delta Kappan,* 51 (January, 1970), p. 292.

[52] See Arthur S. Wise, *Rich Schools, Poor Schools* (Chicago: The University of Chicago Press, 1969).

[53] One discussion of such plans is Robert M. Krughoff, "Private Schools for the Public," in *Education and Urban Society* II (November, 1969), pp. 54–79.

would represent a great departure from traditional patterns of school finance.

SUGGESTED ACTIVITIES

1. Examine the 1950, 1960, and 1970 census figures for your school district or attendance areas. What changes have occurred, and what are their implications for schooling?
2. Spend a day visiting a school and social agencies in a neighborhood different from your own. How are neighborhood characteristics reflected in these institutions?
3. Determine what federal assistance programs are in operation in your school district.
4. Interview a principal or superintendent about the processes he employs to be sensitive to community expectations.
5. Compare two or more contracts or professional negotiations agreements developed in the same school district over a period of time. What do these documents indicate about teacher participation in district affairs?

SELECTED READINGS

BURKHEAD, JESS.. *Public School Finance: Economics and Politics.* (Syracuse, N.Y.: Syracuse University Press, 1964).

CAMPBELL, ROALD F., and BUNNELL, ROBERT A., eds., *Nationalizing Influences on Secondary Education.* (Chicago: Midwest Administration Center, University of Chicago, 1963).

————— and LAYTON, DONALD H. *Policy Making for American Education.* (Chicago: The Midwest Administration Center, 1969).

ROALD F. CAMPBELL, *et al. The Organization and Control of American Schools,* 2nd ed. (Columbus, Ohio: Charles E. Merrill Books, 1970).

CRAIN, ROBERT L. *The Politics of School Desegregation.* (Chicago: Aldine Publishing Co., 1968).

GOLDHAMMER, KEITH. *The School Board.* (New York: Center for Applied Research in Education, 1964).

—————, *et al. Issues and Problems in Contemporary Educational Administration.* Eugene, Oregon: Center for the Advanced Study of Educational Administration, 1967.

HAVIGHURST, ROBERT J., ed. Sixty-seventh Yearbook, Part I, National Society for the Study of Education, *Metropolitanism: Its Challenge to Education.* (Chicago: University of Chicago Press, 1968).

KIRST, MICHAEL W., ed. *The Politics of Education at the Local State and Federal Levels* (Berkeley, Calif.: McCutchan Publishing, 1970).

MORPHET, EDGAR L., and RYAN, CHARLES O., eds., *Designing Education for the Future.* (New York: Citation Press, 1967), Vol. 1–111.

ROSENTHAL, ALAN. *Pedagogues and Power: Teacher Groups in School Politics.* (Syracuse, N.Y.: Syracuse University Press, 1969).

SKOLNICK, JEROME A. *The Politics of Protest: Violent Aspects of Protest and Confrontation.* (Washington, D.C.: U.S. Government Printing Office, 1969). Also available from Simon and Schuster and Ballantine Books, New York.

4

Development And Meaning
Of Administration

In Chapter 1, we were confronted with some brief exposures to the reality of administration. In Chapter 2, we noted certain historical developments that appear to have had relevance to the evolution of schools and to the emergence of the function of administration in those schools and school systems. In Chapter 3, we considered some characteristics of the current setting in which administration operates. We shall now examine more explicitly the development and meaning of administration—first in its general sense and, second, in its application to education. We shall conclude this chapter by suggesting the place and limitations of theory in administration and by indicating specific ways in which administration will be viewed in Chapters 5 through 8.

THE DEVELOPMENT OF ADMINISTRATION

Educational administration, like many other branches of administration, has suffered from too much emphasis on the adjective and too little on the noun. To understand educational administration, one must acquire some sense of the development of administration generally. This may be found in treatises on public administration, business management, industrial psychology, military leadership, and in other writings. Analysis in all of these settings has dealt with mobilizing the efforts of a number of people toward the achievement of a common goal.

Activating members of a group toward a common objective is as old as history itself. Whether we look at the public regulation of the waterways in ancient Egypt, the duties of the magistrates in the far-flung Roman Empire, or the efficient use of resources in the German states more than 200 years ago—growing largely from the work of the Cameralists—the significance of administration becomes clear. While other sources must be consulted for a history of administration,[1] we would mention that both Alexander Hamilton and Woodrow Wilson made contributions to the understanding and practice of the field.

Some aspects of the conflict between Hamilton and Jefferson— both members of Washington's cabinet—are well known. It may not be as fully appreciated that Hamilton became the chief Federalist philosopher and perhaps its most brilliant practitioner. The Federalists must be credited with creating an administrative system from practically nothing. White explains that the system they created included an independent chief executive, a plan of effective delegation by the chief executive to the department heads, an administrative organization separate from the several states, canons of personal integrity on the part of public officers, and approval of the right of public criticism.[2]

This centralization of power and responsibility was often opposed by Jefferson, who was disposed to place confidence in legislative as opposed to executive action, and who emphasized states' rights more than federal responsibility. Hamilton, however, continued to stress the need for an energetic executive, and the customs service in his own department was perhaps the best example of his ideal of government. This page in our history serves to highlight some of the persistent issues found in administration.

In 1887 Wilson attempted to distinguish between politics and administration. He said:

> . . . administration lies outside the proper sphere of politics. Administrative questions are not political questions. Although politics sets the tasks for administration, it should not be suffered to manipulate its offices.[3]

What appears to be a clear differentiation between policy and administration is probably intended for quite another purpose. The cue is in Wilson's last sentence; he was greatly concerned lest special interest groups manipulate public officeholders and thus prevent them

---

[1] For example, see Albert Lepawsky, *Administration* (New York: Alfred A. Knopf, 1949), Chap. 4.

[2] Leonard D. White, *The Federalists* (New York: The Macmillan Co., 1948), p. 512.

[3] Woodrow Wilson, "The Study of Administration," *Political Science Quarterly,* XLI (December, 1941), p. 494. Reprinted from 1887 issue.

from serving the general welfare. Even so, the relationship between policy and administration was raised, and the question is still being vigorously debated.

RECENT HISTORICAL EMPHASES

Let us turn from this brief exploration of the emergence of the concept of administration and look more specifically at some of the recent historical emphases in administration. In each case, we shall deal with a major emphasis by citing the work of a few contributors. These contributors were in reality students of administration; they described or rationalized what was being said about administration and, at least to some extent, what was being practiced in administration. Some of them were also practicing administrators themselves, and all of them had many direct relationships with practitioners.

Job analysis. The first approach to administration was that of job analysis. We shall note the work of two major contributors to this approach. Frederick Taylor, often called the father of the scientific management movement, was born in 1856. He studied in France, Germany, and Italy in his youth, and later earned an M.E. degree at Stevens Institute. From 1878 to 1889, he was employed by the Midvale Steel Company; first as a laborer, then as clerk, machinist, foreman, chief draftsman, and finally chief engineer. Taylor noticed that workers were in charge of both planning and performing their jobs, a situation that led, he thought, to much waste and inefficiency. His experience at all levels of industry led him to formulate his principles, which were condensed in *The Principles of Scientific Management,* published in 1911.[4]

His essential points have been summarized by Villers as follows:

1. *Time-study principle.* All productive effort should be measured by accurate time study and a standard time established for all work done in the shop.
2. *Piece-rate principle.* Wages should be proportional to output and their rates based on the standards determined by time study. As a corollary, a worker should be given the highest grade of work of which he is capable.
3. *Separation-of-planning-from-performance   principle.* Management should take over from the workers the responsibility for planning

---

[4] This and other works appear in Frederick W. Taylor, *Scientific Management* (New York: Harper & Brothers, 1947).

the work and making the performance physically possible. Planning should be based on time studies and other data related to production, which are scientifically determined and systematically classified; it should be facilitated by standardization of tools, implements, and methods.

4. *Scientific-methods-of-work principle.* Management should take over from the workers the responsibility for their methods of work, determine scientifically the best methods, and train the workers accordingly.

5. *Managerial-control principle.* Managers should be trained and taught to apply scientific principles of management and control (such as management by exception and comparison with valid standards).

6. *Functional-management principle.* The strict application of military principles should be reconsidered and the industrial organization should be so designed that it best serves the purpose of improving the co-ordination of activities among the various specialists.[5]

Taylor and other spokesmen of the scientific management movement were influential in seeing many of their principles applied to such firms as the Midland Steel Company, Bethlehem Steel Company, Santa Fe Railway, and Acme Wire Company. Labor, on the other hand, resisted time and motion studies, and other activities which were perceived as treating men as though they were machines. The whole movement became the object of an investigation by the Social Committee of the House of Representatives in 1912. Following extended hearings, Congress attached a rider to the military appropriations bill prohibiting the use of such funds for time and motion studies.

From the perspective of our day, we find that Taylor took a narrow view of management, and that, moreover, he tended to ignore the psychological or personal aspects of mobilizing human effort. At the same time, he did demonstrate that many jobs could be done more efficiently. Even more important, his work stands as a monument to the concept that management can be studied scientifically. No aspect of administration has remained immune to this idea.

Henri Fayol was another major contributor to the job analysis approach to administration. He was born in 1841 of a family of the French *petite bourgeoisie*. At the age of nineteen, he graduated from the national School of Mines at St. Etienne. In a sense, he had four careers: twelve years as a mining engineer, sixteen years as a geologist, thirty years as the very able managing director of a large

---

[5] Raymond Villers, *Dynamic Management in Industry* (Englewood Cliffs, N.J.: Prentice-Hall, 1960), p. 29.

metallurgical firm, and seven years—after retirement at age seventy-seven—as a teacher of administration. In the fourth period, he undertook two main tasks: the first was the formation of a Centre of Administrative Studies; the second was an effort to persuade the French government to pay some attention to the principles of administration.

Although Fayol wrote his book, *Administration Industrielle et Générale,* in 1916, it did not appear in an English translation until 1929, and it was not made generally available in the United States until 1949.[6] Containing the first two parts of the eventual treatise Fayol planned to write, it describes the necessity and the possibility of teaching the principles and elements of management. The now famous elements were planning, organizing, command, co-ordination, and control.

In the early stages of the popularization of Fayol's work, attempts were made by some to represent his approach as antithetical to that of Taylor. But at the Second International Congress held at Brussels in 1925, Fayol himself made clear that such interpretations were false. Actually, both men applied the scientific method. Taylor worked primarily at the operative level, or the bottom of the hierarchal structure, while Fayol began with the managing director at the top of the hierarchy. The work of Fayol has been reflected in the thinking and writing of Gulick, Urwick, Sears, and other students of administration. A more detailed treatment of this approach to administration will be found in Chapter 6.

Both Taylor and Fayol were concerned with industry; both believed that the processes involved in production could be analyzed and studied scientifically. While Taylor concentrated on the worker and Fayol on the manager, both had as an ultimate objective the increased efficiency of industry. To be sure, in his later years Fayol extended the application of his administrative principles to government as well as to industry. Even so, both men tended to stress organizational processes and to ignore individuals as such. The time was ripe for a new emphasis, and Mary Parker Follett helped to supply it.

Human relations. Human relations constituted the second major approach to administration. Again the work of two major contributors will be noted. Mary Parker Follet was born in 1868. She

---

[6] Henri Fayol, *General and Industrial Management* (London: Sir Isaac Pitman & Sons, 1949).

graduated from Radcliffe College, where she followed a course devoted to economics, government, and philosophy. Throughout her life, she worked to help bring about a better-ordered society in which the individual might live a more satisfying life. This motivation was expressed when she served on the Boston Committee on the Extended Use of School Buildings from 1909 to 1911, in the help she gave to establish the Department of Vocational Guidance in Boston in 1912, in her service on the Massachusetts Minimum Wage Board for many years, and in her great interest in the League of Nations.

Her book, *Creative Experience,*[7] has been characterized by Metcalf and Urwick as follows:

. . . mainly psychological in interest and content, [it] marks a definite advance both in the crystallization of thought and in style and phraseology. Its thesis is the reciprocal character—the interpenetration—of all psychological phenomena, from the simplest to the most complex. Human relationships—the ways and work of society and of industry— are at their best when difference is solved through conference and cooperation, when the parties at interest (1) evoke each other's latent ideas based upon the facts of the situation, (2) come to see each other's viewpoints and to understand each other better, and (3) integrate those viewpoints and become united in the pursuit of their common goal.[8]

Follett contended that the fundamental problem of any enterprise, whether it be local government, national government, a business organization, or an educational system, is the building and maintenance of dynamic, yet harmonious, human relationships. She tended to reduce her principles of organization to four in number, all aspects of what she termed *co-ordination*. The principles were:

1. Co-ordination by direct contact of the responsible people concerned.
2. Co-ordination in the early stages.
3. Co-ordination as the reciprocal relating of all factors in the situation.
4. Co-ordination as a continuing process.[9]

Mary Parker Follett might be characterized as a social philosopher with deep psychological insights. She came onto the scene when the

---

[7] Mary Parker Follett, *Creative Experience* (New York: Longmans, Green, 1924).

[8] Henry C. Metcalf and L. Urwick, eds., *Dynamic Administration* (New York: Harper & Brothers, 1942), p. 14. The collected papers of Mary Parker Follett with an introduction by the editors.

[9] *Ibid.,* p. 297.

process and organizational aspects of administration had been emphasized to the exclusion, perhaps, of the values to be cherished for society and for the most adequate development of individuals in that society. As an academician Miss Follett made a contribution in both the United States and England; but she was also a woman of action. She found much stimulation in the observation of governmental and industrial organizations, and she was welcomed as a consultant by many such enterprises.

While Mary Parker Follett became the first great exponent of the aspect of human relations in administration, it remained for Elton Mayo and his colleagues to supply empirical data in support of such a view. Mayo was born in Adelaide, Australia, in 1880, and received A.B. and M.A. degrees from the University of Adelaide. For twenty years, he served as the senior professor in the Department of Industrial Research of the Harvard Business School. From 1923 to 1932, he and his associates were connected with the now famous experiments done at the Hawthorne plant of the Western Electric Company, near Chicago.

Industry had long assumed that wages and physical working conditions were the chief factors in employee motivation. The first experiment at Hawthorne, 1923–26, was quite simply designed to test the effect of one of these physical conditions—illumination—on worker production. It was found that illumination was not significantly related to production. In the true scientific spirit, the results of the experiment were accepted as proof that the basic assumption needed reconsideration.

A second inquiry was conducted to explore the problem more fully. A group of six girl operatives was selected for study to determine what factors might be related to their job productivity. It was found that whatever factors were changed—whether rest periods, length of day, or methods of payment—and whatever way they were changed, even if the change meant returning to the original conditions, production continued to increase. Moreover, the girls were more and more satisfied with their jobs, and their attendance continued to show greater regularity. Findings of this nature were secured almost without exception over a five-year period of meticulous experimentation between 1927 and 1932.

Mayo has explained the findings as follows:

. . . What the Company actually did for the group was to reconstruct entirely its whole industrial situation.

. . . the consequence was that there was a period during which the individual workers and the group had to re-adapt themselves to a new industrial milieu, a milieu in which their own self-determination and their social well-being ranked first, and the work was incidental.

. . . The Western Electric experiment was primarily directed not to the external condition but to the inner organization. By strengthening the "temperamental" inner equilibrium of the workers, the Company enabled them to achieve a mental "steady state" which offered a high resistance to a variety of external conditions.[10]

Clearly, this and similar experiments demonstrated that economic and mechanistic approaches to human relations in industry were inadequate. While wages and working conditions are important to the worker, they rank second to what Mayo called "a method of living in a social relationship." Apparently, the girls in the Hawthorne experiment had gained a sense of playing an important part in a project instead of being mere cogs in a large productive enterprise.

Mayo's work has been subjected to much examination, and some students find two major biases in his experiments.[11] He may have had a management bias, since he was employed by business to help business solve its problems. He may also have had a clinical bias, in that he began with observation and not with theory. Apparently, Mayo did have some disdain for theory and had more faith in empiricism. Regardless of these criticisms, however, one must recognize that through long and meticulous experimentation Mayo and his associates collected a large body of data that make it clear that what goes on inside the worker is even more significant for production than what goes on outside.

Were one to accept the work of Follett and Mayo uncritically, he might assume that adequate human relations is the sum total of administration. Indeed, the so-called "democratic" emphasis in administration of the 1940's and 50's may have sprung from the work of these contributors or, more likely, the inadequate interpretations of some of their disciples. Fortunately, Chester Barnard had turned his great talent to the examination of administration.

Behavioral science and administration. Chester Barnard appears to have been the first to relate administration to the behavioral sciences. Born in 1886, Barnard attended Harvard College from 1906 to 1909. He served for many years as the president of the New Jersey Bell Telephone Company and for four years as president of the

[10] Elton Mayo, *The Human Problems of an Industrial Civilization* (Boston: Graduate School of Business Administration, Harvard University, 1946), pp. 73, 75.

[11] See Delbert C. Miller and William H. Form, *Industrial Sociology*, 2nd ed. (New York: Harper & Brothers, 1964), pp. 78–83.

Rockefeller Foundation. During this time he demonstrated an unusual capacity to deal with theoretical abstractions and with practical problems of management. He found himself consulting with clergymen, military men, government officials, university officials, and leaders of widely diversified businesses on problems of organization.

In 1937, he prepared eight lectures for the Lowell Institute in Boston. These lectures, revised and expanded, became his very important book, *The Functions of the Executive*.[12] Barnard himself suggests that the book has two parts: ". . . an exposition of a theory of co-operation and organization" and "a study of the functions . . . of executives in formal organizations." The book emphasizes the universal character of formal organizations and stresses the need for a theory to explain their behavior.

The development of an appropriate theory, Barnard suggested, has been retarded because of a misconception about the nature of authority, a misconception growing out of interpretations of the church; and because of the unwarranted emphasis given to the economic motivation of man. He saw an organization as a complex social organism— an organism whose peripheral aspects had been dealt with by the various social sciences, but whose core had never been analyzed. His own work did much to promote analyses of organizations as such.

A formal organization, Barnard maintained, is

. . . an impersonal system of co-ordinated human efforts; always there is purpose as the co-ordinating and unifying principle; always there is the indispensable ability to communicate, always the necessity of personal willingness, and for effectiveness and efficiency in maintaining the integrity of purpose and the continuity of contributions.[13]

While Barnard dealt mainly with formal organizations, he also pointed out that in each formal organization there are informal organizations. He characterized informal organization as the contacts or interactions of people without a specific conscious joint purpose. While these organizations may not be governed by joint purposes, such informal interactions do change the experience, knowledge, attitudes, and emotions of the people affected. Since informal organization may perform important roles in a formal organization by way of communication and even in terms of helping build self-respect in

[12] Chester I. Barnard, *The Functions of the Executive* (Cambridge, Mass.: Harvard University Press, 1938).

[13] *Ibid.*, pp. 94–95.

organization members, Barnard thought that informal organization could not be ignored.

One of Barnard's major contributions was the concept of effectiveness and efficiency. Effectiveness is system-oriented and has to do with the achievement of the organization goals. Efficiency, on the other hand, is person-oriented and has to do with the feelings of satisfaction a worker derives from membership in an organization. For the first time, the interrelationship of organization achievement and individual satisfaction was noted. This conception did much to put the work of Taylor and Fayol, who had concentrated on organization achievement, and Follett and Mayo, who had tended to emphasize individual satisfaction, in appropriate perspective.

A second contributor to the science of administration was Herbert A. Simon. Simon was born in 1916 and received A.B. and Ph.D. degrees from the University of Chicago. His graduate work was in political science and he became particularly interested in public administration. His Ph.D. dissertation became the basis for *Administrative Behavior*,[14] the book that established him as a scholar in the field. Simon has spent much of his professional career at Carnegie Institute of Technology as a professor of administration.

Simon contended that he wrote *Administrative Behavior* in an attempt to develop a set of tools—a set of concepts and a vocabulary—suitable for describing an organization. He did give meaning to such terms as administrative behavior, decision-making, organization, rational behavior, and many others. He relied not only on political science to develop his concepts, but on economics, psychology, and sociology as well. In a very real sense he used the behavioral sciences to explain organizations and the behavior of people in them. In a number of books and journal articles, Simon has continued to provide additional insight into the field of administration.

Following Barnard and Simon, a great many behavioral scientists have turned their attention to the study of organizations. Many of these scholars based their work on that of Max Weber, who first developed the concept of bureaucracy.[15] One of these organization theorists, Etzioni, compared complex organizations and noted that bureaucratic concepts did not apply equally to all of them.[16] He

[14] Herbert A. Simon, *Administrative Behavior* (New York: The Macmillan Co., 1945).

[15] See H. H. Girth and C. Wright Mills (Translators and editors), *From Max Weber: Essays in Sociology.* (New York: Oxford University Press, 1958).

[16] Amitai Etzioni, *A Comparative Analysis of Complex Organizations.* (New York: Free Press of Glencoe, 1961).

developed a classification for organizations as follows: coercive, such as prisons and most mental hospitals; utilitarian, such as most businesses; and normative, such as religious orders and universities. Etzioni used compliance as his basic concept, and suggested that one could identify in organizations coercive compliance, calculative compliance, and normative compliance. One has but to refer to the rather complete bibliography at the end of the Etzioni book to realize how extensively the work of scholars from a variety of disciplines has dealt with organizations and their administration.

Roughly speaking, the three periods in the development of administration might be established as follows: job analysis, 1910–1930; human relations, 1930–1950; and behavioral science, 1950 to the present. But the transition from one period to the next has been neither complete nor uniform. Moreover, there is something to be said for job analysis and for human relations. Hopefully, the scientific study of administration will provide a way by which these and other approaches can be more adequately examined.

THE DEVELOPMENT OF EDUCATIONAL ADMINISTRATION

We have examined some of the major developments in the general field of administration. We shall turn now to developments in educational administration.

EARLY SCHOOL ADMINISTRATION

It seems appropriate to recall that for most of our history the organization and management of schools has been a function of laymen and not of professional administrators. Suzzalo has traced, with considerable care, the supervision of the schools in Massachusetts.[17] For almost two hundred years, the school committee was, in one way or another, made up of the town selectmen. It was 1827 before school government was differentiated from general government, and it was some years later before the lay school committee or board of education was ready to employ a school administrator. Thus school administration did not evolve as a field of practice until the latter part

---

[17] Henry Suzzalo, *The Rise of Local School Supervision in Massachusetts.* Teachers College Contribution No. 1 (New York: Teachers College, Columbia University, 1906).

of the nineteenth century, nor become a field of study until the twentieth century.

While much of our discussion above has dealt with major concepts and ideas about administration, any consideration of the development of educational administration must deal chiefly with its practice. The development of concepts about educational administration and the testing of those concepts empirically is at best a relatively new and unexplored field.

State and county school administration have both played important parts in the development of educational administration in America, but the major surge has been at the local level, chiefly in the growth of the school superintendency and of the school principalship. This phenomenon is largely a result of the decentralization of education in this country. The usual connotation of school administration to this day is local school administration. Any other meaning requires an adjective such as state school administration or county school administration.

Leadership in local school administration came first in our cities. Gradually, as multiple school districts within a single city were merged, the board of education found itself in need of a full-time executive. The first cities to establish the office of the superintendent of schools were Buffalo and Louisville in 1837, and St. Louis and Providence in 1839.[18] The practice soon spread throughout the country. Although a number of cities were unsuccessful in their experimentation with the office and abolished it for a while, they eventually returned to it as the best solution to meet the need for district-wide administration. Duties varied from city to city, with some stressing the examining and visiting function while others placed emphasis on business and clerical functions.

In the beginning, the variations in the duties to be performed, the uncertainty regarding the competence needed for the position, and the lack of any specific preparation for it made it difficult to secure people who could serve satisfactorily. Adams spoke disparagingly of the early superintendent, saying that "the ordinary superintendent is apt to be a grammar school teacher run to seed, or some retired clergyman or local politician out of a job."[19] Northend, writing of

[18] Theodore Lee Reller, *The Development of the City Superintendency of Schools in the United States* (Philadelphia: published by the author, 1935), p. 7.

[19] Charles Francis Adams, quoted in J. D. Philbrick, "Which Is the True Ideal?" *Education* I (January, 1881), pp. 300–302.

the situation in Connecticut, described the candidates for the position as follows:

> Lawyers, whose business could not "wane" because it never "waxed"; doctors, whose patients were not troublesomely numerous; clergymen, afflicted with bronchitis or some other malady, or not overburdened with hearers; office seekers of various kinds and all sorts of "do nothings" all become suddenly and wonderfully impressed with the importance of common schools, accompanied by a sort of feeling that in themselves was the only power for truly elevating those schools.[20]

But this was not the general evaluation of the superintendency, or the position would not have survived. The outstanding contributions of some of the early superintendents—such as Gove of Denver, Jones of Cleveland, Philbrick of Boston, and Harris of St. Louis—are recorded as examples of the sort of leadership that was being sought for the schools. However, the controversy over the need for the position and the brilliance of a few people holding the office had caused a thorough examination and study of the superintendency.

The growth of cities not only created populous school districts, but also populous attendance areas for single schools. The increased size of schools, in conjunction with the new practice of classifying pupils by grades, led to the need for an executive or principal for each school building. This official was first called a principal teacher, and we learn that Cincinnati had designated principal teachers for each school within that city as early as 1838. Quincy School in Boston in 1847, however, was probably the first school to have a full-time executive or supervising principal.[21] St. Louis reported in 1859 that all schools of that city had been placed in charge of full-time administrators. This practice is now common in many schools over the country.

To begin with, the work of the principal—particularly while he was still the principal teacher—was largely clerical in nature. Reports on enrollment and attendance, and other matters, were needed in the central office. With the increase in enrollments, pupils had to be classified—by grade and otherwise—and assigned to teachers and rooms. As time went on, instruction, particularly in the upper grades, was departmentalized. These and other developments tended to high-

---

[20] *Connecticut Common School Journal and Annals of Education,* VIII (August 1960).

[21] Paul R. Pierce, *The Origin and Development of the School Principalship* (Chicago: University of Chicago Press, 1934).

light the organization and management functions of the principal. In recent decades, these clerical and management functions of the principal have received less stress, and his instructional leadership role more. With the current emphasis on decentralization, the place of the principal in community relationships is under scrutiny.

While educational administration has tended to focus on the superintendent of schools as the chief executive officer of the school system and on the principal as the executive officer of a single school within a school system, it should be clear, as will be made explicit in Chapter 14, that there are many other administrative positions in education. All of these administrative personnel have unique and complementary roles to perform, as we shall see in Chapter 9.

FEW SCHOLARS

We can find in the history of American education a number of notable administrators. On the other hand, there are relatively few notable scholars of administration. Yet the contributions of such men as Cubberley of Stanford, Strayer of Columbia, Reavis of Chicago, Hart of California, and Reeder of Ohio State should not be overlooked. These and a number of other men had a hand in shaping the organization and management of public education in this country. Each of these men, moreover, had hundreds of students who became school administrators and occupied major administrative posts at all levels of education.

Many of these early professors of educational administration approached school administration through the school survey. The surveys of Boise, Idaho, in 1910, and of Montclair, New Jersey, and Baltimore, Maryland, in 1911 appear to be the first.[22] Such surveys provided some of the first literature in educational administration; and indeed, some of the early ones are still very useful reading.

Since the chief purpose of the survey, however, was to improve practice, the approach often dealt with what *ought* to be, in place of determining basic relationships. The surveys tended to reflect the value judgments of the surveyors and, as such, often proved most useful in pointing the way to improved practice. At the same time, such surveys were not designed to deal with basic concepts or to test such concepts in an empirical setting.

[22] Dan H. Cooper, "School Surveys," *Encyclopedia of Educational Research* (New York: The Macmillan Co., 1960), pp. 1211–1216.

More than anything else, these early students of educational administration approached the field from the standpoint of job analysis. They observed administrators at work, noted the tasks they were required to perform, and then suggested how these tasks might be performed more effectively. Consciously or unconsciously, perhaps both, this attitude was a reflection of the work Taylor was doing in scientific management. In 1913, Bobbitt devoted a long article to principles of management and their applications, as he saw them, in school systems.[23]

The faithful application of Taylor's principles to school operation is illustrated in the following statement from Bobbitt:

> The primary functions of educational directors and supervisors, as relating to methods, are therefore: first, the discovery of the best methods of procedure in the performance of any particular educational task; and second, the giving of these discovered best methods over to the teachers for their guidance in securing a maximum product. Since so few methods, demonstrably the best, have yet been discovered with entire certainty, it is impossible yet to devote any very large amount of time to the function of distribution of this information to the teachers. This leaves the major work at the present moment in the realm of discovery of best methods, it would appear.[24]

The early textbooks in educational administration written by Cubberley, Strayer, Reeder, and others may not have followed Taylor as faithfully as did Bobbitt, but their approach was essentially that of job analysis. Callahan[25] has made a penetrating analysis of how the schools, particularly during the period from 1910 to 1930, responded to the cult of efficiency that appeared to characterize the business ideology, and perhaps the entire American culture, of that time.

A somewhat similar approach or theory of educational administration is found in the work of Sears—for many years a professor at Stanford University. He was familiar with the work of Fayol, Gulick, Urwick, and other students of public administration. In a notable book, he attempted to adapt the administrative process—first suggested by Fayol—to the administration of the public schools.[26] Sears saw the process as including the following activities: planning, or-

---

[23] Franklin Bobbitt, "Some General Principles of Management Applied to the Problems of City School Systems," *The Supervision of City Schools,* Twelfth Yearbook of the National Society for the Study of Education, Part I (Chicago: University of Chicago Press, 1913), pp. 7–96.

[24] *Ibid.,* p. 53.

[25] Raymond E. Callahan, *Education and the Cult of Efficiency* (Chicago: University of Chicago Press, 1962).

[26] Jesse B. Sears, *The Nature of the Administrative Process* (New York: McGraw-Hill, 1950).

ganization, direction, co-ordination, and control. After developing each aspect of the process, he related the whole to such concepts as authority, delegation, and policy-making. Further treatment of the process will be given in Chapter 6.

While Sears appears to have been one of the early scholars of educational administration, his contribution created no great stir—a lack of general recognition that may be due to a number of circumstances. First, since Sears' major treatment of the administrative process appeared after his retirement, he had little opportunity to work directly with other students of administration. Second, and perhaps more significant, only in recent years have professors and some practitioners of educational administration become interested in theoretical approaches to the field. Third, the process is a useful concept in administration, but it has not stimulated the formulation of many hypotheses to be tested.

Taylor's concept of scientific management in industry, we have seen, had a counterpart in education given its clearest expression by Bobbitt; likewise the formulation of Fayol became a major inspiration to Sears, who adapted it to educational administration. In both cases there was an attempt at job analysis—Bobbitt concentrating on the work of the teacher and supervisor, Sears concentrating on the work of the administrator. The emphasis on human relations supplied by Follett and Mayo has also influenced educational administration. This emphasis was reflected in the "democratic administration" movement. Democratic administration had many exponents,[27] but for the most part they dealt in hortatory expositions and did little to give greater insight into the realities of school organizations and their operation. The current emphasis on behavioral sciences and administration, reflecting the work of Barnard and others, likewise has been applied directly to educational administration, as can be noted in a recent yearbook of the National Society for the Study of Education.[28]

SOME RECENT DEVELOPMENTS

Scholarship in educational administration, generally meager during the first part of the present century, seems to be getting some genuine bolstering in the last two or three decades. Four major events, each of

[27] For instance, see G. Robert Koopman, *et al., Democracy in School Administration* (New York: Appleton-Century-Crofts, 1943).

[28] National Society for the Study of Education, *Behavioral Science and Educational Administration,* Sixty-Third Yearbook, Part II (Chicago: University of Chicago Press, 1964).

which will be dealt with briefly, have been part of this dramatic development.

In 1947, the first meeting of a group later to be known as the National Conference of Professors of Educational Administrators was held at Endicott, New York. This meeting was largely the idea of, and was made possible through the influence of, Walter D. Cocking. The succeeding annual meetings of NCPEA have permitted those who teach educational administration to become acquainted with each other, have encouraged an examination of what is known and what is not known in the field, and have helped shape the other events noted here.

A second event of great importance to educational administration was the Cooperative Program in Educational Administration underwritten, to a large extent, by the W. K. Kellogg Foundation. From its beginning in 1950 until most projects were closed out about a decade later, Kellogg spent about $7 million on the program. This money was supplemented by the funds of many universities, state departments of education, and local school districts. Eight Kellogg centers were established in the United States and one in Canada; each of them was encouraged to develop a regional program devoted to the improvement of educational administration.

Initially, CPEA placed more emphasis on the improved practice of administration than on its study. It soon became apparent, however, that improved practice was dependent, in part, upon more knowledge about administration. Some participants in the CPEA program found substantial stimulation in studies done in public and business administration, and in the concepts and research findings of the social sciences. Thus, in the closing period of CPEA, theory and research in educational administration emerged as the most important concern of several of the centers.[29]

One of the CPEA centers, Teachers College at Columbia University, proposed that the major universities with programs in educational administration form an organization for the purpose of continuing the work thus started. Hence, in 1956, representatives from thirty-three universities organized the University Council for Educational Administration. At first the Council was located at Columbia University; in 1959, UCEA was incorporated under the laws of Ohio and moved to

---

[29] More information about the influence of CPEA may be found in Hollis A. Moore, Jr., *Studies in School Administration* (Washington, D.C.: American Association of School Administrators, 1957); and Roald F. Campbell and Russell T. Gregg, eds., *Administrative Behavior in Education* (New York: Harper & Brothers, 1957).

the campus of The Ohio State University. The W. K. Kellogg Foundation made substantial initial and subsequent grants to UCEA to help the new organization get established.

UCEA has three major purposes:

1. To improve the pre-service and in-service training of school administrators.
2. To stimulate and produce research in educational administration.
3. To disseminate materials growing out of research and training practices.

Among its activities, UCEA has organized career seminars for professors of educational administration, participated in large-scale research projects, set up a number of task forces on particular problems in administration, sought foundation and government assistance for fellowships and other aspects of training programs, alerted member institutions to possible sources of support for research and training projects in administration, and published a number of books and monographs growing out of its many activities.

From the beginning, UCEA has maintained a small but competent central office staff. Staff members have visited member institutions, have ascertained much about the interests and strengths of those institutions, have helped bring professors of similar interests in different institutions into touch with each other, and have, in general, served as an important communication link among over fifty universities now belonging to the organization. UCEA, like CPEA and NCPEA, continues to be useful in helping students of administration define the field and learn more about it. Related to these efforts was the funding in 1964 by the U.S. Office of Education of a research and development center in educational administration at the University of Oregon, site of one of the earlier CPEA centers.

In reviewing recent developments in educational administration, a fourth event also seems important. The American Association of School Administrators had taken a part in urging the Kellogg Foundation to support CPEA and had maintained a relationship with that program from the beginning. In 1955, AASA created the Committee for the Advancement of School Administration and received a grant from Kellogg to help it become operative. The purpose of that Committee was to assist in getting action designed to improve the preservice and inservice programs of preparation for school administrators.

The Committee for the Advancement of School Administration has done much to communicate research findings in administration to school administrators; to encourage national, regional, and local groups to work for improved school administration; to help develop plans for the accreditation of training programs for administrators; to urge more adequate regulations for certification in all the states; to influence boards of education regarding procedures to be used in selecting administrators; and to make its concerns about improved training clear to universities with programs in administration. Another noteworthy step taken by AASA at the behest of the Committee was approval, by vote of its members in 1959, of the completion of a two-year accredited graduate program as a requirement for membership, which became effective in 1964. In the late 1960's, AASA also established the National Academy for School Executives specifically for the purpose of improving the inservice or continuing education of superintendents.

Recent developments in educational administration have affected both students and practitioners. Those who would teach administration are becoming more conscious of the place of theory and careful research in the field. Selection and training, moreover, are also receiving additional attention. Criteria for selection are being established, and selection procedures developed and evaluated. New approaches in instruction, such as the case method and the use of simulated material, are being used and appraised. A recognition that good training and research programs are expensive is also dawning. In this whole effort those who practice administration are, for the most part, supportive, as these efforts to raise standards for organization membership and certification suggest. Social conditions generally have deepened the concerns about the role of the administrator, but the field is still characterized by considerable challenge and excitement.

AN OVERVIEW OF EDUCATIONAL ADMINISTRATION

PURPOSE AND ACTIVITIES OF ADMINISTRATION

As we see it, the central purpose of administration in any organization is that of co-ordinating the efforts of people toward the achievement of its goals. In education these goals have to do with teaching and learning. Thus, administration in an educational organization has as its central purpose the enhancement of teaching and learning. All activities of the administrator—whether working with the public, the board of education, or the professional staff—should ultimately contribute to this end.

To enhance teaching and learning, administrators are required to perform four major functions: (1) to discern and influence the development of goals and policies; (2) to stimulate and direct the development of programs designed to achieve the goals and purposes; (3) to establish and coordinate an organization concerned with planning and implementing the programs; and (4) to procure and manage resources, money, and material necessary to support the organization and its program.

While all four of these administrative functions have the improvement of teaching and learning as their end purpose, more than the classroom is, clearly, involved. In order to influence goals and policies, the administrator must work with the board of education and the lay community, as well as with the school organization itself. To stimulate the development of programs, the efforts of many persons in and out of the organization must be brought into productive relationships. To establish the organization, the administrator must see that the proper personnel are selected for it; then he must see that the efforts of these personnel are co-ordinated. To secure resources, the administrator must secure approval from three sources —the board of education, the voters of the school district, and the appropriate state and national agencies.

Clearly, the managerial decisions of administrators may be pointless unless they are geared to the implementation of programs that have, in turn, grown out of the goals. Or, to put it differently, administrators who raise money, build buildings, institute accounting procedures, set up computer programs, organize transportation systems, and do many other things without visualizing a clear relationship between these activities and the teaching and learning programs they are to enhance, may forget that administration is always instrumental, not primary. For administrators to relate managerial acts to program decisions requires some knowledge of education—its purposes and procedures. It is at this point that the school administrator transposed from business or the military may encounter some difficulty.

In suggesting that the administrator not only discern but influence goals and policies, we recognize that we have departed from the formulations of some students of administration.[30] But this is more than a mere difference of opinion. In a study of 272 school districts in Illinois, Allison[31] found that boards of education rely heavily on

[30] John Walton, *Administration and Policy-Making in Education,* Rev. ed. (Baltimore: Johns Hopkins Press, 1969).

[31] Howard C. Allison, "Professional and Lay Influences on School Board Decision-Making," (Unpublished doctoral dissertation, Department of Education, University of Chicago, 1965).

the recommendations of their superintendents on both policy and implementation matters. In effect, we are suggesting that the division between policy-making and administration is not a clear one, and that inevitably the administrator influences policy even as he attempts to discern and clarify policy. This influence is a function of both the knowledge and the values of administration. To the extent that the administrator knows something about education, he can supply information, note alternatives, and suggest probable outcomes. His professional orientation or values permit him to prefer one alternative above another and to explain the reasons for his choice. At this point he is speaking as a professional and giving professional information, which any lay group needs if policy is to be well conceived.

To be sure, the administrator may find it desirable to use other professionals more expert than he in many aspects of education. Thus the contributions of the philosopher, the sociologist, the psychologist, the curriculum theorist, and the able teacher may all be used. Even so, someone must serve as the generalist to suggest how these various specialties are to be related to the problem at hand. While this function may be shared with able laymen, it is also a role that administrators cannot escape.

Obviously, it is at the level of policy-making that professional knowledge and values must make sense to laymen. With knowledge exploding in every field of study, this juncture of special and general understanding is becoming fraught with more and more difficulty. In every public endeavor, however—whether foreign affairs, public health, or public education—there seems to be no alternative to the forging of policy decisions by laymen who have been enlightened by the experts. We are suggesting that foreign affairs are too important to be left to the army, public health too important to be left to the medical profession, and public education too important to be left to the educators. However, we are also insisting that laymen would make even more blunders in these areas if they refused to use the specialized knowledge available to them.

Administration in a Complex World

As was noted in Chapter 3, one cannot understand the administration of any organization in isolation; there is always a context within which the administrative process operates. In the first place, the world is an ever-expanding one geographically. Although we may begin with an attendance area in which we have a single school, we soon discover that this attendance area is part of a school district, that the district is part of a state, that the state is part of the nation, and that the nation is part of the world; and we are now in a period in which we are constantly reminded that this world is part of a mammoth universe.

The administrator of the attendance area, the principal, cannot perform his major administrative functions without reference to the larger world. Policy decisions are not a product of the people of the local school community alone, but often reflect the desires of the people of the school district, the state, and in some sense the world beyond. In like manner program decisions are not made by the professionals of a single school in isolation. The professionals at the district, state, and national levels have an influence on these decisions.

Second, the administrator's world is most complex sociologically. Many people and groups of people performing different roles are involved. In a school district, for instance, there are lay citizens who hold expectations for schools and school administrators, who determine the membership of the board of education, and to some extent the expenditure level of the district. The board of education becomes a major interstitial body between school and community and also determines, within limits, the policies of the school district. The superintendent of schools finds that he must deal with the aspirations and expectations of the people and serve as executive officer and professional adviser to the board of education. But the superintendent also has a professional staff composed of supervisors, principals, and teachers. These people perform different roles in the school system, and somehow their activities must be co-ordinated toward common objectives.

Third, the administrator's world is complex in terms of the many public services to be provided by government. In addition to public education, there are health and welfare, fire and police protection, public roads, and other public services. This means, particularly at district and state levels, that support for public education is always in competition with support for other public services. Inevitably, such a condition places the school administrator within all the complexities of the political world.

Not only must schools compete with highways and welfare; all public services must compete with private services. In government there is the perennial question: Shall we leave matters to individual initiative, or shall we use tax resources to provide the service for all? Clearly there is need to do some of both, a concept Galbraith has called social balance.[32] With growth in any private realm (let us say the manufacture of more automobiles) there is also need for growth in the public realm—in this case the building of more highways.

We have shown that the world of the administrator is a complex one geographically, socially, and politically. Let us now examine a little more carefully the legal realtionships between state and school district. The legal responsibility for education rests with the state. The state through the legislature has established school districts to help the state perform its educational function. The legislature has also created boards of education to preside over these districts, and the boards have the powers delegated to them by the legislature. In legal theory the districts are the creatures of the state, not the product of local autonomy. When there is need to alter districts or school boards, the state can take such action.

It is within this legal framework that the school district and legislature interact, that the superintendent of schools and the state superintendent interact, that the professional staff of a school district and the professional staff of the state department interact. But these legal relationships cannot ignore the geographical, sociological, and political relationships we have already noted. We must recognize, too, as will be demonstrated in later chapters, that the psychological needs and dispositions of people provide still another dimension in the complex world of the administrator.

The major functions of administration must go forward within this complex geographical, social, political, legal, and psychological world. Not all administrators perform all of these activities. We suspect that an able superintendent of schools actually performs at all four levels —he discerns and influences goals and policies, stimulates and directs the development of programs, establishes and co-ordinates an organization, and procures and manages resources. Most school principals, on the other hand, probably concentrate more on co-ordinating the efforts of staff members in building a total program and somewhat less on seeking resources to support the program. Supervisors of instruction, even more than principals, probably devote most of their efforts to co-ordinating staff activities as they relate to instructional programs.

But whether differentiated by position or by level of operation, administration operates in a complex and interdependent world. To

32 John K. Galbraith, *The Affluent Society* (Boston: Houghton Mifflin, 1958).

approach administration in terms of one set of dimensions yields only a partial view of the phenomenon. He who concentrates, for instance, on intra-organizational behavior will soon run aground, for extra-organizational influences are also inevitable.[33]

UNIQUE ASPECTS OF EDUCATIONAL ADMINISTRATION

As noted earlier, educational administration has much in common with public administration, hospital administration, business administration, and administration in other organizational settings. This recognition represents a gain, for the insights and research findings thus available to educational administration have been multiplied many times.

Still, this new-found knowledge has caused some uneasiness. Perhaps dwelling on common elements in administration, useful as such an approach is, oversimplifies the picture. Instead of trying to define either common or unique elements, it might be useful to develop some continua on which administration in a variety of organizational settings might be placed.

Parsons has suggested three levels of systems within organizations—the technical, managerial, and institutional levels.[34] In schools, for example, teaching is at the technical level of operation, action to direct the efforts of groups of teachers toward a common goal or program is at the managerial level, and moves to seek financial support for the school from the larger society are at the institutional level. In the study of administration, according to Parsons, we have dealt mainly with the managerial level and have neglected the technical and institutional levels somewhat.

As we think of various kinds of organizations in our society and realize that all organizations, whether public or private, must be legitimized by that society, we find questions that might be asked regarding any organization:

[33] This point is elaborated in Roald F. Campbell, Luvern L. Cunningham, Roderick F. McPhee, and Raphael O. Nystrand, *The Organization and Control of American Schools,* 2nd ed. (Columbus, Ohio: Charles E. Merrill, 1970).

[34] Talcott Parsons, "Some Ingredients of a General Theory of Formal Organizations." In Andrew W. Halpin, ed., *Administrative Theory in Education* (Chicago: Midwest Administration Center, University of Chicago, 1958), pp. 166–185.

1. What is the service that the organization is designed to provide?
2. What is the nature of the activity in which the organization will engage to perform this service?
3. What are the characteristics of the people who work in the organization?
4. How may the activities of the organization be appraised?

These considerations led us to develop six continua. Two of these, cruciality and visibility, were in response to our first question on the service to be rendered. Two others, complexity and intimacy, were in response to the second question on the nature of the activity. Staff professionalization grew out of question three on characteristics of the people. Difficulty of appraisal seemed to be a part of the general appraisal problem found in question four. While other continua may have been developed, these six will be discussed as one way of suggesting what may be unique about educational organizations and their administration. The organizations cited are for illustrative purposes only and organizational activities have been oversimplified to make the major point.

CRUCIALITY TO SOCIETY

Cruciality to society, as a continuum, obviously rests at the institutional level. We are suggesting that important as the making of ping-pong balls is to some people, this activity is not as crucial to society as fire protection. Likewise, important as fire protection is, we suspect that if a choice had to be made between schools and fire departments, society, particularly our kind of society, would choose schools. Or, to put it differently, we suspect that our society would settle for minimum fire protection before it would settle for minimum school programs.

LEAST CRUCIAL ⟶　　　　⟶　　　　⟶ MOST CRUCIAL

FACTORY:	FIRE DEPARTMENT:	SCHOOL:
PING-PONG	FIRE	TEACHING
BALLS	PROTECTION	AND LEARNING

The crucial place of the school in our society has been suggested by Thelen and Getzels:

> But education as a system is also unique in certain respects. It is a system whose major functions seem to be delegated to it by the other systems, and, to a degree, the effective functioning of the other systems

depends directly on the effective functioning of the educational system. Our geographer, for example, wants education to prepare us for the wise utilization of natural resources; in this sense the school is very much part of the geographer's domain. Our political scientist wants education to prepare us for the wise exercise of political power; in this sense the school is part of *his* domain. Our economist wants education to prepare us for the wise selection of economic alternatives; in this sense the school is also part of *his* domain. In short, the educational system seems unique in the range of its functions and the centrality of its relationship, at least theoretically, to the other social institutions. It is the institution that is charged with responsibility for the "socialization," "politicalization," "acculturation," and so on of the child (and other newcomers) in our society.[35]

The cruciality continuum has interesting implications for the fiscal dependent-independent argument in education. To place all public services at the same point of cruciality to society seems unrealistic. Thus, those who would have all-purpose government, or fiscal dependence for education, whether at local, state, or national levels, should also devise ways by which services thought by citizens to be most crucial to society can be given priority. Similarly, those who would have special-purpose government, or fiscal independence for education, should recognize that some mechanism for weighing the need of various public services is necessary. Under either system, cruciality to society ought to determine the allocation of public financial resources.

PUBLIC VISIBILITY AND SENSITIVITY

The continuum of public visibility and sensitivity seems to reside at the institutional level. Here the factory as an organization, particularly in its internal operations, is far less visible than the college and the school. Furthermore, the management of the factory need not be particularly sensitive to public opinion except as that opinion is connected with the product of the factory. To be sure, in times of labor crises, management must tell its story to the public; but such circumstances are the exception, not the rule.

LEAST VISIBILITY AND SENSITIVITY——▶MOST VISIBILITY AND SENSITIVITY

FACTORY   COLLEGE   SCHOOL

[35] Herbert A. Thelen and Jacob W. Getzels, "The Social Sciences: Conceptual Framework for Education," *School Review*, LXV (Autumn, 1957), p. 346.

In contrast, the school, particularly the public school, highly visible at all times, must be sensitive to its many publics. The high visibility is connected in part with the intimacy of relationships discussed below. Even more important is the fact that most schools are a public, not a private, enterprise. But, as school administrators soon discover, there is not one but many publics, which often hold sharply different views about the task of the school. In spite of the high visibility of the school, it is only in recent years that school administration has begun a serious examination of the relationship of the school to the broader society and the implications of that relationship to administrative behavior.

COMPLEXITY OF FUNCTION

The continuum of complexity of function applies to the technical level of the organization. Some organizations perform more complex technical functions than others. The exact placement of the four organizations on the continuum might be argued, but the process of teaching and learning, at least to one who knows little about making bolts, seems to be complex. In teaching and learning, for instance, the teachers who are charged with the responsibility of guiding the process are not in complete control of it. The learners may or may not respond to the stimulation provided. In contrast, workers who guide the process of bolt-making seem to be more nearly in control of their materials.

LEAST COMPLEX ⟶   ⟶   ⟶ MOST COMPLEX

FACTORY:	GOVERNMENT:	SCHOOL:	PSYCHIATRIC STAFF:
MAKING	COLLECTING	TEACHING AND	CHANGING
BOLTS	TAXES	LEARNING	PERSONALITY

Still, the task of teaching and learning is probably not so complex as the task that confronts a psychiatric staff. Perhaps a more explicit way of making the point would be to say that in terms of results acceptable to the organization, the teaching-learning task is less complex than personality change as attempted in the psychiatrist-patient relationship. Learning and bolt-making, for that matter, may both be highly complex processes, but we are concerned here with results acceptable to the respective organizations.

The main point seems to be that in each organization the administrator must have some knowledge of the complexity of the task acceptable to his organization if he is to function as co-ordinator of the organization.

INTIMACY OF NECESSARY RELATIONSHIPS

The continuum of intimacy, too, may be applied to the technical level of the organization. Exact placement of various organizations on the continuum is unnecessary to illustrate the point that relationships necessary to achieve organizational goals vary in intimacy from organization to organization. They are least intimate in a bolt factory, somewhat more intimate in tax-collecting by a government agency, appreciably more intimate in a school, and perhaps even more intimate in a hospital.

LEAST INTIMATE ⟶ ⟶ ⟶ MOST INTIMATE

FACTORY:	GOVERNMENT:	SCHOOL:	HOSPITAL:
MAKING	COLLECTING	TEACHING CHIL-	TREATING
BOLTS	TAXES	DREN AND YOUTH	THE ILL

It should be noted that school organizations involve the relationship of teacher to pupil, pupil to pupil, teacher to teacher, teacher to parent, and pupil to parent. Nor are school relationships confined to the formal learning of skills or knowledge. Because all human behavior is interrelated and much learning is concomitant in nature, these relationships often spill over into problems of person adjustment, family membership, and social acceptance. Only in medical practice, in hospital care, and perhaps in the church, are personal relationships more intimate.

STAFF PROFESSIONALIZATION

Staff professionalization seems to be part of a managerial continuum. We are using the term professionalization to represent competence that requires specialized preparation through which the individual acquires in marked degree the knowledge and values of his colleagues. Factories have relatively fewer professionals than skilled and unskilled workers. In a hospital, doctors and nurses are professionals, but practical nurses, nurses aides, and attendants of various kinds are not.

LEAST PROFESSIONALIZATION ⟶ MOST PROFESSIONALIZATION

FACTORY	HOSPITAL	SCHOOL	COLLEGE

In a school, however, teachers and administrative personnel make up two-thirds to three-fourths of all employees. They at least tend to be, and many are, professional in education and outlook. On this continuum, the college ranks higher than the school only because, on the average, college teachers possess more specialized knowledge than school teachers.

To the extent that personal dispositions of the staff are affected by professional values, superior intelligence, and articulate communication, it seems clear that administrators in schools must pay greater attention to personal dispositions than administrators in factories. Conversely, school administrators can rely less on standard operating procedures than can administrators in industrial plants.

DIFFICULTY OF APPRAISAL

The appraisal continuum also seems to reside at the technical level of the organization. While we do not wish to underestimate the difficulty of the process of appraisal in sales organizations and manufacturing concerns, it does seem that sales and production are fairly simple indexes of performance.

LEAST DIFFICULT ————————→ ————————→ ————————→ MOST DIFFICULT

SALES	MANUFACTURING	SCHOOL:	CHURCH:
ORGANIZATION:	ORGANIZATION:	CHANGE IN	INNER AND
SALES	PRODUCTS	BEHAVIOR	OUTER CHANGE

The school, in contrast, must be concerned with change in behavior, to use behavior in a broad sense. The change may involve knowledge, skills, or attitudes—all of which, presumably, influence behavior itself. But these changes are not immediately or easily perceptible. Often procedures or instruments have to be devised to measure change. But even when special instruments or procedures are used, students may, particularly in short-run evaluation, give what they believe to be appropriate responses. Sustained changes in behavior can be determined only over a period of years and by the accumulation of evidence from many sources. Obviously, the delay and the complexity of the evidence make useful feedback to the school for the purpose of revising practices most difficult.

Evaluation of a church program may be even more difficult than evaluation of a school program, for faith adds a transcendental dimension. The appraisal of school and college programs seems to be fraught with problems. Perhaps only the problems of appraising church programs are more difficult.

The six continua shown here offer a way of analyzing the common and the unique features of administration in various institutional settings. It is significant that three of the dimensions reside at the technical level, two at the institutional, and only one at the managerial level of organizations. This analysis suggests that the common elements in administration tend to be found at the managerial level, and the differentiations at the technical and institutional levels.

THEORY IN ADMINISTRATION

Some of the concepts dealt with above illustrate the quest for administrative theory characteristic of the last decade or two. In attempting to answer the question, "What is theory?" we have two alternatives. We can go full distance and side with Halpin[36] and Griffiths,[37] who both rely on Feigl[38] for a hypothetico-deductive definition. Or we can follow Walton, who suggests that we approach theory through such steps as observation, identification, definition, systematic classification, analysis, and finally, a hypothetico-deductive system.[39]

Our favorite definition of theory comes from Einstein:

In our endeavor to understand reality we are somewhat like a man trying to understand the mechanism of a closed watch. He sees the face and the moving hands, even hears it ticking, but he has no way of opening the case. If he is ingenious he may form some picture of a mechanism which could be responsible for all the things he observes, but he may never be quite sure his picture is the only one which could explain his observations. He will never be able to compare his picture with the real mechanism and he cannot even imagine the possibility or the meaning of such a comparison. But he certainly believes that, as his knowl-

---

[36] Andrew W. Halpin, ed., *Administrative Theory in Education* (Chicago: Midwest Administration Center, University of Chicago, 1958), Chap. I.

[37] Daniel E. Griffiths, *Administrative Theory* (New York: Appleton-Century-Crofts, 1959).

[38] Herbert Feigl, "Principles and Problems of Theory Construction in Psychology." In *Current Trends in Psychological Theory* (Pittsburgh: University of Pittsburgh Press, 1951), p. 182.

[39] John Walton, *op. cit.*

edge increases, his picture of reality will become simpler and simpler and will explain a wider and wider range of his sensuous impressions.[40]

Perhaps Einstein provides the most significant cue in what has been said up to now—"our endeavor to understand reality." In this context, the development of theory is the process whereby we describe reality more and more accurately.

Since the social sciences are newcomers to the scientific field, administration deals with most complex problems, and any theory seems to deal with but a few of the variables found in these phenomena, we are willing to keep the definition broad at this time. In the development of theory careful observation is a step above careless observation. Systematic classification is superior to no classification. To be sure, a series of related concepts from which we may derive testable hypotheses is theory of a higher order.

In any case, let us note some of the characteristics of theory. Theory is conceptual; it exists only in one's mind. Theory is not right or wrong; it is useful or not useful. At best, theory explains what is—never what ought to be. Theory, if it be useful, has within it the seeds of its own destruction and reconstitution. In other words, theory suggests process of thinking, not a recipe for action.

Recent interest in theory has led both students and practitioners of administration to expect a full-blown, grand theory of educational administration. Certainly no such manifestation is currently available, and we suspect that its formulation is a long way off.[41] On the other hand, a number of stimulating and useful theories are available. March and Simon have assessed the literature on organizational theory. They suggest that back of every proposition about organizations is a set of assumptions regarding the behavior of people. They grouped these propositions as follows:

1. Propositions assuming that organization members, and particularly employees, are primarily *passive instruments,* capable of performing work and accepting directions, but not initiating action or exerting influence in any significant way.

2. Propositions assuming that members bring to their organizations *attitudes, values,* and *goals;* that they have to be motivated or in-

[40] Albert Einstein and Leopold Infeld, *The Evolution of Physics* (New York: Simon and Schuster, Inc., 1938), p. 33.

[41] For development of this point, see Joseph J. Schwab, "The Professorship in Educational Administration: Theory—Art—Practice." In *The Professorship in Educational Administration* (Columbus, Ohio: University Council for Educational Administration, 1964), Chap. 4.

duced to participate in the system of organization behavior; that there is incomplete parallelism between their personal goals and organization goals; and that actual or potential goal conflicts make power phenomena, attitudes, and morale centrally important in the explanation of organizational behavior.

3. Propositions assuming that organization members are *decision-makers and problem-solvers,* and that perception and thought processes are central to the explanation of behavior in organizations.[42]

The view of Taylor, described briefly earlier in this chapter, appears to be based on the proposition that people are rather passive instruments. Barnard, as noted earlier, tended to accept the proposition that members bring to an organization their attitudes, values, and goals. Simon, as noted above, appears to have been the first person to suggest decision-making as a central proposition.

As Getzels and others[43] have suggested, to avoid theory leads to a number of untoward consequences. The first of these is factualism, the collection of facts with little or no purpose in mind about how they are to be used. A second consequence is unwarranted respect for the authority of experts, principles, and techniques; in other words, there is no framework for accepting one authority over another. Perhaps even more pernicious is another consequence—emotional identification with one's own personal views. It is fully as important for practitioners as for students of administration to avoid the consequences of lack of theory. Dewey was right many years ago when he contended that "theory is in the end . . . the most practical of all things."[44]

For the practitioner, theory is perhaps most useful in furnishing a number of concepts, or sets of spectacles, with which to view his situation. Such concepts were noted in the work of Taylor, Fayol, Follett, Mayo, Barnard, and Simon. In this chapter we have presented an overview and have suggested the meaning of administration. In Chapters 5 through 8 we shall describe four different ways of viewing administration. Perhaps only Chapter 8 can be seen, in any sophisticated sense, as a theory of administration, but each of the

[42] James G. March and Herbert A. Simon, *Organizations* (New York: Wiley, 1958), p. 6.

[43] J. W. Getzels, J. M. Lipham, and R. F. Campbell, *Educational Administration as a Social Process* (New York: Harper & Row, 1968), Chap. 1.

[44] John Dewey, *Sources of a Science of Education* (New York: Liveright, 1929), p. 17.

other approaches is a useful way of viewing the field. Taken together, these chapters illustrate the difficulty of subjecting a most complex phenomenon to a single theoretical formulation.

SUGGESTED ACTIVITIES

1. For one school district, suggest practices that seem to be related to (a) the scientific management or job analysis movement and (b) to the human relations emphasis in administration.
2. Note the duties suggested for the superintendent, principals, supervisors, and teachers in the rules and regulations of a city school district. How would you improve the statement? What assumptions are back of your recommendations?
3. Interview a superintendent of schools concerning his major activities.
4. Interview five teachers concerning their view of the major activities of the superintendent. Analyze similarities and differences in perceptions.

SELECTED READINGS

BARNARD, CHESTER I. *The Functions of the Executive.* (Cambridge, Mass.: Harvard University Press, 1938).

CALLAHAN, RAYMOND E. *Education and the Cult of Efficiency.* (Chicago: University of Chicago Press, 1962).

FAYOL, HENRI. *General and Industrial Management.* (London: Sir Isaac Pitman & Sons, 1949).

GETZELS, JACOB W., LIPHAM, JAMES M., and CAMPBELL, ROALD F. *Educational Administration as a Social Process.* New York: Harper & Row, 1968.

GRIFFITHS, DANIEL E., ed. *Developing Taxonomies of Organizational Behavior in Education Administration.* (Chicago: Rand McNally, 1969).

HALPIN, ANDREW W., *Theory and Research in Administration.* (New York: The Macmillan Co., 1966).

MARCH, JAMES G., and SIMON, HERBERT A. *Organizations.* (New York: Wiley, 1958).

MAYO, ELTON. *The Human Problems of an Industrial Civilization.* (Boston: Graduate School of Business Administration, Harvard University, 1946).

METCALF, HENRY C., and URWICK, L., eds. *Dynamic Administration.* (New York: Harper & Brothers, 1942). The collected papers of Mary Parker Follett with an introduction by the editors.

National Society for the Study of Education, *Behavioral Science and Educational Administration*, Sixty-Third Yearbook, Part II. (Chicago: University of Chicago Press, 1964).

SIMON, HERBERT A. *Administrative Behavior*, 2nd ed. (New York: The Macmillan Co., 1957).

TAYLOR, FREDERICK W. *Scientific Management*. (New York: Harper & Brothers, 1947).

5

Administrative Tasks

If administration is to facilitate teaching and learning, as we maintained in the preceding chapter, it becomes necessary to examine the major tasks necessary for the achievement of such a purpose. In this chapter we shall suggest the nature and scope of these tasks. We shall show something of the interrelationships among these tasks, though we cannot treat the detailed techniques to be employed in the achievement of them. Such a treatment requires books, not a single chapter!

The task approach to administration is not characterized by any highly developed theory. At best, the organization of the tasks into operational areas is a taxonomy. This classification, however, brings a certain order to the field which will prove useful to both student and practitioner of administration.

The administrative tasks or operational areas of administration may be grouped into categories. We think the six categories shown below represent a convenient grouping:

1. School-community relationships.
2. Curriculum and instruction.
3. Pupil personnel.
4. Staff personnel.
5. Physical facilities.
6. Finance and business management.

The principal of a school and the superintendent of a school system ordinarily have many tasks to perform in each of these operational areas. In large schools or school systems, assistants to principals and superintendents may be given limited responsibilities in one or two of the operational areas. For example, a high school principal may have a vice-principal in charge of pupil activities, discipline, and attendance, to assist him. Or a superintendent of schools may have a director of curriculum and a business manager to assist him. Or a county superintendent may have an elementary supervisor as a major staff member. In these cases a team of administrators has been formed to work at the administrative tasks.

The organization and treatment of administrative tasks in this chapter should in no sense imply that one administrator or even a team of administrators can or should do these things alone. Other people are nearly always involved. These people may be citizens, school board members, or members of the teaching or non-teaching staffs of the school. In some cases the tasks are achieved with the assistance of these people, in other cases entirely by them, and in still other cases these people advise the administrator regarding the tasks. It should be clear, however, that the responsibility for seeing that these jobs are done rests with the administrator. The nature of each of the major operational areas will now be suggested.

SCHOOL-COMMUNITY RELATIONSHIPS

Because education in our country is largely a public venture, and because in the final analysis it can be no better than the citizens of a community will have it, school-community relationships represent both a point of beginning and a continuing concern for any school administrator. As suggested in Chapter 4, we are defining community in operational terms only as the attendance area for a single school or the school district for a school system. We recognize that in some ways the state or even the nation might be thought of as a community, but we shall limit this treatment to local school units. While the tasks incident to school-community relationships are numerous, we shall limit our discussion to what seem to be certain focal points.

CHARACTER OF THE COMMUNITY

School communities may be characterized as urban or rural, as farm or non-farm, as industrial or residential, as middle-class or lower-class. Such common designations may provide the school administrator with some clues as to how he is to work with his community. In actual practice, however, school communities may not lend themselves to such easy categorizing, and such rubrics may not constitute useful approaches to relating school and community.

Bullock was concerned with the community characteristics that the school administrator needed to understand.[1] After preliminary testing he determined that the following questions were important:

1. What is the general community level of approval or disapproval of the school program?
2. What kind of educational philosophy does the community hold?
3. What degree of prestige do teachers as an occupational class hold in the community?
4. What kind of community is this with regard to such characteristics as cohesiveness and unity of action?
5. How does this community define the role of the school administrator?
6. How receptive is this community to change and innovation?

Bullock then proceeded to develop some scales which an administrator might use in a school community in an attempt to answer the questions enumerated above. In one city school district, for example, he found that the level of school approval varied significantly in terms of the geographical location, occupational category, organizational membership of residents, and the amount of formal education completed by residents.

The pertinence of school-community relationships to the other tasks of administration may be seen in the further examination of some of Bullock's questions. According to him, the level of community approval is related to the level of the program for which a community would be willing to spend money. The educational philosophy of a community has a bearing upon the curriculum of the school. The willingness of a community to accept the leadership of teachers in instructional matters is, in part, a function of the prestige in which teachers are held. Community cohesiveness is pertinent to community decisions regarding school building expansion, as it is to other community decisions. Perhaps enough has been said to illustrate how necessary it is that a school administrator understand the composition and character of his school community.

DESIRES AND ASPIRATIONS OF CITIZENS

Some of what was said above has implications for the assessment of the desires and aspirations that citizens have for their schools. We need to note specifically, however, that this is another important

[1] Robert P. Bullock, *School-Community Attitude Analysis for Educational Administrators,* SCDS Monograph #7 (Columbus, Ohio: The Ohio State University, 1959), 112 pp.

aspect of school-community relationships. There are many ways by which assessment might be made, such as through informal conversations with citizens and through the use of rating scales like those developed by Bullock and referred to above.

A number of studies done at the University of Chicago have dealt with the task of the public school as perceived by various sub-publics.[2] Occupation and amount of schooling were found to be the best predictors of educational belief. Fair predictors were also geographic region in which one lives, age, race, and religion. Interestingly enough, the type of community in which a person lives, income, sex, and participation in school programs did not prove to be closely associated with educational viewpoint. Some useful instruments for the assessment of public perceptions were also developed as part of these studies.

The building of a realistic expectation of what the public schools can and should do in a community represents one of the major tasks of any school administrator. Only with such understanding can school procedures make sense to citizens and lead to significant advances in school programs.

Information About the School

We do not subscribe to the public relations concept of "selling" the public schools to the people. Actually, the people already hold title to the public schools. We do believe, however, that after school and community representatives reach agreement on programs and those programs are put into operation, there must be full and frequent reporting to the community on their progress. Thus, dissemination of information about the school to the community is an important obligation of any administrator.

Indeed, information needs to be disseminated on many subjects. It might pertain to a new emphasis in mathematics, a new method of reporting pupil progress, a program for the in-service education of teachers, the extension of the school plant, changes in the tax resources of the school district, the development of school board policies, or any number of other items. Unfortunately, school reporting in some districts still deals more extensively with athletics and the marching band than with any other aspects of the instructional program. Perhaps administrators who report to the public would do well to exercise candor in reporting shortcomings as well as strengths.

[2] Lawrence W. Downey, *The Task of Public Education* (Chicago: Midwest Administration Center, University of Chicago, 1960), 88 pp.

Just as there are many things to report, there are many ways of reporting. Inevitably school pupils become conveyors of school news. Teachers, too, have many community contacts and are often sources of information about schools. Many schools have found letters to parents, room meetings for parents, and regular P.T.A. sessions useful aids in reporting. Some central offices print short brochures about school matters to be included with the report cards of pupils. Other school districts issue annual reports either as booklets or as special editions of the local newspaper. Coverage of school news by newspaper, radio, and television is, of course, a common and important means of disseminating information about the school.

A nine-year study on "the structure and process of school-community relations" undertaken at Stanford University has provided a great deal of information on this topic.[3] Some of the more important findings of the study are that informal citizen communication about the schools is scanty and ineffective, that mediating agencies between the schools and citizens, such as the school board and parent organizations, are little used by citizens, and that consumer orientations of citizens toward the schools and non-issue related concerns tend to influence support for the schools in general and, specifically, voting in school tax and bond referenda.

ROLE OF THE SCHOOL

Another aspect of school-community relations is the development of a consensus on the role of the school in the community. That the establishment of such a consensus is not so simple as it once was is attested by a statement from the White House Conference on Education:

The basic responsibility of the schools is the development of the skills of the mind, but the over-all mission has been enlarged. Schools are now asked to help each child to become as good and as capable in every way as native endowment permits. The schools are asked to help children to acquire any skill or characteristic which a majority of the community deems worthwhile. The order given by the American people to the schools is grand in its simplicity; in addition to intellectual achievement, foster morality, happiness, and any useful ability. The

[3] Richard F. Carter and William R. Odell, *The Structure and Process of School-Community Relations: A Summary*, Vol. V, U.S. Department of Health, Education and Welfare, Office of Education, Cooperative Research Project No. 1039 (Stanford, Calif.: Institute for Communication Research and School of Education (Stanford University, 1966).

talent of each child is to be sought out and developed to the fullest. Each weakness is to be studied and, so far as possible, corrected. This is truly a majestic ideal, and an astonishingly new one. Schools of that kind have never been provided for more than a small fraction of mankind.

Although it is new, this ideal of schools which do everything possible for all children is a natural development in the United States. The moving spirit of this Nation has been from the beginning a sense of fairness. Nowadays equality of educational opportunity for adults means little without equality of educational opportunity for children. Ignorance is a greater obstacle than ever to success of most kinds. The schools have become a major tool for creating a Nation without rigid class barriers. *It is primarily the schools which allow no man's failure to prevent the success of his son.*[4] [Italics in original]

The social, as well as the educational, purpose of the school is also emphasized in a recent study of the Chicago schools:

The future of the city is bound up with the program of the public schools in two basic ways.

First, the schools help to give the next generation and the present generation of citizens and workers the knowledge and the understanding and the attitudes that make them good, bad, or indifferent citizens, workers, and parents.

Second, the program of the schools is the greatest single factor in the decision of middle-income people to live in the central city or to live in the suburbs, and to live in one section of the city or another.[5]

The administrative task suggested here is two-fold. There is first of all the stimulation of school workers and lay citizens in thinking about the role of the school in a particular attendance area or school district, with, of course, the clear recognition that state, regional, national, and world forces also impinge upon every locality. Second, this consideration must be continued until agreements can be reached which will serve as operating bases for the schools.

ROLE OF OTHER COMMUNITY AGENCIES

As lay citizens and school people work together to determine for a particular school community the role of its school or school system, they will inevitably have to give attention to the roles to be played

---

[4] The Committee for the White House Conference on Education, *A Report to the President* (Washington, D.C.: U.S. Government Printing Office, 1956), p. 9.

[5] Robert J. Havighurst, *The Public Schools of Chicago* (Chicago: Board of Education, 1964), p. 28.

by other community agencies and organizations. These organizations and agencies include the home; the churches; the city or county government; farm, labor, or business associations; public libraries; newspapers, radio, and television stations; and many others. In the total development of a community each of these agencies has a part to play.

Goldman examined the perceptions held by educators, non-educators, and high school students regarding the roles of the high school, the family, and the church in the development of a number of qualities in the high school graduate.[6] Educators and non-educators agree that the family should hold primary responsibility for developing most of the qualities of the ideal graduate. To the high school was assigned the responsibility for developing the theoretic and political qualities, while the family was seen as having primary responsibility for developing the religious, economic, altruistic, hedonistic, social, æsthetic, and ethical qualities. While the students themselves saw the church as having primary responsibility for the religious quality, neither educators nor non-educators were of that opinion.

These findings suggest that more work needs to be done in assessing the perceptions people hold regarding the role of the school and the roles of other community agencies in the total program of education. Moreover, current perceptions in any particular community, we suspect, need not be ultimate perceptions. Again, the need to work out community understandings and programs becomes apparent.

In the operational area of school-community relations, we have suggested that the administrative tasks include those of ascertaining the composition and character of the community, and of determining the desires and aspirations the people have for the public school. We have also indicated that with such data at hand administrators must stimulate the development of some agreements in a community regarding the roles of the public school and of other community agencies. In large city school districts with the current emphasis upon decentralization, the principal of a single school will be increasingly challenged to work within this context for his own attendance area.

---

[6] Samuel Goldman, "Sub-Public Perceptions of the High School Graduate and the Roles of Institutions in His Development" (Unpublished doctoral dissertation, Department of Education, University of Chicago, 1961).

CURRICULUM AND INSTRUCTION

A second, and in a sense the basic, operating area for the school administrator is that of curriculum and instruction. By curriculum and instruction we mean those activities in which school workers, sometimes assisted by lay citizens, engage to plan, implement, and evaluate an instructional program.

We recognize, too, that in the final analysis change in instructional content or method does not come through mere talking about it. Actually, changes occur when the understanding and skills of teachers and other workers change. To be effective, therefore, curriculum development activities should provide ways by which school workers may acquire new insights or develop new skills. Such insights and skills are related to the following curriculum categories: determination of objectives, the development of a program of instruction, the use of instructional procedures, and the appraising of instruction. Each of these will be treated briefly here.

DETERMINING OBJECTIVES

Each school staff needs to develop, in the light of all the evidence available, a concept of the specific objectives of the school or school system in a particular community. Setting the conditions so that this procedure can be carried out effectively is another important administrative task.

General statements of policy, like those found in *Goals for Americans,* are provocative.[7] Gardner suggested, it will be recalled, that "our schools must prepare all young people, whatever their talents, for the serious business of being free men and women."[8] These broad objectives seem acceptable enough until one tries to spell them out in more specific terms. For instance, in the interest of intellectual development, are youngsters going to be free to examine controversial issues such as the war in Vietnam? In the moral realm, to what extent can and should representatives of religious denominations be used in

---

[7] John W. Gardner, "National Goals in Education." In Report of the President's Commission on National Goals, *Goals for Americans* (New York: Prentice-Hall, 1960), Chap. 3.

[8] *Ibid.,* p. 100.

the school program? In what ways do we challenge the gifted and still provide for their participation in social situations with pupils of a wide range of abilities? The administrator must be concerned with these and similar questions as he tries to develop a plan whereby the professional staff can get at the objectives of the school.

What are some of the elements of such a plan? Basically, two things are necessary: to provide opportunity to learn more about the culture and its demands upon the school, and to provide opportunity to learn more about the growth and development of children and youth. These are the foundations of any kind of curriculum study.

Teachers and other school workers, to be sure, already know a great deal about the culture which determines, in part, what the school ought to be about. In a society as complex and pluralistic as ours, however, such knowledge may be fragmentary, incomplete, and even in error. A comprehension of the way federal expenditures for foreign aid may be related to our own economic well-being may illustrate the world-wide nature and complexity of our society.

Any plan for helping professional workers to make a continuous assessment of the social scene requires that they have an opportunity to examine the culture both first hand and vicariously. To examine first hand, people must have an opportunity to travel in their own locality, in the nation, and the world at large. Such travel can, of course, be supplemented by reading or by hearing the reports of other observers, provided such observers have the ability to see and to report.

Opportunity for extending the knowledge of teachers about human growth and learning is readily at hand. Pupils can be seen not only as people to be taught but as subjects to be studied. Actually, the challenge of teaching is probably not fully appreciated until both approaches are used. To study children and youth, however, certain conditions seem necessary. Teachers need a little time for reflection. They may also need the help of a person who is more capable in study and research approaches if their own studies are to be well conceived and executed. The administrator should try to provide these conditions.

PROGRAM OF INSTRUCTION

After the objectives of an instructional program are formulated, the job of actually determining a program to achieve these objectives still remains. Facilitating the development of such a program is also the task of the administrator. To the extent that programs are district-wide in character, the superintendent and his staff should take major responsibility to facilitate the process. To the extent that each building has autonomy in developing its own program, the building principal and his staff should take major responsibility to facilitate the process.

Many of the conditions suggested above for administrators to promote in the determination of objectives pertain also to the development of instructional programs. It seems desirable, however, to look more specifically at the behavior of administrators, particularly as such behavior may affect the work of teachers and other professional personnel as they engage in program development.

Jenkins and Blackman studied the relationship between the behavior of elementary school principals and the curriculum development activities of their staff members in a large city school district.[9] While many of the findings were suggestive only, the data do indicate rather clearly that there was no significant relationship between the verbalization of democratic attitudes by administrators and the effectiveness of those administrators in putting democracy into action. Or to put it another way, administrators may say they involve teachers in curriculum planning—they may even think that they do involve them—and at the same time this condition may not exist.

In the same study it was also found that the most effective administrators used approaches that were neither strongly "staff-centered" nor strongly "task-centered." Rather, principals who had some facility to help teachers define jobs and who at the same time were able to exhibit warmth toward teachers were the ones who, in general, had the most effective staffs in terms of developing curriculum programs.

While organizational arrangements for curriculum study were not a significant variable in the Jenkins-Blackman study, a school administrator does have certain organizational responsibilities if he is to foster program-building among his staff members. At the district level, for instance, it would seem appropriate that some kind of district-wide curriculum council be formed. This council should have on it representative teachers, principals, and staff members from the central office, so that instructional plans for the entire system might be appropriately reviewed. Existence of such a council in form only

[9] David H. Jenkins and Charles A. Blackman, *Antecedents and Effects of Administrator Behavior,* SCDS Monograph No. 3 (Columbus, Ohio: College of Education, The Ohio State University, 1956).

will, of course, guarantee nothing. The council must come to represent a genuine forum where ideas, not status positions, are important. Organization of instructional programs is also important at the building level. Mackenzie[10] analyzed a number of descriptions of educational changes at the building level and reported that school principals were influential participants in such changes.

NATIONAL CURRICULUM PROGRAMS

But development and implementation of the program of instruction is no longer an activity carried on chiefly by a school district or a single school. Under the auspices of the National Science Foundation and other groups, national curriculum programs have been developed, and they have had decided impact upon the instructional practices of many schools.[11] Beginning in 1956 with the Physical Science Study Committee, with headquarters at the Massachusetts Institute of Technology, extensive programs have also been developed in mathematics, biology, and chemistry.[12] The United States Office of Education has also supported projects in English and social studies whose results may have national impact.

These national programs raise several important issues. For one, control of education in this country has, in the past, been assumed to be a state and local matter. Legally, this is still the case for the most part, but actually the influence of the national programs is widespread and pervasive. At one time, extensive teacher participation was considered essential to the development of curriculum programs. But today relatively few teachers take part in the development of most national programs; in fact, they find that they are, rather, the consumers of these programs. Although very limited resources were once available for curriculum development, the national programs have had at their disposal millions of dollars for holding conferences, developing instructional materials, hiring consultants, and organizing

10 Gordon N. Mackenzie, "Curricular Change: Participants, Power, and Processes." In Matthew B. Miles, ed., *Innovation in Education* (New York: Bureau of Publications, Teachers College, Columbia University, 1964), pp. 410–411.

11 Roald F. Campbell and Robert A. Bunnell, eds., *Nationalizing Influences on Secondary Education* (Chicago: Midwest Administration Center, University of Chicago, 1963).

12 John I. Goodlad, ed., *The Changing American School.* Sixty-Fifth Yearbook of the National Society for the Study of Education, Part II (Chicago: The University of Chicago Press, 1966), Chap. 2.

institutes wherein teachers might become acquainted with the programs.

In addition, these programs create new responsibilities for the administrator, who must acquire some knowledge of them in order to discuss them with his staff. He also will probably wish to encourage his teachers to attend institutes where the new programs are being presented. In any case, those involved in curriculum development at the local level can no longer ignore the ideas growing out of the national programs, nor can they ignore the instructional materials these programs make available.

INSTRUCTIONAL MATERIALS

Another closely related task for which the administrator takes responsibility is the selection and procurement of instructional materials. The teacher, to be sure, is central to adequate instruction, but even good teachers can do better when they are provided with appropriate tools.

The first task in this area is that of budget provision. Budget-building at its best assumes that program development, discussed briefly above, has gone forward, and that the materials needed to implement such a program will now become the basis for the budget request. For instance, if it has been decided that every biology student should have actual experience using laboratory equipment and supplies, the budget request will be quite different from one based upon a course that is to be taught with the textbook-demonstration-lecture approach.

Even assuming this kind of budget approach, however, it will usually be the administrator who must convince the superintendent's staff, the board of education, and finally the community that expenditures for instructional materials are indispensable to an adequate program of instruction. Sometimes elaborate plant and grounds—the outside façade of the school—win out over books, maps, and other instructional aids when budgets become tight. Without deprecating adequate programs of plant operation and maintenance, administrators need to be able to hold the line for budget items intimately related to the instructional program.

In the actual selection of instructional materials, teachers should play a large part. It has been found that teachers feel strongly the need to assume responsibility for those activities which have to do with instruction. It behooves administrators, therefore, to devise ways by which teacher participation in instructional matters, including the selection of instructional materials, can be encouraged. It should be recognized, however, that since such participation does take time, it must be regarded as a part of the total load of the teacher.

When budget provision for instructional materials has been made and when teachers have assisted in the actual selection of materials, there still remain the problems of procurement and delivery. These are tasks which the administration of a school district should perform with the greatest possible dispatch. Nothing is as exasperating to a teacher as to participate in a budget-building or a materials-selection program and then have purchase or delivery of materials delayed indefinitely by administrative red tape. The principal and the superintendent must cut through any such maze or avoid creating it.

APPRAISING INSTRUCTION

Another major responsibility confronting any administrator in the area of curriculum development is that of appraising instruction. Some industries allocate as much as one-sixth of their manpower to quality control. In education, unfortunately, evaluation has tended to be done with the left hand, if at all.

Space here will not permit a full treatment of evaluation. It does seem appropriate to suggest, however, that evaluation as a process has the following steps:

1. The formulation of objectives.
2. The definition of these objectives in behavioral terms.
3. Determination of places where these behaviors may be observed.
4. Selection or development of instruments upon which to record these behaviors when observed.
5. Appraisal and interpretation of the evidence thus collected.

If done carefully this process is, of course, a rather laborious one. All aspects of an instructional program probably cannot be submitted continuously to such a careful procedure. On the other hand, the spirit of the evaluative approach can be applied much more generally than is now the case. Essentially, such an approach stresses careful formulation of purposes and collection of evidence in terms of those purposes.

Administrators need to help school workers and lay citizens alike to see that evaluation is a necessary complement to planning and doing. If we devise a new program for the teaching of reading, we must, of course, try it out, and we must evaluate, as best we can, how effective the program has been. Planning, doing, and evaluating are, in a real sense, just parts of a whole.

If this view is taken, it becomes clear that teachers must have time to participate in planning and evaluating as much as in doing. Such a statement has implications for teacher selection, job expectation, and teacher load. Moreover, the assistance of specialists in evaluation should probably be made available to teachers and others in the school system if the process is to be done well. It seems clear that only with regular and adequate evaluation can the administrator fulfill his responsibilities to his staff, his board of education, and his community. Recent demands for accountability and the application of cost-benefit analyses make it clear that citizens insist on knowing "how we are doing."

We have suggested that, in the operational area of curriculum and instruction, administrators have the responsibility for setting conditions that will promote the determination of objectives, the development of instructional programs, and the procurement of instructional materials. We have also indicated that, as programs are planned, plans for their evaluation should be formulated.

PUPIL PERSONNEL

Curriculum and instruction as discussed above had to do essentially with that part of the school program which is concerned with regular classroom instruction. Activities included within the operational area of pupil personnel embrace those services to pupils that supplement regular classroom instruction. Except in schools with very small enrollments, the chief role of the administrator in the pupil personnel area is one of integrating the personnel functions with instruction and of co-ordinating the various kinds of personnel services. Recent developments, such as special programs for the talented and the growth of external testing, have placed even more emphasis on pupil personnel services. A discussion of a few of the major tasks in pupil personnel follows.

PUPIL INVENTORY AND ORGANIZATION

Some staff member in a school or school district must first of all determine how many youngsters there are of school age in the attendance area or district. He does so by means of a school census, by the keeping of enrollment and attendance data, and by other means that will be discussed later. It is usually necessary that the number of pupils be determined by grade level and by school or attendance area.

With this information in hand, the administrator is in a position to determine to what extent school rooms in the existing buildings will house the pupils of the district. If certain buildings appear to be overcrowded and others have capacity to spare, the administrator may find that attendance boundaries need to be altered. In recent years, with charges of de facto segregation in many cities, the establishment of attendance areas has taken on new significance. The social and racial composition of the attendance area is fully as important as the consideration of number of pupils to be enrolled in the school.

The continual or yearly enumeration of pupils also furnishes one of the bases for determining new building needs. Often this enumeration furnishes data having to do with the direction of growth in a school district. In city school districts, particularly, population growth is usually toward the outskirts or even beyond the boundaries of the district to the suburbs. At the same time, enrollments in schools near the center of the city may actually be decreasing.

Enrollment data also furnish the administrator with the best single index of teaching personnel needed by grades, by subject area, and by school or attendance area. For example, if the projected enrollment data for a new elementary school indicated that 456 pupils would attend, and if the district had a policy of providing a teacher for each 28 elementary pupils, it is clear that the new school would require no fewer than 16 teachers.

Up to this point we have spoken of gross enumeration of pupils. It is also necessary that much be known about the characteristics of the pupils found within a school district. How many are gifted, how many are slow learners, how many are hard of hearing, how many are orthopedic cases? Ordinary census or enrollment data will not, of course, provide the kind of information suggested here. The identification of pupils with special problems will require the co-operation of teachers, parents, and specially trained personnel. Again, however, such information is necessary in order that a school or school system can plan a program of services for all, including its deviate pupils.

PUPIL ACCOUNTING

We have already alluded to the first task of pupil accounting, the enumeration of pupils. Ordinarily a school census system is established to help with this task. There is a compulsory education law in nearly every state, and a school census is a necessary step in the enforcement of such laws. While census-taking was once seen as a yearly task, many school systems now use the continuing census approach. Specific procedures to be followed have been described in detail elsewhere.[13]

Another task facing every school system is the development and the operation of a pupil-accounting system. A plan for dealing with pupil absence and tardiness must be developed. If such a plan is to be followed by teachers and principals as part of their regular duties, it needs to be relatively simple. If specialized attendance personnel are to be employed, the plan may be somewhat more ambitious. In any case, teachers should have some voice in deciding upon the plan, and their own part in its operation will need to be clearly understood.

It seems appropriate to say at this point that the "hooky cop" approach to attendance leaves much to be desired. There is usually substantial cause back of nonattendance of school pupils. The school needs personnel who can both determine these basic causes and work toward their alleviation. Such causes often reside in the family, or the culture of which the family is a part, and thus non-attendance may actually be a social symptom toward which school workers, social agencies, and society itself ought to be directing their efforts.

Another duty common in pupil accounting is the issuance of work permits. In most states pupils may be excused at age fourteen or sixteen if they are needed to help support a family or if they can benefit no further from school attendance. These are important decisions in the life of a child and should be made only after facts are ascertained and appropriate counseling has been given the pupil and the family. In small school districts, principals and superintendents ordinarily perform these functions. In larger districts, specialized personnel are usually employed.

Pupil Personnel Services

A very important aspect of the pupil personnel area is the provision of appropriate pupil personnel services. Large school districts may have services such as the following:

1. Child study.
2. Guidance and counseling advisement.

[13] Dean L. Hummel and S. J. Bonham, *Pupil Personnel Services in Schools: Organization and Coordination* (Chicago: Rand McNally, 1968).

3. Testing.
4. Visiting teacher and social worker.
5. Speech and hearing therapy.
6. Medical and nursing.
7. Special education
   a. Physically handicapped
   b. Emotionally disturbed
   c. Mental deviates
   d. Gifted.

To some of these services we have already alluded. For instance, tests and measurements would be helpful in any program of evaluation; the school social worker might be skilled in getting at causes behind nonattendance of pupils. Some school systems see special education as a part of the curriculum program, but even so the workers in special education need to have close affiliation with the workers in the pupil personnel area.

If pupil personnel services are really going to supplement regular classroom instruction, it seems quite clear that some specialized personnel will be necessary. The welfare federation of a large city has suggested that a minimum staff for pupil personnel services should be composed of specialized people for each of the following:

1. Director (or co-ordinator) of pupil personnel services.
2. Health service.
3. Secondary school counseling service.
4. Speech and hearing therapy.
5. Child study service (psychological service and psychiatric consultation).
6. School social work service.

To be sure, small school districts cannot ordinarily employ all of the specialists suggested above. Such districts might start by getting one guidance counselor and by determining where the other services could be obtained on a part-time basis. For instance, in many states the county or intermediate school district is becoming a service unit to smaller school districts. In such cases most of the services noted above can be provided on a co-operative basis. Again, the job of the administrator is that of seeing that these services are made available and co-ordinated.

CONTROL OF PUPIL BEHAVIOR

While schools should attempt to determine the cause of misbehavior in pupils, and to treat the cause and not the symptom of such actions, there are times when pupils must be corrected or disciplined. Policies governing these matters should be clear, and the responsibilities of teachers and other staff members in this area should be understood. Competent teachers can and should exercise appropriate controls over their pupils. Actually, and contrary to the views of some beginning teachers, pupils prefer those teachers who are seen as fair, helpful, setting high standards, and allowing no "monkey business."

Even with the best of teachers, however, there are times when the principal, guidance counselor, or some other non-teaching staff member is placed in the role of disciplinarian. Many contend that guidance counselors and other pupil personnel workers should have no disciplinary function; that function, they insist, should be carried by the principal or some other administrative officer. The logic behind such an argument is that the guidance counselor should be individual- and not group-oriented—or, perhaps better stated, pupil-centered in place of school-centered.

In general, we accept this position; but carried to its extreme it would mean that both guidance counselors and principals would become less effective than they should be. When it is necessary for a principal to take part in a discipline problem, he should get the best picture possible of the circumstances surrounding the misbehavior prior to arriving at a plan of action. Some of this information he may get from the pupil, some he should get from those workers who have specialized knowledge and the competence to place such knowledge in its appropriate context. The best diagnosis possible is needed if the principal is to be effective in helping youngsters toward the ultimate goal of self-discipline.

Recent developments require a reexamination of the traditional concepts of pupil control. The student activist movement, first prominent among college students, has acquired many adherents among high school students. Westin[14] surveyed 1,800 newspapers over a

[14] Alan F. Westin, *The New York Times,* May 9, 1969.

four-month period and found reports of 239 serious episodes such as strikes, sit-ins, riots, and other forms of violence in high schools located in 38 states. Westin categorized the causes of these disturbances in order as follows: racial, political, dress, discipline, and educational reform. While there are no ready made panaceas for dealing with student activities, it seems clear that high school administrators should hear what the students are saying. Some of their contentions are sound and should lead to reform; others are not and in such cases some firmness in making boundaries clear seems to be in order.

We have suggested that in the area of pupil personnel the major administrative tasks have to do with pupil inventory and organization, pupil accounting, provisions for pupil services, and control of pupil behavior. These services should complement the program provided all pupils through regular classroom instruction.

STAFF PERSONNEL

To implement any of the programs suggested above under curriculum development or pupil personnel, appropriate staff must be provided. Here, therefore, we should like to examine staff personnel as one of the major operational areas in administration. Our discussion will be focused on certificated personnel such as teachers, guidance workers, and administrators. Many of the approaches suggested also have application to non-certificated personnel (custodians, lunchroom workers, and bus drivers). Some additional comments regarding non-certificated personnel will be made when business management is discussed.

PERSONNEL POLICIES

In personnel administration, as with all other aspects of administration, one of the first tasks is the development of appropriate personnel policies. Often school districts recognize the necessity for personnel policies even before they see the need for more general policy statements. Perhaps a word should be said here about the meaning of policy. As we use the term here, and as it might be applied more broadly to school administration, policies refer to a set of guiding principles that establish a framework to give consistency to a school board's actions. In a sense, then, a policy statement represents the framework, in terms of law and of the philosophy of the board, upon which action is to be based.

To be sure, many boards of education will need help in thinking through possible alternatives if they are to express what we would deem sound personnel policies. This means that the administrator will think with both staff members and lay citizens concerning policy matters, and from such deliberation will gain assistance in arriving at policy statements to be recommended to his board of education. These policies will probably most often pertain to working conditions and to the salary program.

Personnel policies pertaining to working conditions, we believe, should meet the following criteria:

1. Appear reasonable and not capricious.
2. Have a positive and not a punitive flavor.
3. Be suggestive and not merely prescriptive.
4. Establish the fact that full information on school operation is available to teachers.
5. Provide clear channels of communication.
6. Make plain the bases for promotion.
7. Provide for staff participation in the formulation and operation of policies.

One illustration of policy statement, having to do with the participation of staff personnel in policy formation, has been taken from the handbook of a city school district. The statement follows:

Personnel policies for the Union District shall be co-operatively formulated and written in concise form. In the development of the same the Superintendent is directed to create and maintain a committee system in which the teaching personnel and all others affected by the policies under consideration may participate in their formulation.

The Committee (a) may direct their recommendations directly to the Board through the Superintendent and he is directed not to interrupt, obstruct, or delay transmittal of said recommendations. The Superintendent will provide every means whereby the certificated personnel receive full information and explanation of all personnel policies, rules and regulations that may affect them directly or indirectly. Copies of such policies shall be distributed at least once each year to all employees not having the same. Professional Standards and Staff Relationships will also be discussed in at least one meeting per year.

Personnel policies shall be reviewed at least once per year by a joint committee of teachers, administrators, and board members.[15]

It will be noted that the place of the committee system has been made clear. Participation of staff members in discussing major school problems is given official endorsement, and the need for face-to-face communication among the superintendent, professional staff members, and board of trustees is recognized.

The increasing militancy of teachers and teachers' organizations has added a new dimension to the problem of formulating personnel policies. The day when school boards and administrators could take a rather paternalistic attitude toward teachers seems to be drawing to a close. Teachers' associations and unions are ever more frequently demanding some type of collective relationship with the board of education.

Lieberman and Moskow[16] have dealt extensively with the evolving field of collective negotiations. They suggest that there are at least three approaches: the marketplace or short-range approach, the professional approach, and the problem-solving approach. They deal extensively with each of these approaches, with the procedures involved in collective negotiations, and they include samples of many documents which have been evolved in actual negotiations. One of these documents is the agreement between the New Haven Board of Education and the New Haven Teachers' League.[17] The agreement is twenty-five printed pages in length and includes the following major items: recognition of the league, teaching hours and load, teaching assignments and transfers, promotions, teacher facilities, class size, textbooks, specialists, teacher aids, summer school programs, protection, accident benefits, sick leave, leaves of absence, salaries, grievance procedures, dues deduction, and negotiation of successor agreement.

Collective negotiations have changed the world of most school administrators. At its worst, negotiated agreements can negate any leadership role the administrator may attempt to play. At its best, negotiated agreements can clarify the roles of teachers and administrators and provide for each. In these situations, much can be made

---

[15] Union School District, San Jose, Calif. "Policies, Rules and Regulations, and Administrative Code," p. 31, no date.

[16] Myron Lieberman and Michael H. Moskow, *Collective Negotiations for Teachers* (Chicago: Rand McNally, 1966).

[17] *Ibid.*, pp. 594–618.

of the ground that is common, and the bases for working out differences will probably be more easily established. In shifting from school board domination of teachers, we should not accept teacher domination of school boards. Negotiations imply bargaining in good faith, with recognition of the constraints operating on both sides.

SECURING PERSONNEL

The administrator must also determine the kinds and numbers of people needed to man the various programs of the school and must then proceed to secure the people. This task, always a critical one, has become in recent years, with the general manpower shortage, a most difficult one. While there are indications that the teacher shortage is coming to an end, it seems clear that for some positions and for some schools the shortage will remain. Schools will continue to confront such factors as competition in the labor market for highly trained people, expanded occupational opportunities for women, and the fact that teaching in some situations is a most difficult task.

These circumstances suggest at least two courses of action for the administrator. He must find ways of helping lay citizens understand the facts pertaining to the manpower shortage, and he must help them see its implications, particularly from the standpoint of the teachers' needs. Only as citizens become thoroughly aroused about the matter will higher levels of compensation and more desirable working conditions for teachers—such as reasonable size of classes—be fully supported by the public.

A second task for the administrator, in view of the manpower situation, is the establishment of employment, assignment, induction, and supervision procedures which will attract and hold capable people. Teachers prefer to work in schools and school systems where they feel wanted, where they believe the program is on the move, where they think their contribution is important, and where they feel that the "boss" is understanding and fair. Important as adequate pay is, a number of studies have shown that work conditions are even more significant.[18]

In essence the personnel policies of boards of education and the personnel practices of administrators can do much to relieve the

[18] For instance, see Francis S. Chase, "Professional Leadership and Teacher Morale," *Administrator's Notebook* 1, No. 8 (March, 1953). See also Daniel Katz and Robert L. Kahn, *The Social Psychology of Organizations* (New York: Wiley, 1966), pp. 368–373.

teacher shortage. This is particularly true at the point of encouraging teachers not to drop out of the profession after they have entered it. Moreover the personnel policies and practices that tend to keep teachers in the profession are the same factors that help teachers perform at their highest levels. In short, the relationships an administrator establishes with his staff to achieve the purpose of the school may well be the essence of administration.

Perhaps brief mention should be made of the procedures to be followed in the selection and assignment of personnel.[19] The first task confronting the administrator is the preparation of a job description. Ordinarily, responsibility for the preparation of this statement will be given to the building principal. He may, of course, consult his staff in the process of deciding just what is needed for a particular job. Moreover, it must be assumed that job openings are determined within the framework of personnel policies that have been previously formulated.

With job descriptions in hand the superintendent is in a position to seek candidates from a file of applicants, from college placement bureaus, and from other sources of supply. The objective will be to find the best possible people for each of the openings. Often good people must be approached in terms of professional opportunities present in the school system and not merely in terms of an available vacancy and salary to be paid. In other words, selection of personnel is a two-way process: the prospective teacher is appraised by the school system, and the school system is appraised by the teacher. In this kind of approach the superintendent will often find that principals and teachers in the school where the teacher may be placed are key people in the exploration.

When the candidate and the school system have reached agreement, the superintendent is in a position to recommend the prospective teacher to the board of education for employment. It should be quite clear that seeking out and selecting candidates is a professional task. Actual employment of the teacher is, of course, the prerogative of the board of education.

SUPERVISING PERSONNEL

After personnel have been employed and assigned to various positions of responsibility within a school system, there is still the need for the administrative leader—be he called superintendent, principal,

---

[19] For more detail, see Wm. B. Castetter, *Administering the School Personnel Program* (New York: The Macmillan Co., 1962).

or supervisor—to supervise the work. Three terms—supervision, curriculum development, and in-service education—are closely related. Each suggests that teachers and administrators need to work together to decide what the program ought to be, how it should be implemented, and how it is to be evaluated. For detailed treatment of these tasks other sources should be consulted.[20]

One of the first tasks in supervision is that of teacher orientation. Whether teachers are beginning their first year of teaching or joining a new school system, certain induction procedures are in order. Often these involve helping new people understand the terms and conditions of employment, become acquainted with the community, develop an understanding of the school system and the people in it, and adjust to the job. The process, which may begin even before employment, probably will not be completed until the end of the first year of service.

It should be quite clear that the working relationships existing between the administrator and his staff and among the members of the staff, discussed earlier in this chapter, have much to do with staff productivity. Stated otherwise, the development of an atmosphere of mutual respect and confidence, a commendable objective in itself, in a school situation is also a necessary condition if the purpose of the school is to be fostered. Adequate human relations are thus both ends and means.

Activities related to supervision ordinarily focus on the educational program and incidentally upon teachers and others who implement such a program. Thus supervision may include, as Burton and Brueckner suggest, such activities as the following[21]:

1. An appraisal of the educational product.
2. A study of the learner: diagnosis of learning difficulties.
3. A study of instruction.
4. A study of curriculum in operation.
5. A study of materials of instruction, including the socio-physical environment.

Each of these endeavors may suggest improvements that should be tried in practice and evaluated.

---

[20] For example, see W. H. Burton and Leo J. Brueckner, *Supervision—A Social Process* (New York: Appleton-Century-Crofts, 1955).

[21] *Ibid.*, Chap. I.

APPRAISING TEACHING EFFECTIVENESS

Administrators who have been given responsibility for the operation of a school or a school district must develop some plan of appraising the work of the certificated and non-certificated personnel who work in the school or the district. We suggest that the appraisal be based on the work or performance of the teachers or other personnel rather than on their personal characteristics. The latter involves looking at traits in isolation, an approach that has been largely discredited. Moreover most of us can look more objectively at our performance than we can at our persons.

The major objective of any plan designed to appraise the work of teachers and other personnel should be that of improving performance. It seems clear that when teacher and principal, both of whom comprehend the teaching-learning process, can discuss quite frankly the performance of the teacher, some ways of improving that performance can be determined.

While the primary purpose of performance appraisal should remain that of improving such performance, certain secondary purposes may also need to be served. Decisions pertaining to the retention or dismissal of teachers must be made. Decisions to place or not to place teachers on tenure status are required in many school systems. Many school districts also have a policy of promotion from within the system. Such a plan is based upon the assumption that some teachers have the competencies for such jobs as assistant principals, pupil personnel workers, and other posts, and that those competencies can be recognized. If all of these purposes are to be served well, there must also be appraisal of performance.

In recent years lay citizens and school board members in many school districts have demanded that teaching performance be evaluated in relation to salary. This issue has been debated more than it has been studied. We are convinced that if merit performance is to become a factor in salary determination, most school districts have a long process of "getting ready" for such a program. This eventuality, however, does suggest an additional reason for appraising teaching performance.

Several approaches have been made to the appraisal of teacher performance. One of these might be termed the change-in-pupil-achievement approach. Notable experimentation along this line was carried out by Barr and his students.[22] It rests on the assumption that the effectiveness of teaching performance can be determined by the growth in achievement of pupils while under the direction of the teacher. While there is much to support such an assumption, influences on pupil learning other than the teacher's do not seem to be adequately recognized.

A second approach to the appraisal of teaching performance might be termed the pupil-rating method, to which Bryan has been a major contributor.[23] This plan rests on the assumption that pupils know when they are being well taught. Again, there seems to be some truth in such a contention, but it is doubtful that pupils are acquainted with all of the expectations which most school systems have for teachers. Then too, pupils in the early years of school seem less able than older pupils to make a judgment about the quality of teaching performance.

If both of the approaches noted above have limitations, what approach can an administrator use in appraising teaching performance? In our judgment the evaluation approach discussed earlier in this chapter seems to be the most fruitful one. It includes the following steps:

1. The characteristics or criteria of good teaching will be determined.
2. These characteristics will be defined in behavioral terms.
3. A method of observing and recording these behaviors will be evolved.
4. The evidence collected will be appraised.

If these four steps seem formidable, the essence of this approach might be reduced to two major points: (1) there is joint decision as to what good teaching is and (2) a procedure for collecting and appraising evidence concerning good teaching is evolved.

A series of articles in a recent issue of *The National Elementary School Principal*[24] deal with the question of teacher evaluation. Conceptual approaches, actual experience with evaluation programs, and studies of evaluation procedures are reported. The problem is a complex one but apparently in some schools a cooperative definition

---

[22] A. S. Barr, *et al.*, "The Measurement of Teaching Ability," *Journal of Experimental Education*, 14 (September, 1945), 1–100.

[23] R. C. Bryan, *Student Reactions and Merit Salary Schedules* (Kalamazoo, Mich.: School of Graduate Studies, Western Michigan University, 1958), 67 pp.

[24] *The National Elementary School Principal*, 43 (November, 1963), pp. 3–67.

of good teaching has been developed and acceptable procedures have been established.

In the discussion above we have suggested that the major administrative tasks in the area of staff personnel include developing personnel policies, securing personnel needed to man programs of instruction and pupil services, providing appropriate stimulation and encouragement to staff members as they work at their jobs, and appraising the performance of staff members in terms of their assigned responsibilities in the school system.

PHYSICAL FACILITIES

Most programs of instruction and of pupil services require some physical facilities. We include under such a term school buildings, school grounds, and equipment needed in instruction and incidental to instruction. We have also chosen to include school buses and other transportation equipment under the general term of physical facilities. The major tasks of school administration in this area are what we turn to next.

SCHOOL PLANTS FOR INSTRUCTION

We would like to emphasize the point that school plants exist to facilitate the instructional program. To be sure, these plants may be impressive or they may be beautiful, but neither monumental character nor artistic expression should be achieved at the expense of functional arrangement. Actually, we would suggest that artistry and impressiveness be achieved through assigning function its highest type of physical expression.

Perhaps we can illustrate the relationship we see between program and plant. If the program calls for self-contained classrooms, these rooms must be large enough to permit a variety of activities. If the program includes gardening or camping, clearly the plant must provide for these activities. If television is to be used extensively in instruction, the plant must be designed to permit closed circuit hookups or other necessary arrangements. If part-time farmers are to be given help with their problems, land for agricultural demonstration should be provided. If the school is also to serve as a center for many community activities, it must be so located and so constructed as to permit such use.

Prediction of the educational program of tomorrow is hazardous, but it seems clear that education will undergo change. Hence modern designers attempt to make school plants highly flexible. The problem facing planners is well put by a commission report:

> If the educational program never changed; if the culture were static and scientists had ceased probing into the unknown; if inventors had gone on a long holiday and discoveries and innovations were at a standstill; if population mobility had ceased and the birth rate had become a constant factor; if community life always remained the same; if towns and cities were all alike; if there were no differences in school sites; if no new jobs were being created; if no new educational needs were emerging and the specific purposes of the school were rigidly defined; if the researchers had concluded that all the answers to the problems of teaching and learning had been found; if there were no more content to be added to the curriculum; if the producers of instructional materials and equipment had ceased to experiment and had settled down to producing a standard product; if people were entirely content with present accomplishments; if the dynamic forces of society had all been securely grounded and had ceased to function, then school-building planning would be a simple matter. Stock plans and standard classrooms would be the answer to the school districts' needs for building space. But such is not the case nor is it likely to be.[25]

PLANT DEVELOPMENT PROGRAM

The many problems involved in developing a plant to house a school program are dealt with in the report mentioned above.[26] This volume details the steps to be taken in the development of a school plant program. In order to determine what school plants are needed, an administrator must have data of four kinds: a picture of the educational program to be housed, a projection of the school population to be served, a plan for usage of the existing plant, and an indication of money available for plant expansion. The character of the data needed in each of these areas will be noted briefly.

The school program is a matter of prime importance. For instance, are schools to be organized on a K6–3–3 basis or on a K8–4 basis? Are elementary schools to be designed for 300 pupils or 1,000 pupils? Are rooms to be designed to house 25 pupils or 40 pupils? Is the seventh grade to be organized largely on a self-contained basis or

[25] Report of the AASA School-Building Commission: *Planning America's School Buildings* (Washington, D.C.: The Association, 1960), p. 5.

[26] *Ibid.*, 229.

on a departmental plan? Is science to be taught by the laboratory or by the demonstration method? Is team teaching, where large and small rooms are needed, to be a part of the program? Is closed-circuit TV to be provided?

These questions suggest that the plant should be built to house a program. In a recent report[27] on educational change and architectural consequences,

> Educators have pointed out how innovative approaches as disparate as nongradedness and televised instruction are handicapped by facilities that block groups of students and teachers off from one another, making mobility onerous, impose a tight-ship kind of discipline and a custodial attitude toward resources, and prohibit full use of technology. . . . The school program should dictate school space and not the other way around.

The report concludes that what is needed are flexible school facilities that provide for five general kinds of settings for learning: the conventional classroom, independent study facilities, teacher-pupil one-to-one dialogue, small group discussions, and large group lecture-presentations.

The second area of concern has to do with the pupils to be served, and in this case the administrator is dealing in futures. Such questions as the following must be answered: What changes are anticipated in the school population? How do these changes affect each grade level? How do these changes affect each part or attendance area of the district? What are the prospects of changes in district boundaries, and how are they likely to affect pupil population, including racial composition? What housing developments are in prospect, and what effect are they likely to have on pupil population?

A third body of data necessary in planning for the school plant has to do with the proposed use of the existing plant. Again, key questions must be answered. Are the present buildings safe? Are they located where they will be needed? Can they be adapted to serve the educational needs of the district? What capacities do the existing buildings have in terms of the educational program and pupil population of the future?

Results of these three types of studies begin to suggest the kind, amount, and location of school plants needed by the district. At this

---

[27] *Educational Change and Architectural Consequences* (New York: Educational Facilities Laboratories, 1968), pp. 15–16. Also, the entire issue of the *Harvard Educational Review,* 39, 4, (1969), is devoted to an exploration of the reciprocal relationships between architectural values and educational goals, particularly at a time when the basic values of society are undergoing change.

point the financial resources available for capital outlay must be examined. Since most districts must rely on a bond issue for capital outlay, the bonding possibilities of a district, usually limited by statute, must be noted. Moreover, practical considerations usually require that attention be given to tax levies already in effect for capital outlay and for current operation of the school. These considerations may require that the relative cost of reconditioning existing buildings as opposed to costs of constructing new buildings be determined. All in all, the financial data help answer the big question of whether or not the needed plant expansion is practicable.

In a school district of any size the four kinds of data mentioned above are necessary to a program for the development of the school plant. In a small school district the superintendent will work directly with principals, teachers, and citizens on the problem. In a larger school district he may have one or more staff members who will assist with these studies. In some cases, the help of outside consultants can be secured to guide or supplement the work of local people. In any case, however, the superintendent must see that these studies are made. With such information in hand the board of education and the people of a community are in a better position to make decisions regarding the modification of the existing plant and the securing of additional plant facilities. After such decisions have been made, the superintendent will have other tasks as he works with architects and contractors, but his basic responsibility lies in the tasks enumerated above. Unless the administrator and his staff have given attention to the program to be housed, the planning aspect of the plant program will not be adequate.

In addition to a program designed to expand the physical facilities of a school district, administrators are confronted with the operation and maintenance of the existing school plant. Operation, as the word implies, has to do with the day-to-day running of the plant. The major objectives of operation are to keep the plant safe, sanitary, attractive, and in readiness for teaching and learning. All of this is to be done as efficiently as possible. Extravagance in plant operation may mean that less money is available for those aspects of the program which are more directly related to teaching and learning.

School plants, like other physical facilities, require a constant program of maintenance. Equipment wears out and must be replaced. Paint deteriorates and must be replaced. Mortar loosens and must be repaired. Roofs eventually leak and require repair. A hundred other examples could be given. Most maintenance jobs require skilled craftsmen, including plumbers, painters, electricians, masons, roofers, and many others.

A perennial issue in the plant maintenance field is how to get these skilled workmen. Should the school set up a maintenance department and employ many of these craftsmen on an annual basis so as to have them available when needed? Or should maintenance work be let out on contract at times when there is work to be done? This problem and many allied problems will require administrative attention in any school district.

As suggested above, we have made transportation a part of our discussion of physical facilities, a decision which seems to be logical for two reasons. First, the transportation service is carried on with a rather high capital investment in equipment, for which the problems of procurement and maintenance are somewhat similar to the procurement and maintenance of other equipment. Second, the transportation program is auxiliary to the instructional program in somewhat the same manner as are building facilities. Pupils are housed or transported so as to be available for instruction.

In rural areas the transportation function has become so extensive as to require in some places as much as 25 percent of the school budget. In such instances administrative responsibility for establishing the transportation program, for purchasing equipment, for securing bus drivers and mechanics, for supervising their work, and for maintaining relationships with parents of transported pupils is a major task. In all but the very small districts, supervisors of transportation are usually added to the administrative staff.

FINANCE AND BUSINESS MANAGEMENT

In a money economy such as ours, the services of personnel, the buildings, the equipment, the supplies, and the other items necessary to the operation of a school or a school system must be paid for. Thus another operational area of administration, that of finance and business management, is indicated. The administrative tasks included in this area, whether they have to do with securing revenues or making expenditures, are instrumental, not primary, in character. In other words, money is useful only as it is used to purchase a program of teaching and learning. The details of both finance and business management have been described elsewhere.[28] For our purposes, we

[28] For instance, see Roe L. Johns and Edgar L. Morphet, *Economics and Financing the Education,* 2nd ed. (Englewood Cliffs, N.J.: Prentice-Hall, 1969), and John E. Corbally, Jr., *School Finance* (Boston: Allyn and Bacon, 1962).

shall deal with budget-making, securing revenue, managing expenditures, and managing non-certificated personnel.

BUDGET-MAKING

The school budget is often defined as a school program expressed in fiscal terms. Actually, a good budget will have three major aspects: the proposed program of the school district, the expenditures necessary to support such a program, and the anticipated revenues to cover such expenditures.

Again, the basic position of the instructional program is stressed. The budget should not provide simply for personnel, but rather for particular personnel to carry out particular parts of the program. The budget should not call simply for new or remodeled buildings, but rather for particular buildings with particular facilities to permit particular parts of the program to go forward. The budget should stipulate not simply money for equipment, but money for particular equipment to facilitate teaching and learning for particular parts of the program.

If the budget is to reflect the school program to the extent here indicated, it is clear that budget-building becomes a most important process within a school system. We would like to comment upon some aspects of that process.

It is important that the people within the school system who actually operate the program have a large part in budget-building. This means that teachers will have a real voice in suggesting what is necessary by way of working conditions, equipment, supplies, books, and other items to make instruction most effective. This means also that non-certificated employees who clean floors, repair roofs, or do other tasks will also have a voice in suggesting what is needed to do these jobs efficiently. To be sure, all of these suggestions may not be accepted, but they should be considered.

Budget-making is also a continuous process. It has both short-range and long-range aspects. Filling out a budget estimate for the ensuing year may be essentially a short-range task. On the other hand, teachers may work for a year or two in projecting an improved program for the teaching of the social studies. We submit that such planning is long-range budget-making as truly as it is curriculum development. In brief, we suggest that all planning for program improvement, whether it be for instruction or for services, should also be considered as budget-making.

In recent years, largely based on experience in the Department of Defense, the federal government has stressed program planning and budgeting systems (PPBS). Such systems are seen as methods which require long-range planning, the choice of alternatives, and the relating of costs and benefits. While such procedures are most difficult when applied to an enterprise as complex as education, the concept behind PPBS, and similar formulations, seems worthy of further scrutiny. James[29] has provided one of the more insightful analyses of the movement.

The concept of the budget suggested here means that it is a major policy statement in any school district. Unfortunately, there are still many school districts in which the budget is seen only in its short-range aspects, where the deliberations of staff members are seldom reflected, where the program which the budget proposes to buy is meagerly portrayed, and where the format is unattractive. Such an important document deserves better treatment.

Securing Revenue

Another important administrative task in the area of finance and business management is the securing of revenue. The financing of schools is, of course, but one aspect of public finance. Numerous governmental services at local, state, and national levels must be financed. The securing of money for these services, chiefly through taxation, is intimately related to the general economy of the nation. These interrelationships are often not fully appreciated by citizens, or for that matter by school administrators. Benson[30] has dealt extensively with school finance as an area of public finance, and he has applied economic analyses to a comprehensive selection of topics in the financing of education.

School districts ordinarily receive revenues from local, state, and federal sources as was shown in Chapter 3. There is great variability among the states with regard to the percentage of school revenues received from each level of government, as can be seen in Table 5.1.

At the local level, the source of school revenue is almost entirely the property tax. At the state level, legislative appropriation from the general fund is the usual practice. While revenues accruing to the

---

[29] H. Thomas James, *The New Cult of Efficiency and Education* (Pittsburgh: University of Pittsburgh Press, 1969.)

[30] Charles S. Benson, *The Economics of Public Education,* 2nd ed., (Boston: Houghton Mifflin, 1968).

TABLE 5.1 **Estimated Percent of Revenue for Public Elementary and Secondary Schools for Selected States by Levels of Government (1968–1969)**

	LOCAL	STATE	FEDERAL
Alabama	24.1	60.0	15.9
California	59.8	34.3	5.9
Illinois	68.1	26.7	5.2
Nebraska	74.8	17.6	7.6
New Mexico	23.1	61.8	15.1
New York	48.0	47.8	4.2
Ohio	59.8	34.9	5.3
Texas	41.3	47.1	11.6
United States	51.8	40.9	7.3

Source: Research Division, National Education Association, *Ranking of the States, 1969.*

states upon which legislative appropriations may draw are from several sources, the retail sales tax, the state income tax, or both, have become major sources of such revenue in most states.

In about the last quarter of a century, the federal government has become the chief tax collector. Whereas in 1929 approximately 75 percent of the taxes were collected at local and state levels, and the remaining 25 percent at the federal level, during World War II these percentages were almost reversed, thus making the federal government the chief tax collector. This shift has, of course, been accompanied by a great increase in total taxes collected and by unprecedented expenditures on the part of the federal government for services at home and abroad.

Large sums of federal money have been allocated for such services as hospital construction and road building. Because state and local sources have been shown to be inadequate for these and other public services, many doubt that public schools can be supported adequately from state and local sources alone. Certainly the flow of goods, services, and money tends to be national and international rather than local and state in character.

With the clear recognition that the various states must play a major role in financing public education, and with the likelihood that the federal government will also share more significantly in such financing, school administrators must be prepared to give leadership in public school finance at both state and federal levels. The administrator cannot see his responsibilities in the finance realm as limited to his own school district.

At the state level this means that the whole plan of state support for public education must come under the purview of the school administrator. Most states have some kind of foundation program for the financial support of schools, an arrangement which is supposed to guarantee a minimum educational program for every district of the state. School administrators must be able to help state boards of education, state legislatures, and citizens generally to understand the purposes and operations of such a foundation program. Without such study and vigilance, state aid may actually subsidize conditions that militate against good educational practice.

At the federal level, too, administrators should have insights based upon the economic realities of a highly industrialized and inter-dependent economy. With such insights, and with facts based upon careful research, the appropriate role of the federal government in school finance might be determined. Recent legislation enacted by the Congress suggests that the role of the federal government in financing education in the future will be an expanding one. The task ahead seems to be the evolution of an appropriate local-state-national partnership in the financing of the schools.

Though school administration should provide statesmanship in school finance at both state and federal levels, the concern with the revenues available to one's own school district must also have atten-tion. For instance, the superintendent or members of his staff must check to see that taxes levied for the school district are properly calculated and distributed. In many states this will require close working arrangements with the county assessor and the county auditor.

In similar manner the superintendent or members of his staff must ascertain all ways by which the school district might become eligible for state funds; and when the district is eligible, he must check to see that allocations due the district are being made. Ordinarily, then, the local superintendent must have a working relationship with the state department of education.

While federal funds are a minor part of total school revenue, they are exceedingly important to many school districts. Public Laws 874 and 815, for instance, have provided federal funds for operation and capital outlay to school districts where enrollments have been in-creased due to population movements caused by federal installations. Recent congressional action has also authorized appreciable revenues for the improvement of vocational education and for the education of the culturally deprived. As with local and state revenues, the admin-istrator has the obligation to determine the eligibility of the school district for federal funds and then to see that such funds are made available.

Managing Expenditures

The management of expenditures made by a school district is another administrative responsibility. There are many tasks in this aspect of administration, including purchasing, payroll operation, supply management, accounting and reporting, insurance management, and the keeping of a property inventory. The adequate performance of each of these tasks requires considerable knowledge and skill.[31] In small school districts, the superintendent will be expected to perform many of these functions. In larger school districts, specialized help may be secured, but it is still the superintendent's responsibility to see that these jobs are completely performed.

One important part of the accounting procedures of a school district is the budget-control record. As will be recalled, we advocated that the budget be formulated in considerable detail so as to depict the educational program for which the money was to be spent, and the sources from which the money was to come. With such a budget as a beginning point, a budget control system should be developed so that at least once a month the conditions of expenditures and revenues might be ascertained. Such a report can both help the superintendent and his staff in their administration of the budget, and prove an indispensable aid to a board of education in its efforts to understand how the school enterprise is going forward. For budget control, bookkeeping, and other aspects of business management, a machine technology, including the use of computers, has been developed.

Managing Noncertificated Personnel

Ordinarily the management of noncertificated personnel is made a part of business management. In small school districts this distinction is of little consequence. In larger districts, however, the business management function, including responsibility for noncertificated personnel, is delegated by the superintendent to a business manager or assistant superintendent in charge of business. Noncertificated personnel include a wide variety of workers such as custodians, skilled craftsmen, cafeteria employees, bus drivers, and secretaries. In many

[31] John E. Corbally, Jr., *op. cit.*

school districts, these employees number approximately one-half the number of instructional or certificated workers.

For each of these categories of workers, a plan of personnel management needs to be evolved. In many respects the details of such a plan are similar to those which were developed at some length in the discussion of staff personnel above. For each group of workers, appropriate personnel policies must be developed, suitable people must be selected and employed, supervision must be provided, and appraisal of work performance made.

The components of job satisfaction for noncertificated workers are similar to those of certificated workers. People like to feel wanted, they like to feel that the institution has a desirable program, and they like to feel that their contribution is valued.

We have suggested that administrative activities in finance and business management are instrumental to the achievement of the major purpose of the school. The major tasks of this area have been presented as budget-making, securing revenues, managing expenditures, and directing noncertificated personnel.

ORGANIZING TO ACHIEVE THE TASKS

Achievement of the tasks enumerated above requires an organization or structure. The establishment of this structure represents, in a sense, an additional task area. However, we have chosen to view the development of such a structure as a way of implementing the tasks already suggested rather than as a set of additional tasks.

By structure we refer to the relationships of people as they work to achieve a common goal, and it is these relationships with which this section will deal. In this connection it is necessary to discuss briefly the meaning of formal organization, the controlling board, administrative organization, and channels for communication and participation.

Meaning of Formal Organization

Most people belong to both formal and informal organizations. A group of women may get together regularly to play bridge, a group of men may become a golf foursome, children on a particular street may become a play group, or a half-dozen members of a high school faculty may meet frequently for lunch. All of these are examples of informal organizations.

On the other hand, a business corporation, a military battalion, a church congregation, and a school district are examples of formal organizations. What are the basic differences between these two kinds of groups? There are several worthy of mention. With respect to origin, informal groups tend to be voluntary while formal groups are usually official. An informal organization may terminate when the present membership leaves, while a formal organization persists beyond its immediate membership. The task or purpose of an informal group is probably not known or, at least, not clear to outsiders, while the task of a formal group is usually adequately perceived by people out of the organization. An informal organization ordinarily has no assigned status hierarchy while a formal organization does. In an informal organization there may be little regular differentiation of assigned work (or play), while in a formal organization there is definite allocation of work responsibilities.

The people who work in a school or school district are definitely members of a formal organization. The school or school district came into being by official governmental act. The organization will go on beyond the lives of the present members. The task of the school or school district is clear to those outside the organization. In all except the smallest schools, there is a recognized hierarchy of position. The work of administrators, teachers, custodians, and other workers is clearly differentiated. This concept of the school as a formal organization is relevant to the remainder of this discussion.

We are well aware of the fact that a school or school district, in addition to being a formal organization, may have one or more informal organizations within it. A clique within a faculty, for instance, may greatly influence decisions of the faculty or of the administrator, entirely outside the formal organizational channels. It is not our purpose here to explore the ramifications of informal organizations within formal organizations. Suffice it to say that formal organization cannot replace informal organization.

We also recognize that the formal organization established by the school district will often be called upon to deal with one or more other formal organizations established by the teaching employees, and in many cases by the nonteaching employees of the district.

CONTROLLING BOARD

As with most other formal organizations, workers of a school district are subject to the direction of a controlling board, in most states known as the board of education. In some states the terminology is board of trustees or board of directors. In all cases these boards are created by the respective state legislatures and given by them broad grants of power to organize and conduct schools within their respective school districts. In addition to the specified powers enumerated in the respective state codes, boards of education also have the powers implied as necessary to the proper exercise of the specified powers. The breadth of these responsibilities is illustrated by two sections of the laws of Wisconsin relating to the public schools:

> . . . the school district board shall have the possession, care, control, and management of the property and affairs of the district. (40.29) The board may make rules for the organization, graduation, and government of the schools. . . . (40.30)

While the language shown above makes clear the fact that the board of education has complete legal control, within the limitations of state and federal law, to operate a school district, the board of education has found it necessary in actual practice to create an organization to operate the schools. In a small school district this may be a very simple organization of a few teachers and a custodian with the board itself attempting to retain the administrative function. In most school districts, however, the board of education employs a superintendent of schools as its chief administrator. In turn, the superintendent is expected to organize separate schools under the direction of building principals, and to secure instructional and non-instructional personnel, usually subject to approval of the board, to man the school enterprise.

With the employment of a superintendent of schools, the differentiation of function between the controlling board and its chief executive officer becomes a matter of importance. In general, a board of education does or should become chiefly a legislative and judicial body, while the administrative function is or should be given to the superintendent. This distinction is not as simple as it sounds and many boards and superintendents have difficulty in establishing their respective roles. Since legal control, even for administration, rests finally with the board, the superintendent cannot exercise an executive role except as his board permits.

To assist in this kind of understanding, the role of the board is often defined as part of the rules and regulations of the school district. In Cincinnati the duties of the board have been defined in the following language:

> Recognizing the legal definitions of its duties, the board of education considers its major responsibilities to be:

a. To select a superintendent of schools.
b. To provide for the preparation of and to adopt the annual budget.
c. To provide by the exercise of its taxing power the funds necessary to finance the operation of the schools.
d. To make rules and regulations for the operation of the schools under its control.
e. To initiate questions of policy for consideration and report by the superintendent.
f. To consider and pass upon the recommendations of the superintendent in all matters of policy, appointment or dismissal of employees, salary schedules or other personnel regulations, courses of study, selection of textbooks or other matters pertaining to the welfare of the schools.
g. To appraise the effectiveness with which the schools are achieving the educational purposes of the board.
h. To inform the public concerning the progress and needs of the schools, and to solicit and weigh public opinion as its affects the schools.[32]

To perform the duties enumerated above in a few meetings per month—all the time lay citizens can ordinarily devote to the school board—it is clear that the Cincinnati Board of Education would have to deal with questions of policy and not with the details of operation. Often the establishment of policy, upon the recommendation of the superintendent and his staff, constitutes the legislative activity of the board of education. Examination of how that policy has worked in practice, often with the help of rather complete reports supplied by the superintendent and his staff, permits the board to exercise its judicial function.

This discussion has already implied much concerning the role of the superintendent, but let us look more specifically at that matter. Cincinnati has also defined the superintendent's job as follows:

The superintendent of schools shall be the chief executive and administrative officer of the board of education, and shall have, in addition to the powers and duties specifically imposed upon his office by statute, all executive and administrative powers and duties in connection with the conduct of the schools which are not required by statute to be exercised directly by the board or by some other officer. It shall be the duty of the superintendent to complete all executive and administrative transactions not by law or resolution required to be brought before the board of education; and to prepare all other matters of administrative procedure or policy for board approval. The enumeration in this section, or elsewhere in these rules and regulations, of specific powers and

[32] Cincinnati, Ohio, Board of Education, *Rules and Regulations* (1964), p. 1.

duties shall not be construed to derogate from the generality of duties hereby imposed[33]:

In general terms the superintendent of schools should have two major functions: that of being the chief executive officer of the board of education, and that of being the chief professional adviser to the board of education. These two roles must go hand in hand if a board is to have the help it needs. If the superintendent performs as executive officer only, the board will not be able to establish its policies in light of the professional knowledge with which the superintendent should be familiar. In other words, the superintendent should, with the assistance of his staff, help the board of education be its best self.

ADMINISTRATIVE ORGANIZATION

The school enterprise of many school districts is of such magnitude that a single administrator cannot give it adequate direction and supervision. In these cases an administrative organization must be established. In some districts this organization may include only the superintendent and three or four building principals; in others a much more complex structure becomes necessary.

While we maintain that no form or amount of administrative organization will, per se, guarantee an effective school system, we do believe that appropriate administrative organization can facilitate the achievement of the goals of a school system. There are some telltale signs that betray ineffective administrative organization. Some of these are: a large proportion of administrative time spent on "emergencies," unexplained delays in carrying out plans, or frequent complaints that "no one told me." These and similar breakdowns warn that the concepts and principles of administrative organization should be examined.

Let us mention some of the concepts that require attention. One of these is the question of centralization versus decentralization. In the centralized plan the superintendent's office exercises tight control over all of the schools of the district. In the decentralized arrangement building principals and their staffs are given considerable autonomy with regard to many aspects of school operation. Centralization requires a relatively large central office staff of directors

---

[33] *Ibid.*, p. 15.

and supervisors, whereas decentralization may mean that each principal will be given administrative assistance. Centralized control usually requires considerable uniformity of practice among the various schools; decentralized control ordinarily results in more diversity of practice among the schools. A decade ago this discussion was somewhat academic; but with the recent demand in major cities for community control, new attention must be given to the possibilities of decentralization.

Another concept in organization is that of line and staff. Line officers are usually thought of as those responsible for the operation of the major units of an organization, i.e., school district or school attendance area. Staff officers usually serve in a fact-gathering or advisory capacity or perform a specialized function for line officers, i.e., director of research or school psychologist. Since these terms have a military connotation, some educators have been prone to condemn them, a rejection which seems rather foolish, for in relatively large school organizations some line and some staff officials seem necessary. Ordinarily building principals are thought of as line people, since they are responsible for the operation of a school. On the other hand, a director of research and a director of in-service education would usually be designated as staff people. Their function is that of assisting the superintendent either by supplying him with research findings or performing some tasks in his name. While staff people do not have the responsibility for a school, they do have functional responsibility.

In any organization there is also the matter of a flat or a pyramidal arrangement. A superintendent working directly with principals represents a flat or a two-level arrangement, while a plan of organization which includes assistant superintendents and directors may mean a pyramid, or a four-level arrangement. More levels seem to increase the feeling of distance between the chief administrator and the teachers, and may easily lead to such remarks as, "Oh, I know nothing about that, for it is handled downtown."

Closely related to flat and pyramidal organization is the concept of span of control. This refers to the number of people reporting directly to a single administrator, usually the chief administrator or superintendent of schools. Often the superintendent is torn between wishing a flat organization, and having so many sub-administrators reporting directly to him that he cannot do justice to those relationships. Some students of organization think that the chief administrator should not have more than five to eight administrative assistants reporting directly to him.

Still another concept is that of horizontal and vertical organization. Assistant superintendents in charge of elementary and secondary education respectively represent a horizontal arrangement, while assistant superintendents in charge of functions or operational areas such as instruction or staff personnel represent a vertical plan.

Griffiths and others have suggested that the establishment of an administrative organization is one of the basic functions of administration. They suggest that the steps necessary in this process are as follows:

1. The purposes of the school should be stated clearly and in operational terms.
2. The conceptual framework on which the organization will be constructed must be agreed upon.
3. The functions of administration necessary to the achievement of the stated purposes must be listed.
4. The present administrative structure must be surveyed to determine which functions are being performed by whom.
5. A plan of organization must be developed consistent with the conceptual framework of organization.
6. The functions of administration must be related to specific administrative positions.
7. Job descriptions must be developed for the administrative positions to which functions are assigned.
8. The administrative positions and the job descriptions must be related to the incumbent administrators.
9. A timetable must be set up to implement the reorganization.[34]

COMMUNICATION AND PARTICIPATION

In any formal organization it becomes necessary to establish channels for communication and participation. Only through adequate communication can members of the organization remain aware of organizational goals, keep clearly in mind how their own work contributes to those goals, understand how the work of others contributes to the goals, and make suggestions for the improvement of operational procedures in the organization. The conditions suggested above make it clear that communication in an organization must flow up, down, and across.

[34] Daniel E. Griffiths, *et al., Organizing Schools for Effective Education* (Danville, Ill.: Interstate Publishers, 1962), p. 309.

Culbertson points out that there are many barriers to communication in an organization.[35] These barriers may include the words used in the communication, many of which carry different emotional overtones to different people; or the barrier may rest with the administrator as the communicator, particularly if he is inclined to emphasize the aspects of his office related to status; or the barrier may rest with members of the organization as communicatees, if their values and motivations are different from those of the communicator.

Erickson and Pedersen[36] reviewed a number of studies having to do with communication within schools, focusing particularly upon impediments to such communication. Some of these impediments were found in the situation such as the hierarchical structure of the school, the large quantity of information needing transmission, the lack of collegial interaction, and the cultural influences on interpretations of the messages.

Impediments were also found in the persons, and included such factors as inept transmission and reception, failure to respond, misplaced quest for power, and aversion to threat. Much of the responsibility for removing these impediments to the communication rests with the administrator.

As part of the conclusion of their comprehensive volume on organizations, Katz and Kahn[37] suggest that the conflict between rising expectations of involvement and the difficulties of communication and participation can have several maladaptive effects such as a feeling of apathy at being outside the system, blind conformity to the system, and ferment without form. Katz and Kahn continue by suggesting that most organizations can profitably move toward decentralization, that there can be some shift of authority from officials to members, that distinctions between classes of citizenship can be reduced, and that role enlargement can often give a sense of greater participation.

We have concluded our overview of the administrative tasks in educational administration by a consideration of organization and structure. We have suggested that organization and structure imply arrangements designed to facilitate the other administrative tasks;

[35] Jack Culbertson, "Recognizing Roadblocks in Communication Channels," *Administrator's Notebook,* 7 (March 1959), pp. 1–4.

[36] Donald A. Erickson and K. George Pedersen, "Major Communication Problems in the Schools," *Administrators Notebook* 14 (March 1966) 7, pp. 1–4.

[37] Daniel Katz and Robert L. Kahn, *The Social Psychology of Organizations* (New York: Wiley, 1966), pp. 470–471.

and all administrative tasks, it will be recalled, have their *raison d'être* in improving the programs for teaching and learning in a school or school district.

SUGGESTED ACTIVITIES

1. Compare the operational areas of this chapter with those suggested by Miller. Which categorization do you prefer? Why?
2. In the light of the criteria suggested for personnel policies in this chapter, appraise the personnel policies of your district.
3. Determine what percentage of the budget of your school district over the past ten years has been allocated for (a) instruction and (b) capital outlay and debt service.
4. Taking account of recent legislation enacted by the Congress, project the school revenues from federal sources for your state during the next three years.

SELECTED READINGS

BENSON, CHARLES S. *The Economics of Public Education.* 2nd ed., Boston: Houghton Mifflin Co., 1968.

CAMPBELL, ROALD F., CUNNINGHAM, LUVERN L., McPHEE, RODERICK, and NYSTRAND, RAPHAEL O. *The Organization and Control of American Schools,* 2nd ed., (Columbus, Ohio: Charles E. Merrill, 1970).

CASTETTER, W. B. *Administering the School Personnel Program.* (New York: The Macmillan Co., 1962).

CORBALLY, JOHN E., JR. *School Finance.* (Boston: Allyn and Bacon, 1962).

FROST, JOE L., and ROWLAND, G. THOMAS. *Curricula for the Seventies.* (Boston: Houghton Mifflin, 1969).

HUMMEL, DEAN L., and BONHAM, S. J. *Pupil Personnel Services in Schools.* (Chicago: Rand McNally, 1968).

IANNACCONE, LAURENCE. *Politics in Education.* (New York: Center for Applied Research in Education, 1967).

JOHNS, ROE L., and MORPHET, EDGAR L. *Economics and Financing Education,* 2nd ed. (Englewood Cliffs, N.J.: Prentice Hall, 1969).

MILLER, VAN. *The Public Administration of American School Systems.* (New York: The Macmillan Co., 1965).

Report of the AASA School-Building Commission, *Planning America's School Buildings.* (Washington, D.C.: The American Association of School Administrators, 1960).

6

The Administrative Process

Thus far we have examined administration from the standpoint of its development and meaning, and in terms of the major tasks confronting a school organization. We shall now look at administration as a process. Since this view of administration had its origins in business and public administration, we shall first examine the meaning of the term "administrative process" as it has developed in these two fields, and then note its applications to the field of educational administration. Our own definition of the administrative process, which is the major focus of the balance of this chapter, builds upon these earlier developments and applications.

THE GENERAL CONCEPT

Developments in Business and Public Administration

As noted in Chapter 4, Fayol, as early as 1916 in his *Administration Industrielle et Generale,* dealt with what he called the "elements of management."[1] He described them as planning, organizing, commanding, co-ordinating, and controlling; together these activities constituted the administrative function. These five components of what we would call the administrative process resulted from thoughtful observation on the part of Fayol, an engineer who turned administrator. Urwick, a student of public administration, has this to say of Fayol:

His life embraced four careers rather than one, and in each of them he was pre-eminent. As a technical man he achieved national distinction

[1] See translation by Constance Starrs, *General and Industrial Management* (London: Sir Isaac Pitman and Sons, 1949).

for work in mining engineering. As a geologist he propounded a completely new theory of the formation of coal-bearing strata and supported it with a detailed study of the Commentry district, almost unique as a piece of geological research. As a scientist turned industrial leader his success in both fields was phenomenal. The days of his own detailed research were over, but he applied the scientific approach to problems in every direction and encouraged those associated with him to do likewise. . . . But he always declared that that success was not due to personal qualities, but to the steady application of certain simple principles. Finally, as a philosopher of administration and as a statesman he left a mark on the thinking of his own and of many other European countries. . . .[2]

Because his treatment of the administrative function had a major impact on subsequent formulations of the administrative process, we shall comment further about what Fayol meant by planning, organizing, commanding, co-ordinating, and controlling. Fayol used the term "planning" to represent the activity involved in foretelling the future and preparing for it. The most important instrument of planning was the *plan of operations* which contained the object in view, the course of actions to be followed, the various stages on the way, and the means to be used. Fayol maintained that the characteristics of a good plan of operations were unity, continuity, flexibility, and precision.

Although he recognized that organizing involved both human and material elements, his chief concern was with the human organization. The principal instrument for achieving an effective human organization was the organization chart which showed "the whole of the staff, the constitution and limits of each department, the man occupying each position, the man whom an employee must obey and the subordinates whom he commands."[3] Even at that time, Fayol recognized the problems posed by a peopled organization and mentioned the need to invest time and energy in the selection of employees, to situate men where they could be of most service, and to adapt organizational requirements in light of available personnel.

For Fayol, commanding meant more than enforcement of obedience; it involved getting the best out of employees in the interest of the concern as a whole. To facilitate command, he suggested that the manager should perform such activities as these: acquire a thorough knowledge of his personnel; eliminate the incompetent; avoid pre-

[2] *Ibid.,* p. ix.

[3] See translation by J. A. Coubrough, *Industrial and General Administration* (London: Sir Isaac Pitman and Sons, 1900), p. 58.

occupation with detail; set a good example; and foster *esprit de corps,* initiative, and loyalty among his staff.

Fayol conceived of co-ordination as being principally concerned with harmonizing all the operations of the organization and with unifying disconnected efforts. He argued that a well-co-ordinated organization was evidenced by such conditions as an up-to-date program of work for each department and exact instructions about how the various units and sub-units were to combine their efforts. Lack of co-ordination, on the other hand, was signaled when each department made no effort to consider the firm as a whole and willfully ignored the work of other departments. To help staff members co-ordinate their efforts, Fayol recommended regular meetings of departmental managers.

Controlling, as used by Fayol, signified appraisal and examination of results. The object of control was to uncover weaknesses and errors in order to rectify them and prevent their recurrence. The relationship of control to planning, organizing, commanding, and co-ordinating was stated clearly by Fayol:

> In an undertaking, control consists in verifying whether everything occurs in conformity with the plan adopted, the instructions issued and principles established. . . . It operates on everything, things, people, actions. From the management standpoint it must be ensured that a plan does exist, that it is put into operation and kept up-to-date, that the human organization is complete, the summarized personnel charts in use, and that command is exercised in line with principles, that co-ordinating conferences are held, etc., etc.[4]

According to Fayol, the administrative function (planning, organizing, commanding, co-ordinating, and controlling) was present in all business undertakings—simple or complex, large or small. Furthermore, the administrative function was carried out by all members of the organization; however, the relative importance of the ability to perform this function increased as one ascended the organizational hierarchy. For Fayol the administrative function was the essential condition for a successful operation; if the function was effectively exercised in all parts of the organization, the running of the concern would be satisfactory.

Fayol's "elements" of the administrative function were derived chiefly from his experience with industrial enterprises. Soon, however,

[4] Starrs, *op. cit.,* p. 107.

others were to apply these principles to the public realm. For instance, Gulick[5] suggested how the office of the President of the United States might be organized. He asked the question, "What is the work of the chief executive?" His answer was "POSDCoRB," which sounds a little confusing until one learns that the letters stand for activities necessary to the proper functioning of the office. Gulick himself explains these activities as follows:

> Planning, that is working out in broad outline the things that need to be done and the methods for doing them to accomplish the purpose set for the enterprise;
> Organizing, that is the establishment of the formal structure of authority through which work subdivisions are arranged, defined and co-ordinated for the defined objective;
> Staffing, that is the whole personnel function of bringing and training the staff and maintaining favorable conditions of work;
> Directing, that is the continuous task of making decisions and embodying them in specific and general orders and instructions and serving as the leader of the enterprise;
> Co-ordinating, that is the all-important duty of interrelating the various parts of the work;
> Reporting, that is keeping those to whom the chief executive is responsible informed as to what is going on, which thus includes keeping himself and his subordinates informed through records, research and inspection;
> Budgeting, with all that goes with budgeting in the form of fiscal planning, accounting and control.[6]

Gulick acknowedged that the above formulation was an adaptation of the functional analysis previously elaborated by Fayol. Although Gulick was speaking specifically of the office of the President of the United States, he contended that this analysis would be a helpful pattern into which to place the major activities of any chief executive.

Eight years later, Simon extended the work of Gulick and Fayol by treating administrative functions and activities within a decision-making framework. Simon[7] maintained that administrative processes were decisional ones and that their purpose was to facilitate the application of organized effort to the group task. To accomplish this purpose, the organization deprives the individual of some of his deci-

[5] Luther Gulick and L. Urwick, eds., *Papers on the Science of Administration* (New York: Institute of Public Administration, 1937).

[6] *Ibid.,* p. 13.

[7] Herbert A. Simon, *Administrative Behavior,* 2nd ed. (New York: The Macmillan Co., 1957).

sional autonomy and substitutes an organizational decision-making process.

> The decisions which the organization makes for the individual ordinarily (1) specify his function, that is, the general scope and nature of his duties; (2) allocate authority, that is, determine who in the organization is to have power to make further decisions for the individual; and (3) set such other limits to his choice as are needed to co-ordinate the activities of several individuals in the organization.[8]

Although Simon acknowledged the importance of allocating the decision-making functions, the central problem he addressed was how the decisions and behavior of employees are influenced within and by the organization.

In his analysis of organizational decision processes, Simon, like Gulick and Fayol before him, was also concerned with such issues as planning, budgeting, controlling, and co-ordinating. Simon's approach differed from his predecessors, however, in that he examined each of these problems in decisional terms. For example, the functions of review[9] (Fayol's word was *controlling* while Gulick used *reporting*) were to diagnose the quality of decisions, to correct erroneous decisions already made, and to enforce sanctions against subordinates so that they would make decisions consistent with those expected by organizational authority. Simon's emphasis on decision-making gave his analysis of the administrative process a unity and coherence which earlier formulations lacked.

More recently, Litchfield drew upon the work of Fayol, Gulick, and Simon to formulate a conception of the administrative process which stressed its cyclical nature. Litchfield saw the process as being "at once a large cycle which constitutes the administrative process as a totality and a series of small cycles which provide the means for the performance of specific functions and sub-functions and even for individual technical activities."[10] In the administrative process he included these activities: decision-making, programming, communicating, controlling and reappraising. According to Litchfield, the duty of reappraisal makes the group of activities cyclical by bringing the sequence substantially back to the point at which it began.

---

[8] *Ibid.*, p. 9.

[9] *Ibid.*, pp. 232–234.

[10] Edward H. Litchfield, "Notes on a General Theory of Administration," *Administrative Science Quarterly* (June 1956), pp. 3–29.

In his statement on the administrative process, Litchfield set forth the following propositions concerning the process[11]:

1. Decision making may be rational, deliberative, discretionary, purposive, or it may be irrational, habitual, obligatory, random, or any combination thereof. In its rational, deliberative, discretionary, and purposive form, it is performed by means of the following sub-activities:
    a. Definition of the issue
    b. Analysis of the existing situation
    c. Calculation and delineation of alternatives
    d. Deliberation
    e. Choice
2. Decisions become guides to action after they have been interpreted in the form of specific programs.
3. The effectiveness of a programmed decision will vary with the extent to which it is communicated to those of whom action is required.
4. Action required by a programmed and communicated decision is more nearly assured if standards of performance are established and enforced.
5. Decisions are based on facts, assumptions, and values which are subject to change. To retain their validity, decisions must therefore be reviewed and revised as rapidly as change occurs.

Litchfield made a number of contributions to the thinking about the nature of the administrative process. He articulated the interdependent nature of the activities in the administrative process and introduced the notion that the process applied to the way in which an individual or group handles a particular problem as well as to the activities of the organization as a whole. Furthermore, he formulated a number of theoretical propositions about the process and urged their testing.

APPLICATIONS TO EDUCATIONAL ADMINISTRATION

Conceptualization of the administrative process in the field of educational administration has been heavily influenced by the theoretical developments in business and public administration. Sears,[12]

---

[11] *Ibid.*, pp. 3–29.

[12] Jesse B. Sears, *The Nature of the Administrative Process* (New York: McGraw Hill, 1950).

the first writer to apply the administrative process to educational administration in a comprehensive fashion, acknowledged indebtedness to other students of administration, including Fayol and Gulick, for their work in the field. According to Sears, the process includes the following activities: planning, organizing, directing, co-ordinating, and controlling. With only two minor changes, Fayol's five elements emerge in Sears' formulation. The staffing, reporting, and budgeting functions, as presented by Gulick, are subsumed in the other activities which Sears enumerates. For example, much of what Gulick places under budgeting is treated by Sears under the heading of control. Each of the five elements of the administrative process is examined by Sears in considerable detail.

A yearbook of the American Association of School Administrators took cognizance of the administrative process.[13] After noting that administration is essentially a way of working with people to accomplish the purpose of an enterprise, it enumerates some crucial activities in this relationship. An excerpt from the section in which five crucial activities are described follows:

1. *Planning* or the attempt to control the future in the direction of the desired goals through decisions made on the basis of careful estimates of the probable consequences of possible courses of action.

2. *Allocation* or the procurement and allotment of human and material resources in accordance with the operating plan.

3. *Stimulation* or motivation of behavior in terms of the desired outcomes.

4. *Co-ordination* or the process of fitting together the various groups and operations into an integrated pattern of purpose-achieving work.

5. *Evaluation* or the continuous examination of the effects produced by the ways in which the other functions listed here are performed.

The above formulation of the administrative process seems to contain one new point of emphasis. For "commanding" (Fayol's term) or "directing" (the term used by Gulick and Sears), the word "stimulation" has been suggested. In view of what is known about motivating group action toward a common enterprise, this may be a significant addition.

A careful examination of the administrative process as it applies in education has been made by Gregg.[14] To him the process has seven

[13] American Association of School Administrators, *Staff Relations in School Administration* (Washington: AASA, 1955), Chap. 1.

[14] Russell T. Gregg, "The Administrative Process." In Roald F. Campbell and Russell T. Gregg, eds., *Administrative Behavior in Education* (New York: Harper & Brothers, 1957), Chap. 8.

components as follows: decision-making, planning, organizing, communicating, influencing, co-ordinating, and evaluating. While Gregg uses many of the components with which we are now familiar, he introduces a number of interesting distinctions and ideas. Decision-making is viewed as being different from and perhaps previous to planning. Both communicating and influencing stress the necessity for mobilizing all members of the work group if the organization is to achieve its purpose. In fact, Gregg's treatment stresses time and time again the necessity for involvement of staff if the administrative process is to be effective.

Following the earlier work of Simon, Griffiths asserted that the decision-making process is the central process of administration and that the central function of administration is directing and controlling the decision-making process.[15] His version includes the following steps:

1. Recognize, define, and limit the problem.
2. Analyze and evaluate the problem.
3. Establish criteria and standards by which the solution will be evaluated or judged as acceptable and adequate to the need.
4. Collect data.
5. Formulate and select the preferred solution or solutions.
6. Put into effect the preferred solution.
   a. Program the solution.
   b. Control the activities in the program.
   c. Evaluate the results and the process.[16]

In his later empirical work, more particularly the study of the performance of elementary school principals in a simulated situation, Griffiths uncovered a factor similar to his theoretical conception of the process of decision-making. He named this factor Preparation for Decision v. Taking Final Action. His subsequent attempt to use this re-formulation of the decision-making process in categorizing the performance of executives at work in actual, as opposed to simulated, organizational settings, revealed that the categories were unequal to

---

[15] Daniel E. Griffiths, "Administration as Decision-Making." In Andrew W. Halpin, ed., *Administrative Theory in Education* (Chicago: Midwest Administration Center, The University of Chicago, 1958), Chap. 6.

[16] Daniel E. Griffiths, *Administrative Theory* (New York: Appleton-Century-Crofts, 1959), p. 94.

the task.[17] He found that much of the observed administrative behavior was unrelated to decision-making. As a consequence, he developed a new classification system which included 142 characteristics arranged in an ordered relationship described by the following diagram[18]:

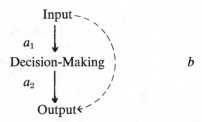

According to Griffiths, outputs may occur either along path a_1, a_2, (involves making a decision), or along path b (without a decision being made). He maintains that the behavior of administrators at work in an actual organizational setting is accounted for by this general schema.

THE ADMINISTRATIVE PROCESS AND THE EDUCATIONAL ADMINISTRATOR

For our purpose, we shall define the administrative process as *the way by which an organization makes decisions and takes action to achieve its goals.* We propose that the process is cyclical and contains the following components:

Decision-making
Programming
Stimulating
Co-ordinating
Appraising

It is obvious that our selection of terms is eclectic. For this we make no apology. Much as we tended to agree with the Litchfield

[17] Daniel E. Griffiths, "A Taxonomy Based on Decision-Making." In Daniel E. Griffiths, ed., *Developing Taxonomies of Organizational Behavior in Educational Administration* (Chicago: Rand McNally, 1969), Chap. 3.

[18] Daniel E. Griffiths and Frank W. Lutz, "Synthesis and Conclusions," in Daniel E. Griffiths, ed., *op. cit.*, Chap. 7.

formulation, we have made certain modifications which we think describe somewhat more accurately what goes on in educational administration.

Lest this formulation seem too pat and its application too obvious, we refer to a warning given by Halpin:

> Unless one is extremely careful he can easily be tempted into talking about "process" as if it were a free-floating affair, detached from the behavior of individuals. . . . An outside observer can never observe "process" *qua* "process"; he can observe only a sequence of behavior or behavior-products from which he may infer "process."[19]

These words bring us to emphasize the point that the administrative process is a conceptualization—not an observed phenomenon. The conceptualization is intended as a useful guide to the practicing administrator and suggests how the educational administrator would behave if he wished his activity to result in the greatest attainment of objectives with available resources. Each of the five components of the administrative process suggested above now will be discussed.

DECISION-MAKING

Decision-making can be irrational or rational. In the first instance the decision maker acts on the basis of whim or caprice whereas in the second he deliberates and acts in terms of a careful diagnosis of the situation and a thorough consideration of the means used to achieve a given end. Our concern is with the latter.

Rational choice has two major phases: problem analysis and decision.[20] Problem analysis is aimed at finding the cause of a difficulty while the task of decision is to select a course of action which will eliminate the problem or reduce its negative effects. At the problem-analysis stage the first step is to describe precisely what is wrong; this description is both a matter of what the problem is and what the problem is not.[21] The second step in problem analysis is to locate what is producing the difficulty; the cause often is *a change*[22]—a change in people, technology, or situational circumstances.

---

[19] Andrew W. Halpin, "A Paradigm for Research on Administrative Behavior," in Roald F. Campbell and Russell T. Gregg, eds., *op. cit.*, p. 195.

[20] See Charles H. Kepner and Benjamin B. Tregoe, *The Rational Manager* (New York: McGraw Hill, 1965).

[21] *Ibid.*, p. 45.

[22] *Ibid.*, pp. 45–46.

When the cause of the difficulty has been identified, the decision maker's consideration shifts to the possible alternative courses of action. For each alternative there are multiple consequences. Some are intended; others are unintended. The unintended side effects may be either positive or negative. A major task of the decision maker during this second principal phase of rational choice is to select the course of action which yields the most favorable consequences and carries with it a minimum of negative ones.

Let us illustrate the decision-making component in the administrative process. Suppose there is a public outcry that the foreign language program in the local high school is failing to prepare students adequately for college level course work in this curriculum area. In analyzing the problem and precisely pinpointing the difficulty, the administrator needs to ask questions such as: *Who* are the students having the difficulty? Which students do not seem to be having the difficulty? *What* is the nature of the difficulty which the students are having? *Where* are the students who are having the difficulties? *When* did the difficulties begin to appear? *To what extent* do the difficulties apply to all the foreign languages offered in the school? In other words, in what foreign languages do students subsequently have difficulty, and in what languages do they apparently have no problems? Information gathered to answer these questions will enable the administrator to state what the problem is with a reasonable degree of precision.

Suppose that the answers to these questions disclose that not all students who take advanced college level work in a foreign language begun in high school are having difficulties. Rather, only students in modern foreign languages (French, German, and Spanish) are experiencing problems at the college level. Furthermore, not all of the students enrolled in a modern foreign language are having such problems—only those attending *X, Y,* and *Z* colleges. Finally, only local graduates of the last two years have been doing below average work when they continued their foreign language study in college.

Having located more exactly what the difficulty is, the administrator is confronted with this question: Is there any change which took place two years ago in the foreign language programs offered at colleges *X, Y,* and *Z?* Suppose that the administrator discovers that the approach has shifted in these three colleges from an emphasis on reading and writing to an emphasis on speaking.

With the cause of the difficulty now clearly identified, the administrator is ready to consider alternative courses of action and their consequences. For instance, the administrator can choose to ignore the information, use the information as the basis for his arriving at a solution to the problem, or report the information to his staff. With respect to the first alternative, he envisions only negative consequences. Students at colleges X, Y, and Z will continue to perform poorly, and the public is likely to increase its pressure for some kind of resolution. The second alternative, on the other hand, might have either negative and positive consequences. By acting alone to solve the problem, the administrator sees a speedy resolution possible but subsequent resistance from the staff to an administrator-conceived solution. The third alternative also poses potential costs as well as benefits. In reviewing the information, the staff may feel that the situation is not really a problem because too few students are involved, or the staff may spend an inordinate amount of time reaching a satisfactory solution. However, since the decision is the staff's own, it is likely to be highly committed to its implementation. What the administrator finally does is a function of the consequences he foresees and the value he assigns to each of these consequences.

Although the choice may finally be made by the chief administrator, in all probability other administrative staff members, counselors, and teachers were involved in framing the questions which would guide the attempts to specify the problem. A whole research department may have been involved in gathering the information to answer the questions. The alternative courses of action may have been discussed at length in a meeting attended by the school principal, the language teachers, the department chairman, and the central office staff. Only after analyzing all of the cues supplied by the involvement of these various people in the organization, does the chief administrator make the decision. In a real sense, the decision is an organization one.

PROGRAMMING

Once a major decision is made, there are a number of implementing decisions to be made. This aspect of the administrative process is often called organizing, but the word "programming" seems to describe it somewhat more accurately. In programming, arrangements for the selection and organization of staff for housing, equipment, and budget must be made. The nature of these tasks has been described in some detail in Chapter 5. At this point, it is necessary to point out that the material treated in Chapter 5 is but a part of the larger framework of the administrative process.

Let us refer·once again to our example of unsatisfactory progress by local high school graduates in modern foreign languages at colleges *X, Y,* and *Z.* Suppose the basic decision made in that situation calls for the provision of experiences to develop students' conversational skills. Such a decision requires considerable programming. For instance, what equipment and materials are needed for such a program? What will the program cost, and how is it to be budgeted? Does the present staff have the requisite abilities to provide such experiences? If not, how will the staff develop these abilities? How will the conversational experiences be introduced into the foreign language course of study? Only after such questions as the above are considered, answered, and acted upon can the decision to offer conversational experiences in Spanish, French, and German be said to be programmed.

Programming, like decision-making, tends to be an organizational action rather than a one-man performance. Therefore, several types of organizational personnel may be involved in the programming phase. The superintendent may set budgetary limits for the deliberations but allow complete freedom in deciding how the money is to be spent. Teachers, department chairmen, the principal, and a technical consultant may be constituted as a committee to review the available equipment and materials and specify the limitations, strengths, and costs of each object that is examined. Other staff members may focus singly or in combination on the intended student behaviors, the range of appropriate conversational experiences to be offered, and the way in which these experiences will be ordered and incorporated into the modern foreign language curriculum. A particular supervisor in the central office may be asked to take over the detailed organization and direction of the curriculum. In all of these activities, the organization is concerned with programming its decision.

STIMULATING

The third step in the administrative process, it will be recalled, has at times been called *command* and, at other times, *direction*. While any administrator may on occasion need to command and at other times to direct, we feel the better term for what is involved here is *stimulating*. The objective of stimulating is to elicit individual efforts and contributions in implementing organizational decisions.

To be sure, there are several kinds of stimulation. At one level the organization or the administrator acting for the organization can exercise considerable pressure upon an individual in that organization. Seldom, if ever, can a formal status leader in an organization free himself completely from exercising such influence. At another level, the administrator stimulates by creating a set of conditions which inherently motivate people to act in the situation. In this case, members of the organization are involved in identifying the information they will take as evidence of an existing problem, examining the information which is gathered, judging whether a problem exists, and deciding upon the course of action to be taken.[23] It is our belief that the latter mode of stimulation is more effective than the former one, which rests on pressure.

We do not wish to oversimplify the problem, however. Involvement as a means of stimulating organizational members is most effective when the decision is outside their zone of indifference. Decisions that clearly fall outside members' zone of indifference are those which have consequences for them. Therefore, when the members' personal stakes in the decision are high, their interest in participation should be high.[24] Members should also be interested in considering matters which are within their scope of experience and sphere of competence.[25] To involve organizational participants in decisions they are not qualified to make is to subject them to frustration. As a result, involvement will be most effective on those occasions when the decision is one in which members have a stake in the outcome and expertise in deciding the matter at issue.

Communication has also been found to be of great importance to the stimulation of organization members. Communication needs to be of three kinds: down, up, and across. The Hawthorne studies[26] and other research have demonstrated that when members of an organization are "in on the know," when they understand clearly what is being attempted by the organization, they tend to be more productive. Face-to-face communication appears to be very important if organization members are to be motivated to do their best.

Let us use our foreign language example above to illustrate

---

[23] For a discussion of the problems involved in using a fact-minded approach, see Alfred J. Marrow and John R. P. French, Jr., "Changing a Stereotype in Industry," *Journal of Social Issues,* 2, 1, 1945, 33–37.

[24] Edwin M. Bridges, "A Model for Shared Decision-Making in the School Principalship," *Educational Administration Quarterly,* III, 1 (Winter, 1967), 49–61.

[25] *Ibid.*

[26] See F. J. Roethlisberger and W. J. Dickson, *Management and the Worker* (Cambridge, Mass.: Harvard University Press, 1939.)

stimulating as a part of the administrative process. Even after the decision has been made to offer conversational experiences as a means of developing students' skills in speaking, there is still the question of stimulating the teachers to provide such experiences. Some teachers may lack the necessary conversational skills to implement the change. They may be required to take additional training to upgrade their own skill level; even so, the question remains as to how they can be stimulated to do something about modifying their instructional techniques. This is clearly a problem of building attitudes, as well as a problem of acquiring new skills.

However, if teachers have been involved in the decision to initiate a particular programmatic change, their attitudes toward it are likely to be different from what they might have been had the decision been imposed upon them. Moreover, if the information about the foreign language situation at the college level has been shared with the teachers, the need for modifying the modern foreign program will be as evident to teachers as to administrators. If staff members fail to define the situation as a problem, then the administrator may find no substitute for a frank face-to-face conference with them concerning the possible internal and external consequences of inaction.

As with the other aspects of the administrative process, stimulating is not merely personal behavior on the part of the administrator. Ideally, stimulation should be directed toward the achievement of the purposes of the organization, not merely toward the personal satisfaction of a status leader. Moreover, the work group itself may often provide or contribute to the stimulation needed to get individual members of an organization to increase their contributions to the organization.

CO-ORDINATING

A further aspect of the administrative process is that of co-ordinating. This activity involves bringing into appropriate relationship the people and things necessary for the organization to achieve its purposes. Often, in co-ordinating, the goals of the organization must be reviewed and made explicit. At times, standards of performance necessary to the achievement of such goals need to be noted. Members of the organization may need to be held to meeting such standards.

The place of co-ordination may also be illustrated in our foreign language example. As the modern foreign language program seeks to develop student conversational skills, there are at least three kinds of co-ordination problems which, if not anticipated and solved, will jeopardize the success of the curriculum change.[27] One such problem stems from the interdependent nature of the classroom content. For instance, what a teacher in French II hopes to teach his pupils is contingent upon their having learned something in French I. If this content-sequencing problem is not solved, then students will experience difficulty in making the transition from French I to French II. The difficulty is similar in certain respects to the one faced by the local high school graduates who have been continuing their language study at colleges X, Y, and Z.

A second type of problem may originate from differences in instructional techniques used by teachers. The way in which one teacher offers conversational experiences may create severe difficulties for students when they move to the next higher level in the sequence. For example, a teacher in Spanish I may interpret the notion of conversational experiences as meaning oral reading and brief responses to questions framed by the teacher. The teacher in Spanish II, however, may interpret conversational experiences as meaning student discussions conducted in a small group setting around issues formulated either by the students themselves or by the teacher. Such inconsistencies in the approaches at the two levels can generate problems for both students and teachers. The possibility of this type of problem occurring foreshadows the need for some form of preventive action.

A third possible co-ordination problem may arise because there is a scarcity of instructional resources. If the new component of the instructional program requires special equipment and it is in limited supply, action must be taken to prevent staff members from making simultaneous demands on the equipment. Anticipation of this co-ordination problem should reduce the likelihood that equipment will be duplicated unnecessarily and that teachers and students will be frustrated by not having equipment available when it is needed.

The administrator is the key person in helping all members of an organization understand the need for co-ordination and the role each person is to play. When he becomes lax in his co-ordinating role,

---

[27] For an insightful discussion of co-ordination problems, their location and resolution, see W. W. Charters, Jr., "An Approach to the Formal Organization of the School." In *Behavioral Science and Educational Administration,* Sixty-Third Yearbook of the National Society for the Study of Education, Part II (Chicago: University of Chicago Press, 1964), Chap. XI.

confusion, ineffectiveness, and job dissatisfaction nearly always follow.

APPRAISING

The last step in the administrative process, as we see it, is that of appraising. Some writers in the field use the term evaluation; and, to be sure, the two terms have many of the same connotations. Because we have used evaluation in a somewhat broader sense in Chapter 5, we have chosen the word "appraising" as more suitable to describe one aspect of the administrative process.

It seems clear that administrative decisions and subsequent actions, if they are rational, are based upon certain facts, values, and assumptions. In time, any or all of these bases may change, and such change may make both the decision and the implementing action obsolete. The need for continuous appraisal, or reappraisal as Litchfield calls it,[28] is apparent.

There appear to be four purposes or concerns in appraisal. They may be stated as follows:

1. Are the objectives and the procedures chosen to achieve them consistent with one another?
2. Are the procedures operating as intended?
3. To what extent and how well have the organizational objectives been met?
4. To what extent and how well has the organization been maintained?

These points emphasize the fact that organizations exist to achieve some purpose. In the case of the public school, the purpose includes the teaching of literacy and critical thinking. In appraisal, then, key questions would have to do with how well literacy and critical thinking are being taught and learned.

But an organization must also take the long view. In addition to looking at the degree to which its objectives are being met at the moment, it must also be aware of how well the organization is being maintained so that it may continue to achieve its ends. Excessive teacher turnover, for instance, implies that the organization is not being maintained. Moreover, unless the members of an organization

---

[28] Litchfield, *op. cit.*

continue to grow in competence, the organization cannot be well maintained. It follows that, in public education, teachers and administrators are continually confronted with new challenges and opportunities to meet those challenges.

Let us see how appraising can be applied to our foreign language example. The shift to a greater emphasis on conversational skills has taken place. The change now needs to be assessed. Questions such as the following must be asked: Is there a consistency among the objectives as stated and the recommended course content, instructional techniques, and student examination procedures?[29] Do the actual content of the courses, the instructional techniques being used, and the means for examining students' performance match the stated intent? Have the changes in practices produced the desired conversational skills in students? Do the students with these skills subsequently perform satisfactorily in colleges *X, Y,* and *Z?* Do the students who continue their language study at colleges which stress skills in reading and writing perform as well as they did before the changes in the local program were introduced?

The last three questions are key ones. If practices have shifted in the desired direction, one kind of evidence concerning the effectiveness of the program has been obtained. However, this evidence is intermediate in nature. A more important test comes in determining whether or not the students are actually able to converse in the foreign language as intended. Perhaps in this case the ultimate test is how the students perform in college. Of interest to the organization is the performance of students who attend colleges which emphasize the reading and writing approach to language instruction as well as those students who are enrolled at colleges which stress the conversational approach. The improved performance of the one type of student must not be at the expense of the other.

An appraisal of the performance of students in college may indicate the extent to which the organization is achieving its purpose so far as foreign language is concerned. But what about the maintenance of the organization? Now another set of questions such as the following must be asked: Have the teachers who participated in the program changes identified more fully with the organization? In case the school needs to tackle another problem, are the teachers disposed to help with it? Did the experience result in an increased feeling of professional competence and status? If these questions can be an-

---

[29] See Michael Scriven, "The Methodology of Evaluation." In *Perspectives of Curriculum and Evaluation* (Chicago: Rand McNally, 1967), pp. 39–83.

swered in the affirmative, there has been organizational maintenance as well as organizational achievement.

A CASE REPORT[30]

To illustrate further the administrative process we shall next present a case report. Subsequent to the presentation of the case, we shall point out certain applications of the administrative process which were followed in the case.

CENTRAL CITY, U.S.A

During the past decade a number of new industries had settled in Central City, and its population had grown to about 40,000. The leaders of these industries found that as they recruited technical and professional personnel for their plants, the adequacy of the local public schools became a question of considerable importance. The schools may have been appropriate for a conservative city of yesterday, but they did not appear to be good enough for the emerging leaders of the community.

This feeling led to the nomination of a slate of three candidates for the board of education who were pledged to improve the schools. These men were elected to the board, and they then began "to cut their eye teeth." Within a few months the board secured state university personnel to help them make a study of their school plant needs. About the time the study findings were reported, the board also employed Mr. Smith, a promising young administrator, as its new superintendent of schools. At this point, many of the problems with which the board had been struggling, including the passage of a large bond issue, were placed in Mr. Smith's lap.

Mr. Smith recognized that it would be no easy task in Central City to pass a bond issue of the size that would be required to meet the needs that were so apparent. The area of Central City had doubled in the last five years, and the survey currently completed by the state university indicated that the enrollment in the schools had increased 40 percent in the last ten years. The survey recommended a new senior high school to accommodate ultimately 2400 students and three additional elementary schools with a total of forty-two ele-

---

[30] The initial report on this case was written by Thomas B. Southard.

mentary classrooms. Central City had not made any sizable capital outlay for school construction for over twenty years, except for additions to elementary schools provided by a $2.5 million bond issue about five years earlier. The issue had failed to receive the simple majority required for passage in the regular election and had scarcely met the 60 percent favorable vote required at a special election. It was apparent to Mr. Smith that if an issue were to be passed this time, the community must see the need for it and feel involved.

The first step was to translate the needs indicated by the survey into dollar amounts. Mr. Smith contacted an architectural firm and, with board approval, retained them on a per diem basis to secure these estimates. The estimate totaled approximately $13 million. To acquire such a sum would require Central City to vote bonds up to the statutory limit of 10 percent of its total assessed valuation.

The problem was now clear. Central City had not kept up with school needs over a long period. Buildings were old and run down. Taxes over the years had been among the lowest in the state, and a certain pride in the low tax rate seemed to be held by at least the older people in the community. There seemed to be also a general dissatisfaction with present school administration, especially among the industrial leaders and the younger people in the community. The problem facing Mr. Smith was, how could such a large issue be passed? What group or groups should spearhead the campaign? How could this modern Rip Van Winkle be awakened to the needs of its schools?

One of the first steps that Mr. Smith took was to meet in his home with the members of the board of education, perhaps ten or twelve times, to "talk shop." Technically speaking, his purpose was to strive for some common perceptions of the campaign on the part of the board of education and himself, with emphasis on the objectives of the campaign and the respective roles of the board and the superintendent in their achievement. During the meetings, the state university survey was inspected and its recommendations discussed. The place of the school in the community was discussed. Mr. Smith familiarized himself with board policies, although the board had no written statement of policy. These informal get-togethers also enabled new and old board members to get acquainted.

Soon Mr. Smith developed a tentative plan for the campaign and prepared a brochure entitled *The Fact of the Matter Is*. The plan had emerged in concert with the board during the informal meetings. The board agreed that the supporting data were appropriate for use in the campaign.

In addition to meeting with the board of education, Mr. Smith made a conscientious effort to become acquainted in the community. By invitation, he joined the local Rotary Club and became well acquainted with a number of leading citizens in the city. He also became a member of the Chamber of Commerce. More by chance than design, one of the most influential leaders of Central City took Mr. Smith under his wing and agreed to help in any way he could for the betterment of the schools and the passage of the bond issue.

The next decision that faced Mr. Smith was who should spearhead the campaign. This was not a simple matter. By this time, Mr. Smith had become acquainted with people representing all service clubs of the community and had acquaintances in each who were sympathetic to the school problem. At the November election, however, a city manager plan backed by the Chamber of Commerce had been defeated; and the expressway issue backed by the Kiwanis Club and independent groups had barely passed. A two-mill school-operating levy supported by the P.T.A., on the other hand, had passed rather easily. It seemed, therefore, that a school bond issue in Central City might be initiated by the local P.T.A. Council.

Mr. Smith was aware, nevertheless, that a two-mill operating levy and a $13 million bond issue were indeed two different things. Historically, Central City had never turned down an operating levy, but bond issues had been defeated. The P.T.A. of course cut across many lines and represented some 6,000 votes. It also had among its members people from all the service clubs in the community.

The greatest single item that concerned Mr. Smith was whether or not the P.T.A. Council had the proper type of leadership to conduct a suitable campaign. After meeting with the P.T.A. leaders, Mr. Smith concluded that it would be best for the P.T.A. Council to spearhead the campaign but that it also seemed wise to organize an advisory committee on the ways and means, or professional know-how, of campaigning. The latter group was to remain in the background to help in any way possible.

The advisory committee was formed by invitation. Its members numbered twenty-three and represented all facets of community organization: radio stations, newspapers, ministers, social groups, labor organizations, financial groups, parochial school leaders, and the federated women's clubs. To co-ordinate this group and to work out relations with the P.T.A. Council, the president of a local bank donated the full-time services of his public relations director. This man, Mr. Fair, worked closely with Mr. Smith in all phases of the actual campaign.

The leaders of the P.T.A. Council and the advisory committee met frequently with Mr. Smith to work out the details of the campaign, after the P.T.A. Council had officially endorsed the bond issue. The first phases of discussion centered around a calendar of activities leading up to election day, May 7. It was decided that a short, all-out effort would be more effective than a campaign over a long period of time. The group first met in December. The all-out effort was to be confined to three weeks before election; dissemination of factual information was to start immediately, but was to be built up slowly.

The committee thought that as a new superintendent Mr. Smith should avail himself of every opportunity to speak publicly, as it seemed important for the residents of Central City to become acquainted with him. Mr. Smith complied by making sixty-nine public addresses between August 1 and May 7.

The campaign actually got under way about mid-December. Before it began, however, the board of education reviewed and approved the whole operation, including committee appointments. Mr. Fair, the co-ordinator, worked with both the P.T.A. Council and the advisory committee to establish a budget after the campaign had been outlined. The budget, which amounted to $3,000, was raised through contributions from local P.T.A. units and local industry. Close records of expenditures were kept and filed with the board of elections within ten days after May 7.

The overall campaign included the following activities:

1. Public addresses to civic groups were given by Mr. Smith from December to the following May.

2. Beginning in late March, school pupils participated in a poster contest on paper furnished by the P.T.A. The poster paper was bordered like a school slate. This same slate theme was carried through on all signs and billboards.

3. A speakers' bureau of teachers, students, and board members was organized and speakers were made available.

4. Daily newspaper releases were made from April 1 to May 7.

5. Students, citizens, and lay leaders were interviewed by the local radio and television stations beginning April 1.

6. Daily advertisements were carried in local newspapers from April 29 to May 7.

7. Advertisements at station breaks on the local radio were broadcast during the last week of the campaign.

8. A weekly fifteen-minute discussion, "Inside Central City Schools," was broadcast by the local radio for a month prior to May 7.

9. Twenty thousand handbills were devised by local Chamber of Commerce officials and Mr. Smith and were handed out by P.T.A. mothers on a house-to-house canvass starting two weeks before election.

10. Fourteen billboards covering all routes into and out of the city were rented for five weeks prior to election.

11. Seven thousand copies of *The Fact of the Matter Is* were distributed through the student body.

12. One thousand professional posters were placed in stores and offices.

13. A thirty-two-page tabloid was organized by the high school journalism group and placed as an insert in the daily newspaper on the Saturday before election. This tabloid included pictures, articles by citizens and teaching staff members, a historical account of the schools in Central City, endorsements by local leaders of business and labor, and accounts of interviews with community leaders.

14. Forty of the forty-five churches in Central City, including church denominations with parochial schools in Central City, devoted their sermons to the bond issue on Sunday, May 5.

15. Twenty-one sign boards (4′ x 8′) were constructed by the high school industrial arts department with material furnished by the P.T.A. and placed in front of each school at least one month before the election.

16. The campaign was climaxed by a torchlight parade the night before election involving approximately 4,000 students, 500 parents, a float representing each local P.T.A. unit, the labor union band, three high school bands, the board of education, and the superintendent of schools. The high school band director assumed the responsibility of organizing and co-ordinating this huge parade.

17. At noon on the day of election, a small printed reminder to vote was sent home with each student.

Two weeks before the election, when no organized opposition had appeared and many of the people normally against changes had' rallied behind the proposal, Mr. Smith sensed that the issue would pass. The parade was indeed the climax of the entire campaign. Mr. Smith could feel the community spirit and enthusiasm at its peak with approximately five thousand people parading and twenty thousand onlookers. After the election, the official count revealed that 68.14 percent of the voters had voted in favor of the bond issue. The building program could now proceed.

In retrospect, Mr. Smith saw many additional values in the campaign other than the successful passage of the bond issue. First, his appearance before many community groups afforded opportunity for him to become acquainted, and the successful passage of the issue could be interpreted as community confidence in the change of administration. Further, new channels of communication were established, which Mr. Smith felt must remain open. With such broad involvement of lay people in the campaign, Mr. Smith noticed that the passage of the bond issue had resulted in a feeling of community pride and accomplishment. Mr. Smith looked forward to continued community participation in solving the school problems in Central City, U.S.A.

SOME INTERPRETATIONS

The following is our interpretation of the application of the administrative process in the case reported above. For the purposes of this chapter, we have reviewed this case to discover examples that will illustrate each of the five steps in the administrative process.

Decision-making. The Central City case illustrates how a change in the socioeconomic composition of the community eventually led to a penetrating analysis of the adequacy of existing school facilities. A rather detailed specification of the building problem was commissioned by the board of education and prepared by consultants from the state univeristy. As a part of this study, population growth was ascertained, the condition of the existing plant was appraised, and the extent of the need for additional facilities was determined. These data were probably more objective and more complete than they would have been had they been gathered without outside assistance.

Data from this study figured prominently in the decision to submit a large bond issue to the electors of the school district. Interestingly, the major impetus for the decision came from citizens and board members; the retiring superintendent of schools was relatively content with the status quo and was basically unwilling to define the current situation as a problem. The study made it possible for the board to take an important step in the organization's activity despite the inertia of the chief administrator; this illustrates that decision-making is an organizational process and not the whim of a single person.

The superintendent did have an important role to play in the decision-making process, however, as evidenced by the behavior of the new superintendent of schools. He helped the board interpret the survey. He also helped clarify the probable cost of the projected building program, ascertained the bonding capacity of the district, and made some assessment of the probable reception the bond issue would get from the people of the community.

The new superintendent also developed a tentative plan for the bond campaign. In this process, various alternatives were undoubtedly considered. Note the ten or twelve meetings that were held in the new superintendent's home. Only with the acceptance of the tentative plan of the superintendent, could it be said that the school district had made a choice: to try for $13 million with which to construct a high school and three elementary schools.

Programming. Like decision-making, programming is well illustrated in the case. There was first the question of who would give leadership to the bond issue campaign. This case illustrates one kind of staffing for school purposes, in which many of the leaders were lay people, rather than professional educators, who contributed their services rather than serving as paid employees of the school system. As it turned out, there were several community leaders who assisted the superintendent and the board of education, including P.T.A. leaders, members of an advisory committee of influential citizens, and Mr. Fair, whose services were loaned by one of the bankers.

A related question was how these leaders should be organized. In a sense, the new superintendent at this point created for himself an *ad hoc* advisory council composed of P.T.A. leaders, advisory council members, and Mr. Fair. This council was to deal with the decisions necessary to implement the basic decision made by the board of education, as already discussed. It should also be noted that many aspects of implementation or programming were also reported back to the board of education in order to keep them fully informed.

The programming actually covered the development of seventeen activities to publicize the bond campaign. These activities included speeches by the superintendent, publicity by news media, house-to-house canvass by P.T.A. workers, preparation of a special edition of the newspaper by pupils, expressed support by ministers, and a torchlight parade.

As in most programming, there was also the question of budget allocation. In this case $3,000 was required. Since state law prohibited the use of school funds for such purposes, other sources of revenue had to be found. Again, the implementing character of the programming step in the administrative process can be noted.

Stimulating. It was previously suggested that in stimulating people to action the administrator often uses the processes of involvement and communication. These devices were used extensively in Central City. To begin with, the plan of the campaign was developed by the superintendent in a series of informal conferences with the board of education. Board members could undoubtedly say with considerable justification, "This is our campaign." Significantly, it did not become Mr. Smith's campaign.

Involvement and communication were again in evidence in the many contacts Mr. Smith established with community leaders, with the P.T.A. Council, and with the appointed advisory committee. A part of Mr. Smith's own enthusiasm for the project rubbed off on a great many other people in Central City. But there was more than enthusiasm. The new board of education was made up of people in whom many community leaders had confidence. The board had studied the problem, had secured outside consultation to examine the building needs, had employed a competent young superintendent to assist them, and had approved a tentative proposal. There was now the question of getting this proposal accepted as a community-wide goal and not as just a goal of the board or of the superintendent. It was with this objective in mind that the superintendent built the factual analysis of the extent of the need.

Another example of communication is found in the sixty-nine speeches made by the superintendent. Had he not been a new superintendent, we think that this would have been too many speeches for any one leader. Under the circumstances, many community groups needed a face-to-face relationship with their new school administrator. His speeches may have seemed like too much one-way communication. We understand, however, that after the presentation, in most cases, the audience was given an opportunity for questions. We suspect that many of these speeches provided the basis for discussions among members of various groups. A good part of that talk probably got back to the superintendent and the board of education. If this was the case, two-way and not merely one-way communication was in operation.

Co-ordinating. In this case there is also evidence of considerable co-ordinating. First of all, the new superintendent, Mr. Smith, had to work out an understanding of his own role and the roles of the board of education, of the *ad hoc* advisory council, and of Mr. Fair in the bond campaign. This he did not do simply by assigning the various roles. While Mr. Smith probably had some idea as to the appropriate role each group or person should play, he discussed these ideas in numerous conferences, and in that process he probably arrived at many modifications of his original ideas. It is significant to note the crucial place that role definition, as a part of co-ordination, has in the administrative process. Unless it is well managed, misunderstanding, confusion, and conflict are likely to follow.

In this case the question of time was also important. The plan involved the release of information on the building problem from December to the following May, a gradual build-up in campaign activity, and an intensive campaign during the final three weeks. This plan was probably based on knowledge of advertising principles, assessment of resources available for campaign activities, and judgment as to how the budget could be most effectively allocated.

In the time span noted above, there was the question of when each of the seventeen activities should take place. Moreover, there was the problem of which people could do these activities most appropriately. It would seem to require some co-ordinating genius to fit together the efforts of preachers, industrial arts pupils, radio announcers, newspaper editors, P.T.A. workers, and the organizer of a torchlight parade. This "fitting together" is a most important aspect of the co-ordinating part of the administrative process.

Appraising. The case shows scant evidence of a formal concern for appraising. In this respect, the Central City episode is similar to, rather than different from, current educational practices. Educational changes are almost never evaluated on a systematic basis. Decisions to terminate or to continue changes in educational practices are seldom grounded on hard data.[31]

Although appraisal was relatively unobtrusive in the case study, there was an occasion when the superintendent did seek to appraise the situation and acted upon the basis of his assessment. As it may be recalled, the superintendent decided to have the P.T.A. Council spearhead the bond campaign. The superintendent recognized that this organization had the manpower to conduct the campaign; however, he suspected that the group had neither the professional know-how nor the brain power to run the campaign successfully. Consistent with his appraisal of the group's expertise, the superintendent formed an advisory committee to decide on the strategy which the council would follow. Although we cannot isolate critical factors which influenced the outcome of the election, the superintendent's appraisal and subsequent action may have been a significant determinant of the outcome.

What was missing were systematic attempts to monitor the campaign while it was in progress. There was no concern for determining how particular people were handling their responsibilities; nor were

---

[31] Matthew B. Miles, "Innovation in Education: Some Generalizations." In Matthew B. Miles, ed., *Innovation in Education* (New York: Bureau of Publications, Teachers College, Columbia University, 1964), Chap. 25.

there efforts to see if the various activities were yielding the hoped-for results. Finally, the issue of organizational maintenance, particularly how people were growing as a consequence of involvement in the campaign, was virtually ignored.

Despite the apparent lack of attention to formal appraisal, the immediate outcome was a positive one. The long-range picture has yet to be painted. What were the unintended, negative side effects which may be lurking beneath the surface only to rise and hamper future efforts? Which activities and people were ineffective? The answers to questions like these would be relevant to future campaigns and would show clearly how appraisal can become a useful guide to action.

OTHER OBSERVATIONS

The analysis of the Central City case from the standpoint of the administrative process brings out certain other aspects of the process. First, it should be quite clear that decision-making, programming, stimulating, co-ordinating, and appraising are simply ways of conceptualizing the administrative process. There is considerable unity among these components. They do not necessarily represent a sequence of acts in administration. In fact, the same act on the part of the administrator may both stimulate and coordinate. Involvement of a person in the basic decision may do much for him by way of stimulation and co-ordination later. And the programming of pupils, editors, P.T.A. workers, and ministers into the bond campaign in Central City was at the same time stimulation and co-ordination.

We would also suggest that the administrative process is, in a sense, a cyclical process. Each time the process is applied to an administrative problem and that problem is solved or appropriate action is taken, other or subsequent problems, which also require application of the administrative process, result. With the passage of the bond issue in Central City, for instance, many other problems emerge. One of these has to do with the facilities that are to be provided in the new high school building. The answer to that question, and many others, will again require decision-making, programming, stimulating, co-ordinating, and appraising.

This brings us to our last point. The administrative process is an economical method of approaching administrative problems. To be sure, the substantive content of problems and the situational factors surrounding them will differ. A bond campaign is not identical to building the educational specifications for a new high school plant.

Both are different from the establishment of a foreign language program, which emphasizes a conversational approach. Each of these problems must be approached in terms of the conditions found to pertain in a particular school community at a particular time. But all three problems can be approached intelligently by application of the administrative process. Thus, knowledge about the administrative process and the ability to apply it do much to make an effective administrator.

SUGGESTED ACTIVITIES

1. Read the case, "Since September," presented in Chapter I of Campbell and Gregg, *Administrative Behavior in Education,* and indicate to what extent the administrative process, as described in this chapter, was followed by Mr. Miner.
2. Use the elements of the administrative process as described in this chapter to appraise the steps taken to solve an administrative problem in your school.
3. Interview a superintendent or principal concerning steps taken in the solution of one of his administrative problems. Write up the case and analyze the extent to which the administrative process as described in this chapter was followed.
4. How do the views of Dill (see below) with respect to the administrative process compare with those presented in this chapter?

SELECTED READINGS

BARNARD, CHESTER I. *The Functions of the Executive.* (Cambridge, Mass.: Harvard University Press, 1938).

DILL, WM. R. "Decision-Making." In National Society for the Study of Education, *Behavioral Science and Educational Administration,* Sixty-Third Yearbook, Part II. (Chicago: University of Chicago Press, 1964), Chap. 9.

GREGG, RUSSELL T. "The Administrative Process." In Roald F. Campbell and Russell T. Gregg, eds., *Administrative Behavior in Education.* (New York: Harper & Brothers, 1957), Chap. 8.

GRIFFITHS, DANIEL E. "A Taxonomy Based on Decision-Making." In Daniel E. Griffiths, ed., *Developing Taxonomies of Organizational Behavior in Educational Administration.* (Chicago: Rand McNally, 1969), Chap. 3.

HEMPHILL, JOHN K., GRIFFITHS, DANIEL E., and FREDERIKSEN, NORMAN. *Administrative Performance and Personality.* (New York: Bureau of Publications, Columbia University, 1962).

KEPNER, CHARLES H. and TREGOE, BENJAMIN B. *The Rational Manager.* (New York: McGraw-Hill, 1965).

LITCHFIELD, EDWARD H. "Notes on a General Theory of Administration," *Administrative Science Quarterly*, 1 (June, 1956), pp. 3–29.

SEARS, JESSE B. *The Nature of the Administrative Process.* (New York: McGraw Hill, 1950).

SIMON, HERBERT A., *Administrative Behavior*, 2nd ed. (New York: The Macmillan Co., 1957), Chap. 1.

SIMON, HERBERT A. *The New Science of Management Decision.* (New York: Harper & Row, 1960).

7

Administrative Behavior And Educational Administration

Having viewed educational administration in terms of its meaning and purpose, its tasks, and its process, we shall now look at the administration of the school from the standpoint of the behavior of those who occupy administrative positions. In this chapter we shall examine the administrator's behavior from two vantage points: the administrator as an initiator of action and the administrator as a recipient of action. Our intent is to sensitize the prospective administrator to the possibility that he will both influence and be influenced, and to increase his knowledge and understanding of both processes.

THE ADMINISTRATOR AS AN INITIATOR OF ACTION

Since the turn of this century, much has been written about the administrator as an initiator of action. Some of it has been prescriptive; some of it has been descriptive. Regardless of its character, this work generally uses the term *leadership* to denote the behavior of administrators who originate action for others. To be considered a leader, the administrator must act as a causal agent for someone else's behavior. The administrator is leading only when he is guiding and influencing what others in the organization are thinking, feeling, valuing, believing, or doing. If the administrator is unable to exert such influence, then he is not a leader.

Consistent with this general usage of the term *leader,* we define a leader as an administrator who has a mission or a special sense of direction for the organization and who is able to secure the commitments and efforts of subordinates in service of this mission. According to this definition, the educational administrator must possess two essential characteristics if he is to be regarded as a leader. First, he must have a special sense of where the organization is going, a vision which excites the imagination and challenges the best in people. This noble purpose gives people something to work for, something which they do not yet know how to do, and something which they will be proud of when they achieve it.[1] Such a vision gives calm perspective to the hot issues of the day and affects the significance of everything the administrator does.[2] The essence of leadership, therefore, is "choice, a singularly individualistic act in which a man [administrator] assumes responsibility for a commitment to direct an organization along a particular path."[3] This commitment stimulates and guides action.

The second essential characteristic which the educational administrator must have if he is to be considered a leader is the ability to influence people, to bind their wills in the accomplishment of purposes beyond their own ends.[4] If the administrator has a worthy organizational objective and a sense of direction which is designed to give continuity to individual actions over time but is unable to elicit the requisite energies and commitments of others, then he is not a leader according to our definition. To be a leader, the administrator must be able to realize his intent in the attitudes, values, and behavior of his subordinates. Functioning as a leader means that the administrator is guiding and shaping what individuals do in service of the organization and its mission.

THE LEADER AND HIS ORGANIZATIONAL MISSION

Given the current state of our society, man reaches out for something to believe in, something that will give meaning to his job. He searches for this meaning because his former psychological anchors are rapidly disappearing.[5] People are on the move; geographical

---

[1] Charles H. Granger, "The Hierarchy of Objectives," *Harvard Business Review,* 42, 3 (May–June 1964), 63–74.

[2] O. A. Ohmann, "Skyhooks," *Harvard Business Review,* 48, 1 (January–February 1970), 4–22 and 166.

[3] Abraham Zaleznik, "The Management of Disappointment," *Harvard Business Review,* 45, 6 (November–December 1967), 59–70.

[4] Chester I. Barnard, *The Functions of the Executive* (Cambridge, Mass.: Harvard University Press, 1962), p. 283.

[5] Harry Levinson, *The Exceptional Executive: A Psychological Conception* (Cambridge, Mass.: Harvard University Press, 1968), p. 28.

mobility is the rule rather than the exception. A mobile society brings with it several disruptive effects. People are now reluctant to establish enduring friendships and ties with others because they wish to avoid the pain of separation. People are unlikely to be living in the same neighborhood for any extended period of time; space is, therefore, no longer the source of psychological support and identity it once was. Nor is the extended family unit likely to be found living in close proximity; people cannot turn to fathers, mothers, sisters, brothers, uncles, and aunts for help and comfort in time of need. With these three traditional threads of continuity and sources of identity disappearing, the individual looks to the organization in which he works to furnish the psychological anchor outside himself which will give meaning to his life. People want and need a leader who believes in something and in whom they can believe. Let us now turn to two concrete examples of such a leader in two quite different educational settings.

A suburban example. Smith and Keith,[6] in describing and analyzing a highly innovative elementary school, highlight an administrator who inspired his staff to pursue a bold new conception of education —a conception free of the myriad ills which characterize the traditional American elementary school. The central thrust of this "School of Tomorrow" was to help students become "fully functioning mature human beings." The objectives of this school were fivefold:

1. to develop each child to the limits of his potentialities
2. to help each child achieve complete living in all phases of his life
3. to assist each child in becoming the architect of his own character
4. to foster self-actualization and self-realization
5. to develop the child intellectually, socially, emotionally, and physically

The administrator proposed to achieve these objectives through individualized instruction—*i.e.*, differentiation in the rate of presentation and content according to the needs of each child.

To create a sense of special significance for this school, the administrator continually contrasted the School of Tomorrow with the schools of today and yesterday. He bestowed the School of Tomorrow with heroic qualities and the traditional schools with vil-

[6] Louis M. Smith and Pat M. Keith, *Anatomy of an Educational Innovation* (New York: Wiley, to be published).

lainous ones. The traditional school was characterized as an "egg crate" whereas the School of Tomorrow reflected an open-space concept. The architecture of the school was distinctive and was used to reinforce the image of a school destined to be distinctive in functioning and having effects on children. The school was going to replace the "lock-step" curriculum with one based on continuous progress for each individual. Goals were to be set by the students rather than by the teachers. Students worked individually and in groups of varying sizes as opposed to the conventional classroom with thirty students. Daily schedules for students were arranged according to the needs and interests of each pupil and not according to a prearranged schedule that was the same for each day. Responsibility for what went on in the school was shifted from the teacher to the pupil. Textbooks were abandoned because they were viewed as a deterrent to instruction and to learning. Divergent thinking rather than rote memorization was stressed.

The overall organization of the school was changed from six grade levels to three divisions—the Basic Skills Division, the Transition Division, and the Independent Study Division. The function of the Basic Skills Division was to provide the competencies in communication and computation which are essential for acquiring knowledge, as well as the social skills which are necessary for the development of mature human beings. As the student moved to the Transition Division, he was taught to pursue knowledge independently but within the structure of the school. In the Independent Study Division, teachers assisted the pupils in discovering knowledge about the world in which they lived. In all three divisions the intent was to provide a flexible program of study based on the individual needs, interests, and abilities of students and to guide them into the repeated experiencing of success rather than failure.

Staff members were totally committed to this conception of education and were convinced of the worthiness of the principal's mission. They labored unceasingly, many to the point of exhaustion, in trying to achieve this grand goal. Smith and Keith report that they had never witnessed such total absorption in the work of an organization. The enthusiasm and the commitment were short-lived, however, and the results deviated dramatically from the ideal. At the beginning of the third year, the school board had been voted out of office, the superintendent had resigned, the principal had departed, the curriculum director had taken a position in another district, and only two of the original teaching staff remained. The program of the school reverted to the traditional pattern, and the wall-less building was transformed into one with self-contained classrooms. Why this undertaking proved so disastrous will be treated in a later section of this chapter.

An inner-city example. McPherson,[7] in a case study of two inner-city elementary schools with radically different teacher turnover patterns during the same five-year period, found a sense of mission evident in the low turnover school. At this school's inception, the principal communicated to prospective staff members his desire to create an intellectual oasis in the inner city—a school where lower class black children would learn to read effectively and succeed academically. The principal was convinced that such an oasis could be created and was instrumental in getting his staff to believe that if it could accomplish this objective, then others would look at the school and say, "How come we can't do it if the Vesey Elementary School can?" Vesey's success would demand more oases. The sense of special significance was the commitment to establishing an exemplary inner-city elementary school which would become the model for inner-city education in the future. By solving the educational problems at the Vesey Elementary School, the staff would be leading the way toward solving the problems in inner-city education everywhere, a noble purpose indeed.

In recruiting teachers for his staff, the principal of Vesey Elementary School looked for experienced, well-educated, and highly competent individuals who had a Peace Corps sense of mission and who shared his conviction that an intellectual oasis was possible in the inner city. He sought teachers who desired to help black students succeed academically and experience joy and happiness while in school. He searched relentlessly for teachers with interests and abilities in more than one area, for teachers who understood and enjoyed working with inner-city black youngsters, and for teachers who regarded their jobs as more than just a way to occupy time between 9 and 3 o'clock. As the result of his efforts, the principal and his staff shared a common understanding of what the school was about, and were convinced that the objective was attainable. There were unusually high expectations for success—a feature missing in most schools in this setting.

At the end of a five-year period, the school was successful by many different criteria. There was virtually no vandalism in the school;

---

[7] R. Bruce McPherson, "A Study of Teacher Turnover in Two Inner-City Elementary Schools" (unpublished doctoral dissertation, Department of Education, University of Chicago, 1970).

windows were not broken, and the washrooms and corridors were free of the usual graffiti. The students enjoyed coming to school and a potentially militant community was supportive of the school's efforts to educate the students in its charge. On the single salient measure of success for teachers, however, the school was a failure. Despite the best efforts of a dedicated, determined group of competent educators fully expecting to be successful in fostering the intellectual development of their students, the academic performance of students was apparently no different than in other inner-city schools. Most of the students who had spent their first four years in Vesey School were reading below grade level, and a number of them actually regressed. As one teacher phrased it, "Some of these kids started out right, but somewhere we lost them." How this school and the one in the suburban setting happened to fail to achieve their mission is the subject of the next section.

MISSION FAILURE AND ITS IMPLICATIONS FOR ADMINISTRATIVE BEHAVIOR

In neither of the two examples which we have cited was the mission achieved. The answer to why the ventures failed may be a simple one. Given the circumstances, both visions may have been unrealistic and unattainable. The educators may have plunged headlong into these undertakings with an extravagant conception of the potentialities of the future and were totally ignorant of the difficulties involved.[8] If so, then the implications for the administrator who wishes to be a leader are rather clear. Before committing the organization to a particular direction, he should seriously ponder this question: "Can this be done?" In this case the peculiar genius of leadership is the ability to distinguish between the possible and the impossible, but with the willingness to get dangerously close to the latter.[9]

We believe that the preceding answer as to why the undertakings failed is inadequate. Another explanation seems more plausible. In neither school did the principals intellectualize the mission fully. There was no deliberate effort to break up the mission into immediate, visible targets; rather, the principals amplified the remote targets

---

[8] Eric Hoffer, *The True Believer* (New York: Harper & Row, 1951), p. 21.
[9] Granger, "The Hierarchy of Objectives," p. 70.

and underplayed the close ones.[10] No one seemed to be asking and seeking answers to this question: "What is it that we should be doing if we are to achieve our mission?" There were general goals but no clear and carefully thought out plan for mission attainment. For example, in the inner-city school both the principal and his staff believed that if a school has an able, dedicated principal and staff who have a high expectancy of success, then high academic achievement will be the result. It was not clear then, nor is it clear now, how these admittedly desirable qualities of principal and staff necessarily lead to high student achievement, particularly in reading. The problem of student reading was never attacked head on; no plan or program for improving the reading performance of students in that school was ever developed. In short, the sentiment of expectancy for student success in reading was never transformed into a plan for action. Important as enthusiasm and commitment are, they are insufficient by themselves for producing the desired results. These sentiments must be accompanied by a reasoned plan of action directly aimed at the problem which the organization is committed to solving.

THE LEADER AND HIS PROBLEM OF INFLUENCE

As we mentioned earlier, in order to be considered a leader an administrator must be able to influence people in addition to having a mission which gives continuity to actions over time. Influencing others in the context of an organization, particularly one which is staffed by people who regard themselves as professionals, will inevitably be problematic for the administrator. In our two earlier examples, the principals were able to minimize the influence problem to a considerable extent because they opened new schools and consciously recruited staff members who found the principals' missions appealing. Most administrators will confront settings and situations with personnel who have life histories in the organization and who have developed vested interests and commitments which are incompatible with the would-be leader's mission. Such people may not readily adopt an organizational objective no matter how worthy it is and may resist attempts by the administrator to influence them in minor, as well as in major, organizational matters. Even those who

---

[10] For an interesting statement on a gradualist approach to change, see Amitai Etzioni, *Studies in Social Change* (New York: Holt, Rinehart & Winston, 1966), Chap. 3.

wholeheartedly embrace the administrator's mission may oppose either covertly or overtly efforts to influence them. Since we believe that the administrator cannot take his capacity to influence others for granted, we will examine this problem in greater detail.

In dealing with the problem of influencing others within the context of a formal organization, we shall consider that influence has occurred when the administrator attempts to modify another person's attitudes, values, beliefs, thoughts, or ways of behaving,[11] and succeeds in his attempt. For example, a principal recognizes that one of his staff members believes that inner-city children simply cannot learn, and the principal seeks to influence the teacher *to adopt the belief that these children can learn.* If the principal succeeds in altering the teacher's belief in the manner desired, we regard him as being a leader in that situation. We assume that such a belief does contribute either directly or indirectly to achieving the organization's mission as envisioned by the principal.

Our treatment of influence will focus on the various ways in which the administrator may seek to influence others and some of the conditions under which each mode of influence may be most effective. No single method is universally applicable since the effectiveness of any given mode is dependent upon the exact nature of the administrator, the person who is the object of the influence attempt, the change desired, and their interrelationships. Therefore, each administrator who aspires to be a leader will have to assess these various factors before he selects the particular mode of influence which he will use. The discussion that follows is aimed at helping the administrator make this selection.

Training. As a mode of influence, training is particularly applicable when a person is willing to change but lacks the requisite skills which may be developed through some type of training program. Furthermore, the person agrees with the administrator that the new belief, value, or way of behaving is a desirable one. For example, a foreign language teacher may be willing to switch her emphasis from teaching students to read and write in the foreign language to teaching them to converse in the language. The major obstacle to be overcome is arranging opportunities for the teacher to acquire the requisite conversational skills before undertaking the new approach. In such a case, the administrator might seize the initiative in identifying

---

[11] H. D. Lasswell and A. Kaplan, *Power and Society* (New Haven: Yale University Press, 1950).

the opportunities which are available, and in helping the teacher take advantage of these opportunities. The latter might even include payment of the costs associated with the training and compensation for time spent in securing the necessary training.

Informing. There is a different type of situation, one which is conducive to influence by informing. In this situation the individual who is the object of influence is both willing and able to change in accordance with the views of the administrator. The major obstacle to change is the person's lack of knowledge about his present behavior and how it departs from some ideal. Therefore, the way in which the administrator influences others is to provide the information which vividly describes the state of the present situation.

For example, let us assume that the teachers in a given school are committed to the idea that a major function of formal education is to develop the powers of critical thinking in students. An important question to be answered is: "Are teachers structuring experiences which demand and foster critical thinking? If so, how frequent are these occasions?" The administrator, with the co-operation of his staff and outside consultant help, may create a plan and a set of procedures for answering this question. The plan may involve a systematic examination of the classroom tests which teachers use, the types of questions posed by teachers to students during question-answer periods, and the nature of the homework which is assigned. The leadership role of the administrator is twofold: to take the initiative in establishing a system which will yield information about the present practices in the school and to feed back the information to the members of his staff.

Supporting. Supporting, as a mode of influence, is appropriate when an individual is predisposed to change his behavior and is capable of making the change, but is fearful and anxious about being able to behave effectively in the new way. As in the preceding two modes of influence, the interpersonal relationship between the individual and the administrator is a positive one. In this type of situation, the major obstacle to change is the individual's anxiety and uncertainty about the future. Consequently, the administrator is likely to be successful in his influence attempt if he can be supportive and understanding while the individual works through his decision about changing and seeks to implement it.

By way of illustration, suppose a principal wishes to embark on a program designed to improve school-community relationships. What he has in mind is a two-year program. In the first year, he intends to meet in the homes of parents with groups ranging in size from eight to fifteen people. The length of these meetings will be one hour and a half, and they will center on topics of interest to the people present. He plans to open each meeting by presenting some ideas for changes which are being contemplated for the following year and indicating that he would be eager to discuss these ideas or to react to specific questions which parents might wish to raise at that time. In the second year, he plans to have parents visit the school, again in small groups of eight to fifteen people, and to witness first-hand the innovations which are being tried in the school program. The principal himself is somewhat uncertain about this course of action, however, and has asked the superintendent for a conference to discuss the matter.

Early in the conference, the superintendent senses that the principal doubts his own ability to handle the program successfully. The superintendent suppresses his tendency to respond in the usual ways. He does not give the principal bland assurances that he will be able to function well in these meetings with parents, nor does the superintendent give bits of wisdom about what to do to make these meetings successful. Rather, he listens and acts as a sounding board[12]; he helps the principal to recognize and to deal with his misgivings about being able to function effectively in these admittedly unpredictable meetings with parents. The superintendent also explores ways in which his office might be of help by asking if the principal has thought about assistance which the superintendent might be able to provide. By acting in this manner, the superintendent is being supportive and is influencing the principal with respect to some future activity.

Advising. Influence by advising is likely to be most effective when a person is dissatisfied with the existing set of circumstances but is unable to determine the particular condition or state which will yield more satisfying outcomes. At the same time, the administrator is perceived to have the knowledge and expertise necessary to extricate the individual from his current problematic situation. The major obstacle to change is the person's inability to identify the state or condition which represents a solution to his problem; therefore, the

[12] Harry Levinson, *Emotional Health: In the World of Work* (New York: Harper and Row, 1964), pp. 223–227.

individual is susceptible to influence by the administrator if the latter has the intellectual resources to solve the problem.

There is evidence[13] which suggests that, in fulfilling their supervisory functions, principals are quite sensitive to this type of situation. Principals report that *unsolicited* advice or suggestion to teachers on matters related to the teaching process has crucially different implications from *requested* advice. The former carries with it a questioning of professional competence, and the professional receiving it is apt to react with considerable effect. A major factor which governs the person's reaction to unsolicited advice is the degree of respect which the person has for the supervisor. Principals who recognize this fact of organizational life consider their qualifications and those of the advisee and adapt the content of their suggestions and advice accordingly.

Involving. On occasion, the administrator will confront a situation in which a person is willing and able to change, but will oppose it if the administrator makes the decision unilaterally. The resistance develops because the person feels that the administrator does not have the legitimate right to make a decision about the change without first consulting the people who have a stake in the outcome. In this situation, the major obstacle to change is one of legitimation; consequently, the administrator can influence the person to behave in a new way by involving him in the decision about whether the change should be made.

For example, let us assume that a principal wishes to change the length of class periods and the number of days a given class meets each week and to drop study halls. The three changes are interrelated. The majority of discipline problems have occurred during study hall periods. As one might expect, students who have been in trouble have not used the study time to do their homework even though homework was assigned. Furthermore, the students report that they do not use the study time to do their homework because they do not understand how to do it. The standardized test results indicate that these students probably are experiencing the difficulties which they report. As a solution to this problem, the principal proposes to lengthen the class periods from forty to seventy minutes, with approximately thirty minutes to be allowed for supervised study by the teacher who has assigned the homework. Classes would meet four

---

[13] Anne E. Trask, "Principals, Teachers and Supervision: Dilemmas and Solutions," *Administrator's Notebook*, XIII, 4 (December, 1964).

days rather than five days each week, and all study halls would be dropped from the schedule.

The principal carefully documents the discipline referrals and when they occur. He notes the reasons for these referrals and indicates the ability levels of those who are referred for some sort of disciplinary action. Armed with this information and his proposed solution, the principal meets with his staff. He presents the findings of his study and what he thinks is a viable means of dealing with the problem. He encourages teachers to find fault with the proposal, to foreshadow the problems which might develop if the plan were implemented, and to express their own personal fears and concerns with respect to what he has proposed. Following a discussion of the plan, the principal might decide the issue in one of three ways: 1. by making the decision himself (sensing that there is no clear opposition to the proposal), 2. reaching the decision by majority vote, or 3. seeking to resolve the matter by reaching consensus.[14]

Rewarding. As a mode of influence, rewarding is appropriate when the individual believes that the benefits associated with the change do not exceed the perceived costs and when the administrator has control over resources which the other person values. In this situation, the major obstacle to change is that the person sees no net gain for himself by altering his behavior. If the administrator is to influence the other person, the administrator must make rewards available which are sufficient to induce the person to change his way of thinking or behaving.

Almost every school system has its own reward system. People quickly come to recognize what kind of behavior counts. Praise, promotions, salary increases, access to scarce organizational resources, and preferential treatment can be important incentives for behavior. The anticipation of these rewards, as well as the actual offering and receipt of them, can motivate people to act in ways which are congruent with the administrator's expectations. In some cases, it must be evident that a positive response to the administrator's influence attempt will lead to certain tangible rewards for compliance.

Commanding. There will be times when the administrator must resort to commanding as the mode for influencing an individual to modify his behavior. When the person has shown himself unwilling

[14] For a more detailed discussion of involvement, see Edwin M. Bridges, "A Model for Shared Decision Making in the School Principalship," *Educational Administration Quarterly*, 3, 1 (Winter, 1967), 49–61.

but able to change his way of behaving and the administrator has the organizational authority to demand compliance, the administrator will need to bring the power of his office to bear on the other person. The major obstacle to change is the person's refusal to behave in accordance with organizational norms; the administrator influences in such cases by insisting that the change be made and by applying the prescribed sanctions if necessary.

By way of illustration, a principal had been working with the Chairman of the Physical Education Department in a concerted effort to develop a program of study. The principal had tried to build upon the ideas of the chariman but he had none. Contrary to the opinions of the members of his department, the chairman indicated that no additional equipment was necessary and that the existing program was more than adequate. He steadfastly refused to consider the changes which his colleagues proposed, and ignored the problems inherent in the present practices. An outside study team with expertise in this area visited the school, examined what was being done, and recommended massive reform in the present program. When the chairman opposed the recommendations, the principal ordered the chairman to implement the recommendations as soon as possible or else he would be replaced.

Designing. Up to this point in our discussion of modes of influence, we have dealt only with methods which are directed specifically at another person by the administrator and which result in awareness by the individual that he is being influenced by the administrator. There is an influence mode called designing, or *ecological control,*[15] in which the administrator takes some action that modifies the other person's social or physical environment on the assumption that the new environment will subsequently bring about the desired change in him. In this mode, the person is unaware that he is being influenced by the administrator. This mode of influence is apt to be used when the other person is committed to the status quo and/or when he would resist more direct influence attempts by the administrator.

For example, a principal during his first year as high school principal noted that the English department was oriented toward the use of anthologies; and, there were no attempts made to use reading materials which appealed to a range of abilities and interests. Most of the teachers appeared to be highly committed to the continued use of these materials primarily because they made the teachers' job a

---

[15] M. Rosenberg and L. Pearlin, "Power-Orientations in the Mental Hospital," *Human Relations,* 1962, 335–350.

relatively easy and undemanding one. The principal felt that one teacher in particular was anxious to try a more differentiated approach because she recognized that many students were bored by the current materials. Also, a number of students were incapable of reading what was available. The principal approached the teacher and asked if she would be interested in having a paperback book library for her room. Together with a consultant secured by the principal, the English teacher put together four separate lists of paperback books; each list contained a variety of books geared to a range of interests and abilities. Within a month after the new materials were put into use, other teachers who were pressured by their own students came to the principal and requested that the same materials be made available for use in their classes.

A CONCLUDING COMMENT ABOUT MODES OF INFLUENCE

Throughout our discussion of influence, we have for ease of presentation showed only one influence mode being used in connection with each influence attempt. For any given situation, the administrator may need to employ several different modes if the person is to be influenced to accept or to adopt a change. By way of illustration, an individual may be confronted with the knowledge that there is a discrepancy between his present state of behaving and some future state (*informing*) but be unable to adjust his behavior because he lacks the requisite skills. To move the person from his present way of behaving, the administrator may need to couple the training, rewarding, and supporting modes with informing. In the final analysis, the particular mode of influence or combination of various modes which the administrator chooses will depend upon his perception of the personal and situational conditions that exist in each concrete case. Hopefully, our discussion of influence modes will improve the administrator's perceptiveness and facilitate his choices.

THE ADMINISTRATOR AS A RECIPIENT OF ACTION[16]

Administrators are recipients, as well as initiators, of action. As a recipient of action, the administrator's behavior is best understood as being guided, shaped, and even controlled by the intent and actions of

[16] This section is based primarily on an article by Edwin M. Bridges, "Administrative Man: Origin or Pawn in Decision Making?" *Educational Administration Quarterly*, 6, 1 (Winter, 1970), 7–25.

others. Influence flows to the administrator, as well as from him. Since our knowledge and understanding of this side of administrative man is quite limited, our discussion of the administrator as a recipient of action will lack the extensive empirical and theoretical base which supported our treatment of administrative man as an initiator of action. Our comments will focus on three different ways in which the behavior of the administrator is guided, shaped, and influenced by others and will be organized around the following rubrics:

1. *Recipient of action by choice.* The administrator, willingly and knowingly, uses the goals of others as the principal basis for choosing the course of action he will take.

2. *Recipient of action against his will.* The administrator is most certainly not acting on his own and is aware that the goals underlying his behavior are primarily those of others and not his own.

3. *Recipient of action without his knowledge.* The administrator clearly is not acting on his own, but he is unaware that his behavior matches the intent of others and is caused by their purposes, desires, and aims.

RECIPIENT OF ACTION BY CHOICE

The administrator governs by consent. This is true because in the final analysis the administrator's authority is determined by the willingness of others to accept his directives, orders, and suggestions as the basis for their behavior.[17] To maintain his authority, the administrator must maintain a balance between the contributions he expects of others and the inducements which they receive for their contributions. In other words, he gives in order to get. The administrator attempts to satisfy the goals of others in the immediate situation in order to elicit their compliance or co-operation with decisions he makes in some future situation.

As the administrator tries to satisfy the goals and needs of others, he confronts a number of problems; these problems are either an intentional or an unintentional consequence of their efforts to originate action for the administrator. One unintended problem stems from the ambiguous way in which people articulate their needs. Their stated goals are ambiguous because their goals or needs are obscure even to themselves. As a result, the person is able to communicate

[17] Barnard, pp. 161–165.

only that he has a strongly felt sense of need. He is aware that something is wrong, but has no clear understanding of what is wrong. The person recognizes that he is in a state of deprivation or in a state of needing, but has no firm notion of what actions, conditions, or objects will eliminate the state of deprivation or will satisfy the need.[18] For example, students in high schools, colleges, and universities are seeking in varying degrees of intensity to become involved in organizational decision-making processes. In some undefined number of cases, administrators are genuinely interested in satisfying students' needs for involvement. The administrator's decisions in these situations are complicated perhaps less by the willingness of faculty members to forego some of their prerogatives than by the students' lack of a clear grasp of what is required to satisfy their need for involvement. The administrator is unable to take action until he can identify or help the students clarify what modes of involvement they deem "good enough"—*i.e.,* capable of meeting their need for involvement. Unfortunately, we know very little about how administrators perform this clarifying role and how they behave when confronted with this type of ambiguity.

Unintended problems also may arise even if the person is aware of his state of deprivation and the conditions which will rectify the deprivation. These difficulties occur when individuals incompletely communicate what their needs are. For example, a subordinate communicates his need in terms of the actions which will eliminate the deprivation, but inadvertently neglects to articulate what the basic need-as-felt is. If the subordinate has erred in judging the capability of the action for achieving his desired state, and the administrator makes his decision consistent with the subordinate's explicit definition of the situation, then the administrator will believe that his decision is "good enough" when in fact it is not.

This is not the major problem posed by the incomplete communication of others, however. If the administrator accepts the need-as-stated as the basic need-as-felt, then he is severely limited in the range of alternatives he can consider as being potentially "good enough." To return to the issue of student involvement, college students may express the desire to have a vote equal to that of the faculty in matters relating to the hiring, firing, and promotion of faculty members. Underlying this stated goal is a firm conviction that faculty members are not adequately fulfilling their responsibilities to

---

[18] This distinction between need as a state of deprivation and need as a material thing or set of conditions which fills a lack is drawn from Joseph J. Schwab, *College Curriculum and Student Protest* (Chicago: The University of Chicago Press, 1969), p. 152.

students; as a result, students are not performing at the level to which they aspire. The administrator, acting in terms of the expressed desire, will fail to locate a satisfactory alternative if the faculty opposes student involvement, or if the institution's bylaws prohibit this form of student participation. Alternative courses of action which are "good enough" are much more likely to be found, however, if the basic need is identified—*i.e.,* "We are not performing at the level to which we aspire." The need, thus redefined, allows a range of other possible solutions to be considered. Conversion of the need-as-stated into the basic need-as-felt is an important facet of the administrative man which has been overlooked.

Difficulties which hamper the administrator's efforts to find a solution that is "good enough" to others also are posed by the intentionally misleading way in which they represent their needs. Under certain conditions, people communicate that they require one thing when they actually require another. Gouldner, for example, in his study of worker-management relationships, describes how complaints stemming from changes in management practices were channeled into a demand for more money.[19] Several factors contributed to this misrepresentation, including the workers' belief that their real complaints were not legitimate in the eyes of management and the workers' desire to have an issue on which unity of action was possible.

Confusing or misleading statements of needs by others, regardless of their intentionality, are not the only sources of problems for the administrator who is a recipient of action by choice. Problems also arise from the administrator's own attribution processes. Prior to reaching unilateral decisions, administrators frequently rehearse in their mind's eye the consequences of the alternatives under consideration. One important source of consequences is the anticipated reactions of others. The goals which administrators attribute to other persons in such cases influence the selection of alternatives. Incorrect inferences are both a persistent fear and a bane of the administrator.

RECIPIENT OF ACTION AGAINST HIS WILL

In a collective bargaining setting, the administrator's behavior is frequently guided by the goals and demands of others. The flow of influence is not unilateral, however. Each side uses a range of tactics

[19] Alvin W. Gouldner, *The Wildcat Strike* (New York: Harper & Row, 1954).

to advance its purposes and to achieve its goals within an institutionalized mechanism for handling intergroup conflict. The tactics used by both sides in this setting—deception, bluff, threats, and threat fulfillment—conform to a power strategy.[20] The process involves a series of demands and counter-demands, offers and counter-offers. There is an expectation by both parties that not all of their goals will be realized and that goal attainment by one party probably means a commitment which satisfies the goals of the other party. For the most part, neither side agrees with alacrity to accept the goals of the other. On those few occasions when one party is willing to satisfy the others' needs or goals, this willingness is concealed; and the object of attraction is used to extract concessions from the other side.

Influence of the administrator against his will is not limited to the collective bargaining setting, however. In his daily organizational routine, the administrator on occasion comes to act contrary to his own wishes and preferences as a consequence of the efforts of others. These occasions are occurring with increased frequency; teachers, students, and citizens are demanding that the school administrator become more sensitive to their goals.[21] There appear to be two approaches which they are using in an effort to realize this end. One approach focuses on the administrator prior to his reaching a decision; the other concentrates on him after he has made a decision, which is inconsistent with the wishes and goals of others.

In using the latter approach, the intent may be to obtain a reversal of the administrator's decision. For example, students and parents may want an administrator to rehire a particular teacher whom he has just fired. The demand may be accompanied by a disruption of the school's activities. Parents picket the school and the district's administrative offices. Students go on strike and refuse to re-enter the school until the teacher is rehired. Violence and damage to the school building may also result unless the administrator changes his decision. Convinced of the rightness of their demands, such groups may resort to any tactic, legal or otherwise, to achieve their ends.

Some decisions, however, are irreversible in that there is no way of undoing the damage which people perceive has been inflicted on

---

[20] Richard E. Walton, "Two Strategies of Social Change and Their Dilemmas," *The Journal of Applied Behavioral Science*, I, 2, 1965, 167–179.

[21] For a discussion of these occasions and how the administrator might deal with them, see Edwin M. Bridges, "Subjective and Objective Aspects of Demands for Involvement," *Administrator's Notebook*, XVII, 6 (February, 1969).

them. In such cases, persons may use tactics which are designed to establish a clear cause-effect relationship in the mind of the administrator. The latter is, in one sense, led to expect negative consequences if he behaves in ways which thwart the goals of the group in question. If the relationship between the group and the administrator is affectively neutral or positive at the time, then the group in all likelihood will limit its tactics to the communication of intensely strong negative affect by means of nonverbal cues. However, if the relationship is such that the group believes the expression of negative sentiments will not make the administrator more responsive to its goals, the group may resort to tactics like sabotage, ritual insubordination, or strict bureaucratic interpretations of its obligations to the administrator. Such tactics frequently are accompanied by a variety of verbal and muted cues to establish an unmistakable relationship between these events and the administrator's action.

Individuals or groups also attempt to influence the administrator before he reaches a decision. This happens when they know that the administrator is considering a particular issue and they want to affect the outcome, or when they want the administrator to take action that they perceive he is unwilling to initiate on his own. In trying to exert influence on the administrator, people find ingenious ways of letting the administrator know how they feel about a situation and what action they consider appropriate. If their stake in the outcome is high and they attribute obduracy to the administrator, then they, in addition, may subtly foreshadow certain difficulties and link them to the administrator's decisions. For example, work groups may let it be known that they have been preparing a list of grievances which they plan to present to the union representative or to the administrator's superior. There may be hints that the group will no longer help out in crisis situations by doing work that is not stipulated in the contract. There may even be threats of a walkout or some other form of harassment, inconvenience, or embarrassment. Regardless of the tactic, the objective is the same. The group hopes to create a decision situation for the administrator which offers only negative choices. The administrator yields to the preferences of others because he dislikes the other alternatives open to him even more.

We suspect that yielding to the preferences of others against his will is likely to be an unusually stressful event for the administrator. The stress is produced in no small measure by the image of administrative man as the initiator of action (leader), which is consistently portrayed in the literature on educational administration. Because of this image, being the influencee rather than the influencer poses far more difficulties for him than for others—particularly his subordinates. How the administrator copes with this role reversal and what the consequences are for his subsequent behavior represent an interesting area for future inquiry.

RECIPIENT OF ACTION WITHOUT HIS KNOWLEDGE

In both of the preceding discussions of the administrator as a recipient of action, the administrator has been portrayed as *knowingly* being guided or governed in his actions by the efforts and goals of others. As recipient of action by choice, he willingly permits this influence to occur. As the recipient of action against his will, the administrator yields to the preferences of others because he wishes to avoid the real or imagined costs of noncompliance. In the third and final recipient-of-action-state to be discussed, stress will be placed on the more subtle tactics people use to influence the behavior of the administrator. Contrary to the popular conception of administrative man as the one who influences, he will be treated as the one who is being influenced without his knowledge.

People seek to influence the administrator without his awareness for a variety of reasons. They wish to elude the unpleasantness and the risks of a direct confrontation with an administrator who might retaliate when he is challenged. They derive a sense of satisfaction from outwitting the bearers of formal authority. They have purposes which, if public, either could not be realized or perhaps would have a lower probability of being achieved. The objective sought determines in part which tactics are considered, for one objective is attained more efficiently and more effectively by one type of maneuver than by another. The choice of tactics is further limited by the availability of the conditions and the resources that the tactic demands. For example, if the tactic requires knowledge of persons on whom the administrator relies for advice and counsel and this knowledge is lacking, then the individual must look for a tactic which can be employed with existing means, knowledge, and circumstances.

Research and theoretical work are relatively silent on the ways in which an administrator's behavior is influenced by others without his knowledge. However, from our own informal observations of organizations at work and from discussions with occupants of subordinate positions within the organizational hierarchy, two types of tactics have emerged. One type depends upon the co-operation of a second party, whereas the other type may be implemented by the would-be influencer alone. Examples of the first type include resorting to disguised flattery and exerting influence through a significant other. Examples of the second type include creating an illusion of influence and biasing the information on which the administrator is apt to base his actions.

Creating an illusion of influence. In one sense, the image of administrative man as a leader provides a potential Achilles' heel for the unwary administrator. As we mentioned earlier in this section, the administrator encounters an idealized conception of his role in the literature which he reads during his preparatory program. This conception is apt to be reinforced by his employer when the administrator assumes his first managerial position. As a consequence, the administrator who believes that he is acting as a leader should derive a strong feeling of satisfaction and a sense of accomplishment. A resourceful person may take advantage of this situation in ways limited only by the extent of his own imagination. Regardless of the method selected to achieve his goal, the person has but one major intent. He is striving to develop a definition of the situation in which the administrator sees himself as trying to persuade or to influence the individual to behave in a particular way. The social reality of the situation, however, is that the individual is both willing and able to act in this fashion but has led the administrator to believe otherwise. The administrator perceives that he has succeeded in influencing the person, and experiences satisfaction from performing this leadership act. One party has been influenced—but the influencee is the administrator, not the other person as the administrator believes.

A classic illustration of this form of influence was discovered in a manual which had been prepared by a creative group of high school students intent on helping their peers to succeed in their academic work. The students were advised to perform poorly on the first examination or two in the class and to seek help and guidance from the teacher. As the teacher provided this assistance, the students were advised to show gradual but steady improvement on subsequent tests and to express their appreciation to the teacher for having helped them to increase their understanding of the course content. Through this technique, the teacher, according to the students, would come to regard herself as the principal cause for the students' improvement, feel good about having reached the students, and reward the students with a higher mark than they might have attained otherwise. (Students reported using this tactic with highly satisfactory results.)

Biasing the information on which the administrator is apt to base his actions. Because other people are often the source of information on which administrators in large part base their decisions, these people have ample opportunity to influence these decisions without the administrator's knowledge. Subordinates, for example, employ a variety of techniques to influence the decisions of their superior as they perform their relay function in the organization's communication network. The tactics that we have identified have one aspect in common. The information that is presented contains no recommendations or advice; the burden of inference is placed on the administrator. The situation is arranged, however, so that the latter arrives at conclusions which are favored by or are favorable to subordinates. Such slanting occurs when the subordinates plant clues which, if detected by the administrator, lead him to expect certain positive outcomes from one course of action and certain negative consequences from other alternatives. Subordinates also affect their superior's decisions by supplying information which points to one particular definition of the problem. By biasing the information to suggest that the cause of the difficulty lies one place rather than another, the subordinate increases the probability that the administrator will restrict the alternatives he considers to those aspects of the situation which the subordinate wants handled. Subordinates also strive to influence administrative decisions by staging their presentation. The subordinate reports in considerable detail how he went about gathering the information, the sources he tapped, the ingenuity he exercised in obtaining the information from unco-operative sources, and the data he has assembled. The subordinate not only slants the information on which the decision is to be made, but seeks to heighten the credibility of the evidence by dramatizing the care and thought which "obviously" went into it.

Exerting influence through a significant other. When people believe that they have a greater likelihood of influencing the administrator's decisions by persuading a second party to initiate the influence attempt, there are at least two basic types of significant others from whom willful or unwitting co-operation is sought. These two types are differentiated by the nature of the party's affiliation with the organization. One member type is the confidant of the administrator (such as his secretary) who functions as an adviser, a sounding board, and a wailing wall. A second member type is one who occupies a position bearing more formal authority than the administrator who is the primary target of influence. Two nonmember types used by individuals, especially subordinates, in an attempt to sway the administrator are clients and the organization's public-in-contact or some segment of it. Accessibility and ease of eliciting co-operation are major determinants of which type people will choose to use. Regardless of the type selected, people hope that the administrator will believe that the source of influence is the significant other and not themselves. So long as this fiction is maintained, the legitimacy of the influence attempt never becomes a salient issue.

Resorting to disguised flattery. A subordinate may wish to obtain preferential treatment from his superior and to enhance his own potential for advancement within the organization. One way subordinates endeavor to accomplish this is to make themselves more personally attractive to their chief administrator through the use of compliments. However, since the administrator controls resources important to subordinates, he expects to be the target of ingratiation attempts[22]; consequently, he is suspicious of compliments from his subordinates. Under these conditions, the major task confronting the subordinate is to create the impression that the compliments are "honest" ones. In order to increase the chances that the compliments will be taken at face value, the subordinate enlists the co-operation of an individual who has no apparent reason to make the compliment. This individual then communicates to the administrator a prearranged compliment, and attributes the opinion to the administrator's subordinate. For example, a teacher subordinate may have a friend who works in another school within the district and whose civic responsibilities bring him into occasional contact with the teacher's building principal. The friend is prompted to ask the principal, when the opportunity arises, if he anticipates a vacancy in the near future. When, as expected, the principal proves curious and seeks a reason for the inquiry, the friend is to respond "spontaneously" that he has heard so many fine comments from Teacher X about the way the school was being run that he was considering a possible transfer. Credibility of the compliment is increased on several grounds—its apparent spontaneity, its source, and its subtle nature.

SUMMARY

In this chapter we have tried to present a balanced view of administrative behavior which is congruent with the realities of organizational life. We have noted that the educational administrator is both

[22] See Edward E. Jones and Keith E. Davis, "From Acts to Dispositions." In Leonard Berkowitz, ed., *Advances in Experimental Social Psychology,* (New York: Academic Press, 1965), Vol. 2, pp. 220–266.

an initiator and a recipient of action. As the initiator of action, the administrator (if he is to be considered a leader) must have a sense of organizational mission and be able to elicit the requisite energies and commitments of others in service of the organization and its mission. Our discussion of administrative man as the initiator of action centered on eight modes of influence which the administrator might use to elicit the desired contributions from others and the conditions under which each mode was likely to be most effective. In dealing with the administrator as the recipient of action, we stressed three sets of conditions under which the administrator is guided, shaped, and influenced by others. We noted that the administrator can be a recipient of action by choice, against his will, and without his knowledge.

In one sense, however, the discusson was imbalanced. We emphasized the ways in which the administrator influences others in service of organizational goals and the ways in which organization members seek to influence the administrator in an effort to achieve their own individual goals. We recognize also that the administrator may attempt to influence others in order to achieve his own goals and that that organization may attempt to influence the administrator in ways which are consistent with organizational purposes. Only as more research is done which takes these various possibilities into account will we be able to present a description of administrative behavior that is even more congruent with the realities of organizations in action.

SUGGESTED ACTIVITIES

1. Interview a number of principals and superintendents to determine the ways in which they try to influence members of their staffs. Focus your discussion with these administrators on concrete examples, and seek to identify what conditions prompted the administrator to use one particular influence mode in preference to another. How do these influence modes and conditions correspond to the discussion in this chapter?

2. Observe several administrators at work. Does their behavior appear to be more usefully understood in terms of the administrator as an initiator of action or as a recipient of action? Support your conclusion.

3. Talk with several teachers and try to discover the ways in which they attempt to influence the administrators with whom they work. See if you can determine why the teachers choose to use one tactic

rather than another. What insights does this information provide you into understanding administrative behavior?

SELECTED READINGS

BRIDGES, EDWIN M. "Instructional Leadership: A Concept Re-examined," *The Journal of Educational Administration,* **V,** 2 (October, 1967), 136–147.

CARTWRIGHT, DORWIN. "Influence, Leadership, Control." In James G. March, ed., *Handbook of Organizations.* (Chicago: Rand McNally, 1965), pp. 1–47.

FIEDLER, FRED E. *A Theory of Leadership Effectiveness.* (New York: McGraw Hill, 1967).

GIBB, CECIL A. "Leadership." In Gardner Lindzey and Elliott Aronson, eds., *The Handbook of Social Psychology* (Reading, Mass.: Addison-Wesley, 1969), Vol. 4, pp. 205–282.

GROSS, NEAL, and HERRIOTT, ROBERT E. *Staff Leadership in Public Schools: A Sociological Inquiry.* (New York: Wiley, 1965).

HALPIN, ANDREW W. *Theory and Research in Administration.* (New York: The Macmillan Co., 1966).

KATZ, DANIEL, and KAHN, ROBERT L. *The Social Psychology of Organizations.* (New York: Wiley, 1966).

LEVINSON, HARRY. *The Exceptional Executive: A Psychological Conception.* (Cambridge, Mass.: Harvard University Press, 1968).

National Society for the Study of Education. *Behavioral Science and Educational Administration.* (Chicago: Sixty-Third Yearbook, Part II, The Society, 1964).

STOGDILL, R. M. "Personal Factors Associated with Leadership: A Survey of the Literature," *Journal of Psychology,* **25** (January, 1948), 35–71.

ZALEZNIK, ABRAHAM. *Human Dilemmas of Leadership.* (New York: Harper & Row, 1966).

8

The School
As
A Social System

We have viewed administration from the standpoint of its purpose, its tasks, its process, and in terms of administrative behavior. We shall now look at administration in the setting of the school as a social system. This is perhaps our most theoretically oriented approach to administration. We shall present the theoretical framework of administration as a social process, examine some of the studies which such a framework has generated, note the limitations and extensions of this formulation, and then suggest some implications for practice growing out of such an approach.

THE CONCEPTUAL WORK

The formulation of the concept of administration as a social process was essentially the work of Getzels and Guba.[1] Our description of this concept follows closely part of a paper given by Getzels at a seminar on administrative theory sponsored by the University Council for Educational Administration and the Midwest Administration Center.[2] The theory has been extended and amplified in a more recent publication.[3]

To comprehend the model described in the next few pages requires

[1] Jacob W. Getzels and Egon G. Guba, "Social Behavior and the Administrative Process," *School Review*, 65 (Winter, 1957), pp. 423–441.

[2] Jacob W. Getzels, "Administration as a Social Process." In A. W. Halpin, ed., *Administrative Theory in Education* (Chicago: Midwest Administration Center, University of Chicago, 1958), pp. 150–165.

[3] Jacob W. Getzels, James M. Lipham, and Roald F. Campbell, *Educational Administration as a Social Process* (New York: Harper & Row, 1968).

236

some knowledge of concepts found in sociology and psychology. For many students, however, careful reading of these pages and some of the material mentioned in the footnotes will be found rewarding.

Getzels suggests that administration may be conceived structurally as the hierarchy of subordinate-superordinate relationships within a social system. Functionally, this hierarchy of relationships is the locus for allocating and integrating roles and facilities in order to achieve the goals of the social system. It is in these relationships that the assignment of positions, the provision of facilities, the organization of procedures, the regulation of activity, and the evaluation of performance take place.

While the functions named above are the responsibility of the superordinate member of the hierarchy, each function becomes effective only as it "takes" with the subordinate members. This interpersonal or social relationship is the crucial factor in administration as a social process.

The model or concept begins with a consideration of the most general context of interpersonal or social behavior, i.e., a given social system. The term "social system" is of course conceptual rather than descriptive and must not be confused with society or state, or thought of as applicable only to large aggregates of human interaction. Within this framework, for one purpose, a community may be considered a social system, with the school a particular organization within the more general social system. For another purpose, the school itself or even a single class within the school may be considered a social system in its own right. The model proposed here is applicable regardless of the level or size of the unit under consideration.

The social system is conceived as involving two classes of phenomena that may be thought of as independent but, in an actual situation, are interactive. There are, first, the institutions characterized by certain roles and expectations in keeping with the goals of the system. And there are, second, the individuals with certain personalities and dispositions inhabiting the system. The social behavior found in this system may be understood as a function of two major elements: institution, role, and expectation, which together constitute the nomothetic or *normative* dimension of activity in a social system; and individual, personality, and need-disposition, which together constitute the idiographic or *personal* dimension of activity in a social system.

THE NORMATIVE DIMENSION

To understand the nature of observed behavior—and to be able to predict and control it—the nature and relationships of these elements must be understood. Certain key terms need further elaboration.

The term "institution" has received a variety of definitions which cannot be reviewed here. It is sufficient to point out that all social systems have certain imperative functions that come in time to be carried out in certain routinized ways. These functions—such as governing, educating, policing within the state—may be said to have become "institutionalized," and the agencies established to carry out these institutionalized functions for the social system as a whole may be termed "institutions." Thus, the school is the institution devoted to educating.

An important part of the institution is the role. Roles are, to use Linton's terminology, the "dynamic aspects" of the positions, offices, and statuses within an institution, and they define the behavior of the role incumbents or actors.[4] In the school these incumbents are superintendents, principals, teachers, and other workers.

Roles are defined in terms of role expectations. A role has certain obligations and responsibilities, which may be termed "role expectations," and when the role incumbent puts these obligations and responsibilities into effect, he is said to be performing his role. For instance, the role expectations for the third grade teacher, the guidance counselor, and the principal are quite different. The expectations define for the actor, whoever he may be, what he should or should not do as long as he is the incumbent of the particular role.

Roles are complementary—interdependent in that each role derives its meaning from other related roles in the organization. In a sense, a role is a prescription not only for the given role incumbent but also for the incumbents of other roles within the organization, so that in a hierarchical setting the expectations of one role may to some extent also form the sanctions for a second interlocking role. Thus, for example, the role of sergeant and the role of private in the army, or of principal and teacher in a school, cannot really be defined or implemented except in relation to each other. It is this quality of complementarity which fuses two or more roles into a coherent,

---

[4] Ralph Linton, *The Study of Man* (New York: Appleton-Century-Crofts, 1936), p. 14.

interactive unit and which makes it possible for us to conceive of an organization as having a characteristic structure.

The elements constituting the nomothetic or normative aspects of social behavior have been examined. At this level of analysis, it was sufficient to conceive of the role incumbents as "actors," devoid of personalistic or other individualizing characteristics—as if all incumbents were exactly alike and as if they implemented a given role in exactly the same way. This permits certain gross understandings and prediction of behavior in an organization. For example, if the roles in a given educational institution are known, some rather accurate predictions of what the people in these organizations do without ever observing the actual people involved can be made.

THE PERSONAL DIMENSION

But roles are of course occupied by real individuals, and no two individuals are alike. Each individual stamps the particular role he occupies with the unique style of his own characteristic pattern of behavior. Even in the case of the relatively inflexible roles of sergeant and private, no two individual sergeants and no two individual privates fulfill their roles in exactly the same way. To understand the observed behavior of specific sergeants and specific privates, it is not enough to know the nature of the roles and expectations—although, to be sure, their behavior cannot be understood apart from these— but the nature of the individuals inhabiting the roles and reacting to the expectations must also be known. That is, in addition to the nomothetic or normative aspects, the idiographic or personal aspects of social behavior must also be considered. Both the sociological level of analysis and the psychological level of analysis must be included.

Just as it was possible to analyze the normative dimension into the component elements of role and expectation, so it is possible, in a parallel manner, to analyze the individual dimension into the component elements of personality and need-disposition. We may turn to a brief consideration of these two terms.

The concept "personality," like that of role or institution, has been given a variety of meanings. Personality is defined by Getzels as the dynamic organization within the individual of those need-dispositions that govern his unique reactions to the environment. The central analytic elements of personality are the need-dispositions, which we can define with Parsons and Shils as "individual tendencies to orient and act with respect to objects in certain manners and to expect certain consequences from these actions."[5]

Returning to the example of the sergeant and the private, an essential distinction can now be made between two sergeants, one of whom has a high need-disposition for "submission" and the other a high need disposition for "ascendance," and a similar distinction between two privates, one with a high need-disposition for "submission" and the other for "ascendance," in the fulfillment of their respective roles, and for the sergeant-private interaction. In short, to understand the behavior of specific role-incumbents in an institution, we must know both the role-expectations and the need-dispositions. Indeed, both needs and expectations may be thought of as motives for behavior, the one deriving from organizational obligations and requirements, the other from personalistic sets and propensities.

One troublesome facet of the model, to which insufficient attention has been given, is the problem of the dynamics of the interaction between these organizationally defined expectations and the personally determined needs. To put the problem concretely, one may ask: How is it, for example, that some sergeants and privates—or to generalize the case, some complementary role-incumbents—understand and agree at once on their mutual obligations and responsibilities, while others take a long time in reaching such agreement and quite frequently do not come to terms either with their roles or with each other?

The essential relevant concept Getzels proposes here is selective interpersonal perception; people see what their own backgrounds permit them to see. In a sense, the prescribed organizational or normative relationships of two complementary role-incumbents may be conceived as being very different. On the one hand, there is the prescribed relationship as perceived by the first organization member in terms of *his* needs, dispositions, and goals. On the other hand, there is the same prescribed relationship as perceived by the second organization member in terms of *his* needs, dispositions, and goals. These private perceptions are related through those aspects of public objects, symbols, values, and expectations which have to some extent a counterpart in the perceptions of both individuals.[6]

When it is said that two role-incumbents—for example, a subordi-

[5] Talcott Parsons and Edward A. Shils, *Toward A General Theory of Action* (Cambridge, Mass.: Harvard University Press, 1951), p. 114.

[6] Jacob W. Getzels, James M. Lipham, and Roald F. Campbell, *op. cit.,* pp. 86–89.

nate and a superordinate—understand each other, it means that their perceptions and their own organization of the prescribed complementary expectations are congruent; when it is said that they misunderstand each other, it means that their perceptions and their own organization of the prescribed complementary expectations are incongruent. The functioning of the social system depends not only on a clear statement of the public expectations, but on the degree of overlap in the perception and individual organization of the expectations by the specific role incumbents. As will be shown, the relevant research suggests that when participants evaluate an interaction, the congruence of the perception of expectations often takes priority over actual observed behavior or even accomplishment.

THE MODEL

By way of summarizing the argument so far, the general model is pictured in Figure 8.1.

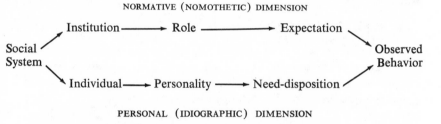

NORMATIVE (NOMOTHETIC) DIMENSION

PERSONAL (IDIOGRAPHIC) DIMENSION

Figure 8.1   General model showing the organizational and personal dimensions of social behavior (from Getzels and Guba)

The normative axis, shown at the top of the diagram, consists of institution, role, and expectation, each term being the analytic unit for the term preceding it. Thus the social system is defined by its institutions, each institution by its constituent roles, each role by the expectations attaching to it. Similarly, the personal axis is shown at the lower portion of the diagram and consists of individual, personality, and need-disposition, each term again serving as the analytic unit for the term preceding it.

A given act is conceived as deriving simultaneously from both the normative and personal dimensions. That is to say, social behavior results as the individual attempts to cope with an environment composed of patterns of expectations for his behavior in ways consistent with his own independent pattern of needs. Thus, one may say that behavior in an organization is a function of a given institutional role defined by the expectations attaching to it, and the personality of the particular role incumbent defined by his need-dispositions.

The proportion of role and personality factors determining behavior will of course vary with the specific act, the specific role, and the specific personality involved. The nature of the interaction can be understood from another graphic representation, as indicated in Figure 8.2.

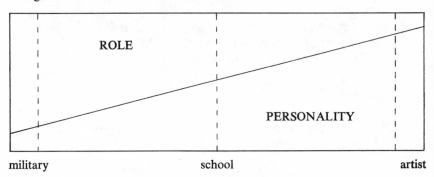

military   school   artist

Figure 8.2   The interplay between role and personality in a behavioral act (from Getzels and Guba)

A given behavioral act may be conceived as occurring at a position represented by the dotted line through the role and personality possibilities represented by the rectangle. At the left, the proportion of the act dictated by considerations of role-expectations is relatively large, while the proportion of the act dictated by considerations of personality is relatively small. At the right, the proportions are reversed, and considerations of personality become greater than those of role-expectation. In these terms one may, for example, have on the one hand the behavior of an army private conforming almost entirely to role demands and on the other the behavior of a freelance artist deriving almost entirely from personality dispositions. Most schools are probably somewhere between these extremes. In a given setting, administration always deals with proportions of both these components.

In any case, whether the proportion tends toward one end or the other, behavior insofar as it is social remains a function of both role and personality, although in different degree. When role is maximized, behavior still retains some personal aspect, because no role is ever so closely defined as to eliminate all individual latitude. When personality is maximized, social behavior still cannot be free from some role prescription. Indeed, the individual who divorces himself from such prescription is said to be autistic, and he ceases to communicate with his fellows.

Some critics of the social process model have maintained that it lacks a dynamic quality. Abbott[7] suggested some intervening variables between the normative and personal dimensions and some feedback mechanisms which may help answer this criticism. He summarizes his argument as follows:

> . . . a formal organization may be viewed as a specific social system in which role expectations become formalized and institutionalized. Such expectations constitute a codified behavior system, which is more or less explicit but which is generally understood by all employees. As specific individuals, with their own patterns of organizationally relevant needs, are socialized in respect to the organization's codified behavior system, they achieve a cognitive orientation to roles and they respond affectively to this orientation. Thus, behavior in a formal organization is conceived as deriving simultaneously from an individual's cognitive orientation to roles and his affective responses to roles.
>
> Both the cognitive orientation to roles and affective responses to roles are modified over time, largely as a function of the operation of two feedback mechanisms within the organization: the reward system and the reference-group norms. Feedback, in this sense, is a perceptual process in which the cognitive orientation is monitored in terms of its congruence with the "real" situation.[8]

The relevance of the general model for administrative theory and practice becomes apparent when it is seen that administration inevitably deals with fulfillment of both organizational and personal requirements within the context of a particular social system, and that these requirements may be modified over time.

SOME EMPIRICAL STUDIES

A theory, as we suggested in Chapter 4, should, among other things, generate hypotheses that can be tested. The theory described above has been the source of a number of hypotheses which have become the bases for empirical studies, some of which will now be reported. These reports should be read not only for their findings, but also to

---

[7] Max G. Abbott, "Intervening Variables in Variables in Organizational Behavior," *Educational Administration Quarterly*, 1 (Winter, 1965) pp. 1–14.

[8] *Ibid.*, pp. 12–13.

illustrate the way by which studies may be derived from a theoretical framework.

SELECTIVE PERCEPTION

One of the early studies dealt with selective interpersonal perception. To Ferneau the theory suggested that when two or more persons come in contact with each other over a sufficient length of time, each begins to have certain expectations as to how the other will act or behave.[9] He wished to examine the expectations of superintendents of schools and consultants from state departments of education as they worked together on curriculum problems.

He reasoned that expectations become generalized; for example, while the contact may have been with only two or three consultants, the school administrator begins to expect much the same behavior from all consultants. In turn, the consultant working with a few administrators begins to have certain expectations as to how all administrators will behave. Expectations on the part of either the administrator or the consultant are not completely rigid. There is what is termed a "range of permissiveness"; either may exhibit a variety of behavior within certain limits and still stay within the expectations of the other. However, when the actions of one fall outside this range, the other rejects such behavior. This situation results in a lack of rapport, in one or both becoming defensive or aggressive, or in some other attitude which makes their contacts useless.

Ferneau was able to describe three possible roles for consultants: the expert, the resource person, and the process person. He then developed a check list of sixty items which required respondents to choose for each item the preferred behavior of the consultant. One hundred thirty-two superintendents in the states of Kansas, Michigan, Nebraska, and Wisconsin who had recently used consultants from their respective state departments of education responded to the instrument. These same superintendents, in another study, had previously given an evaluaton of these consultant services. In these same states forty-three consultants who had given these services to the superintendents also completed the check list and evaluated the effectiveness of the services as they viewed them.

With these data available, it was possible to match the replies of

9 Elmer F. Ferneau, "Which Consultant?" *Administrator's Notebook,* 2, 8 (April 1954).

the consultants with those of the administrators whom they had attempted to help. It was possible also to determine the behavior the administrators had expected the consultants to exhibit and what the consultants had expected of the administrators. Then it was possible to compare the administrator's evaluations of the consultations in which both administrator and consultant behaved as the other expected him to behave and when the behavior of one differed from that which the other expected.

In responding to the various statements used in the questionnaire, the respondents rated each behavior on a six-point scale with regard to its appropriateness. When a consultant and an administrator disagreed by as much as an average of two points in evaluating each statement, nineteen out of twenty times the consultation in which they were involved was rated as of low value by one or both. This finding was tested in three ways; each test gave the same result. Consultants and administrators must perceive each other as functioning in the manner expected if the consultation is to be effective.

Within each of the four states included in the study there was much greater agreement between consultants and administrators as to the behavior that they expected of each other than there was among the consultants and administrators in the states as a group. For example, in one state both administrators and consultants ranked first among the four states in the number of times they expressed preference for behavior classified as the "expert" approach. In another state, both groups ranked last in the number of times they expressed such a preference.

This study seems to support the idea that expectations have more to do with the judged effectiveness of consultant services than the nature of the service itself. There is at least the suggestion that in any interaction between two people the congruence of expectation of behavior may be most important.

ROLE-PERSONALITY CONFLICT

One of the most definitive studies on the model was done by Merton Campbell, who examined the degree of self-role conflict (the amount of spread between the two dimensions of the model) existing among teachers and the relationships between such conflict and satisfaction, effectiveness, and confidence in leadership.[10] Included in the

---

[10] Merton V. Campbell, "Self-Role Conflict Among Teachers and Its Relationship to Satisfaction, Effectiveness, and Confidence in Leadership." (Unpublished doctoral dissertation, Dept. of Education, University of Chicago, 1958).

study were fifteen schools and 284 teachers. Appropriate instruments were developed to test the variables being studied.

Four of the hypotheses developed by Campbell were from the standpoint of an outside observer, as suggested by "A" in Figure 8.3.

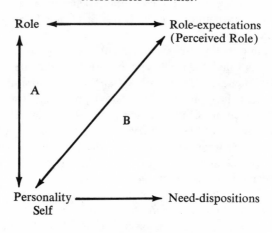

Figure 8.3   Partial social process model showing variables tested

It was hypothesized that teachers with a low degree of self-role conflict in the teaching situation will (1) rate themselves higher in teaching satisfaction, (2) rate themselves higher in teaching effectiveness, (3) be rated by the principal as more effective teachers, and (4) express greater confidence in the leadership of the principal than will those teachers with a high degree of conflict.

Hypotheses 1, 3, and 4 were confirmed. Teachers with a low degree of self-role conflict expressed greater satisfaction in teaching than did high-conflict teachers. Low-conflict teachers were rated as more effective by their principals than were high-conflict teachers. Low-conflict teachers expressed greater confidence in the leadership of their principal than did high-conflict teachers. Hypothesis 2 did not hold: low-conflict and high-conflict teachers were not diffentiated on the basis of their own ratings of effectiveness.

Another set of four hypotheses was developed from the standpoint of the teacher (the actor), suggested by B in Figure 8.3. It was hypothesized that teachers with a low degree of conflict between self and *perceived* role will (1) rate themselves higher in teaching satisfaction, (2) rate themselves higher in teaching effectiveness, (3) be rated by the principal as more effective teachers, and (4) express greater confidence in the leadership of the principal than will those teachers with a high degree of conflict.

Again, hypotheses 1, 3, and 4 held. With respect to the conflict between self and perceived role, the low-conflict teachers expressed greater satisfaction than high-conflict teachers. Principals rated the low-conflict teachers as more effective than the high-conflict teachers. Low-conflict teachers expressed greater confidence in the leadership of their principals than did high-conflict teachers. As before, however, low-conflict and high-conflict teachers did not differ significantly on the basis of their self-ratings of effectiveness.

These findings led the investigator to conclude:

> Teachers do differ from each other in respect to the degree of self-role conflict and the degree of conflict between self and perceived-role. It is possible to order the teachers on each of these two indexes. This tends to substantiate the theoretical framework of this study, that role and personality (self) are two important constructs to be considered when studying the administration of a social system such as the school. This study provides an empirical link with the conceptual creation of a social system, by using an on-going real life setting to test the theoretically contrived hypotheses.[11]

ROLE CONFLICT

Moyer[12] did a study of the principal's leadership role, the attitudes of teachers and principals toward the role, and the relationship between these attitudes and teacher satisfaction. His hypothesis was as follows: close correspondence between teachers' and principals' attitudes toward leadership will be associated with a high degree of teacher satisfaction.

Two styles of leadership—leader-centered and group-centered—were defined, and Q-sort statements were developed to permit teachers and principals to choose items which would describe their ideal principal. A rating scale for teacher satisfaction was also developed. These instruments were administered to the principals and teachers of seven schools—four elementary and three secondary. In the analysis,

---

[11] *Ibid.,* pp. 140–41.

[12] Donald C. Moyer, "Teachers' Attitudes Toward Leadership as They Relate to Teacher Satisfaction." (Unpublished doctoral dissertation, Department of Education, University of Chicago, 1954).

the responses from the principal and teachers of each school, from 12 to 15 in number, were treated separately.

Some of the major findings follow: (1) the closer the correspondence of attitudes and needs toward leadership within a teaching group (group solidarity), the higher the overall satisfaction of the teachers in the group; (2) the closer the members of a teaching group correspond in group-centered attitudes toward leadership, the higher the level of teacher satisfaction in the group; (3) the extent to which a principal defines his ideal principal as one who encourages teachers to be less dependent on him and more interdependent, the higher the overall satisfaction of the teachers in his group.

While Moyer may have been more preoccupied with teacher satisfaction than with role definition and role conflict, his findings do suggest the importance of role perception on the part of both teachers and principals. Moreover, conflict in how the principal's role is perceived does affect the satisfaction and presumably the productivity of members of the organization.

PERSONALITY CONFLICT

The third type of conflict suggested by the model lies within the idiographic or personal dimension. Getzels and Guba did some work at Maxwell Air Force Base in which this aspect of the theory, among other things, was tested.[13] The setting was Air University, an advanced training center for higher echelon officers in the Air Force. At the time the research was undertaken, the university consisted of what they called nine "courses" but which we may call "schools." The institution was staffed by officers, chiefly of field rank, and the study was initiated because of certain strains in the institution and dissatisfaction among the personnel. An analysis of the existing social system in the terms of the model revealed that each officer-instructor occupied two roles which were in fundamental conflict along a number of dimensions. On the one hand, there was the officer role with certain military expectations, and, on the other hand, the instructor role with certain opposing educational expectations. In addition to stimulating the overall study, the model suggested hypotheses for testing both role conflict and personality conflict.

[13] Jacob W. Getzels and Egon G. Guba, "Role, Role Conflict, and Effectiveness: An Empirical Study," *American Sociological Review,* XIX (April 1954), pp. 164–175; "Role Conflict and Personality," *Journal of Personality,* XXIV (September, 1955), pp. 74–85.

We shall report here only the part of the study relating to personality conflict. With respect to individual differences among the faculty in felt conflict, it was hypothesized that the intensity of such conflict would vary as a function of certain emotional characteristics. For example, officer-instructors who were "rigid," "defensive," "extrapunitive," and so on, would be more conflicting than other officer-instructors. Personality data were obtained by three standard instruments: the Guilford-Martin Inventory GAMIN and STDCR, the California E and F Scales, and the Rosenzweig Picture—Frustration Study.

To test the hypothesis having to do with differences in personality conflict among instructors, the quarter of officer-instructors scoring highest in felt conflict was compared with the quarter scoring lowest in felt conflict on each of the personality variables provided by the three experimental instruments. Significant differences were found on seven of the ten factors of the Guilford-Martin, on both the E and F sections of the California Scale, and on five of the six variables of the Rosenzweig; and in each case, the results were in the direction predicted by the model. For example, those high in felt conflict were found on the Guilford-Martin to have a greater "feeling of inferiority," to be more "nervous," "introverted," "depressive," and "cyclical in temperament"; on the California E-F Scale to be more "rigid" and "stereotyped"; and on the Rosenzweig to be more "extrapunitive" and "defensive."

LEADERSHIP STYLE

The model suggests that some leaders may be more nomothetic or normative in their behavior and some more idiographic or personal in their behavior. Moser was able to use these ideas and define three styles of leadership as follows[14]:

1. The nomothetic style is characterized by behavior which stresses goal accomplishment, rules and regulations, and centralized authority at the expense of the individual. Effectiveness is rated in terms of behavior toward accomplishing the school's objectives.

2. The idiographic style is characterized by behavior which stresses the individuality of people, minimum rules and regulations, decentralized authority, and highly individualistic relationships with subordinates. The primary objective is to keep subordinates happy and contented.

[14] Robert F. Moser, "The Leadership Patterns of School Superintendents and School Principals," *Administrator's Notebook,* **6,** 1 (September, 1957).

3. The transactional style is characterized by behavior which stresses goal accomplishment, but which also makes provision for individual need fulfillment. The transactional leader balances nomothetic and idiographic behavior and thus judiciously utilizes each style as the occasion demands.

Moser undertook to examine the relationships between the behavior of superintendents and principals in the performance of their different, yet complementary, roles. He also undertook to assess the relationship between the leader-follower leadership styles of superintendents and principals and their effectiveness ratings, confidence in leadership, and job satisfaction.

Twelve superintendents and twenty-four principals in twelve school systems participated as subjects in the study. The superintendents and principals answered interview questions designed to stimulate subjective responses concerning perceptions of their own and the others' leadership style, their major problems as leaders, and their relationships to each other. In addition, each participant responded to a series of instruments designed to permit analysis which would produce indices related to the following variables: leadership style, agreement or disagreement on role definition, ratings of effectiveness, confidence in leadership, and satisfaction.

In relating the perceived and professed leadership styles of principals and superintendents to the relationships that exist among them, Moser found the following points significant:

1. Superintendents express highest confidence in and give the highest effectiveness ratings to those principals whom they perceive as exhibiting transactional behavior. Superintendents express less confidence in and give the lowest effectiveness ratings to principals whom they perceive as exhibiting idiographic behavior.
2. Superintendents express the highest confidence in and give the highest effectiveness ratings to principals who profess to be nomothetic.
3. Superintendents who profess nomothetic behavior are given the highest effectiveness ratings by principals and enjoy the confidence of principals.
4. Superintendents expect principals to be transactional, with emphasis upon the nomothetic. Likewise, principals expect superintendents to be transactional-nomothetic. Principals want positive leadership from superintendents, and superintendents want principals who are positive leaders.
5. Principals tend to emphasize idiographic behavior in dealing with teachers and nomothetic behavior in their relations with the superintendent. This indicates that the principal is subjected to different

expectations from his superintendent than from his teachers and that the principal behaves differently with his superiors than with his subordinates.

6. The principal's rating of the superintendent's effectiveness is a function of the agreement between the superintendent and the principal on the expectations held for the principal role. On the other hand, the superintendent's rating of principal effectiveness depends upon the superintendent's and principal's agreement on the definition of both roles.

7. High mutual ratings of effectiveness and confidence by superintendents and principals are accompanied by similarities in leadership style, feelings of security, general satisfaction with the relationships, desire to consult with one another on important matters, and clear delineation of duties and authority of decision making.

This short review of some of the studies generated by the social-process model should demonstrate that the model has been useful in suggesting research. The findings of a single study, however, should be accepted with considerable caution. One should recognize that the population included, the nature of the instruments used, the limited variables being tested, and other factors will often limit the generalizations that may be drawn from a single study. We shall have more to say about the implications of these and related studies later.

LIMITATIONS AND EXTENSIONS OF THE THEORY

Initially, the social process view of administration appeared to be a most useful way of looking at the in-organization relationships of a school or school system. It seemed to serve less well as a way of viewing the out-organization relationships of a school or school system. As we shall show later, implications for personnel selection and supervision, for instance, were readily apparent. On the other hand, implications for the relationships between the school organization and the larger society of which the school is a part were not so readily apparent. The theory did little, for instance, to explain operating-levy elections in a community.

Every administrator is aware that he has many out-organization relationships as well as in-organization relationships. One of us participated in a study in which the interactions of four superintendents over an extended period of time were observed and described.[15] In

---

[15] Midwest Administration Center, "Observation of Administrator Behavior" (Chicago: The Center, University of Chicago, 1959), 188 pp.

this study 515 of the interactions of the four superintendents, observed a half-day each week over a six-month period, were with organizational members, but 256 of the interactions were with the board of education, community groups, and professional groups. Community groups included governmental agencies at local, state, and national levels, and nongovernmental organizations and individuals of many kinds. The reality of these out-organization relationships is illustrated in the following description of one incident from the study:

> The newspaper reporter pulled a chair up to the front of the superintendent's desk, moved the name plate and calendar to one side, and started taking notes. After several questions the reporter said, "Now about that budget hearing this week, I think I ought to tell you that the industrial group is going to be down at County Seat to fight the budget you have proposed, along with the Tax Committee of the industrial group, though I don't know why."
>
> The superintendent replied, "Well, I'm a little surprised at that, as I thought they were on our side."
>
> The reporter then asked who all would represent the schools at the hearing, and he added, "I suspect it will be a knock-down, drag-out affair."
>
> The superintendent told him that the director of finance, the attorney, the principals, the PTA president, the representatives of the teachers' union, the representatives of the labor organization in industry, the voters' organizations, the legal organizations, and certain civic groups would represent the schools. In addition, he said, "It may be that the president of one of the big industries will be there, also, to say that they do not go along with the members of the opposition group." Then the superintendent laughed and said, "Now don't go list all of this, or you will really stir up the opposition." The reporter added that he would not, but he said, "We'll have someone down covering the hearing by telephone, and I'll be writing the story at the *Herald,* so all of this background helps. Hell, I wouldn't have told you about who was planning to oppose this unless I had a little judgment, although this bit about their industry people jumping the traces is really 'hot' and would break the opposition right into two camps."
>
> "That's exactly what we hope to do," replied the superintendent.
>
> "That's fine for now; we'll see you tonight at the meeting," the reporter concluded.[16]

Getzels and Thelen, recognizing the limitations of the initial social process model, developed a new dimension designed to picture more

[16] *Ibid.,* p. 85.

adequately the reality of the school in the larger society.[17] Just as one is able to think of organizations in sociological terms, one may also think of them in cultural terms, for the organization is embedded in a culture with certain mores and values. The expectations of the roles must in some way be related to the ethos or cultural values. This relationship, however, is by no means clear. Parsons and Shils, for example, view cultural elements as a highly complex constellation of elements that tend to become organized into systems.[18] Yet this system is not viewed as a motivated system, but as patterned symbols and value-orientations which may become embodied either in institutionalized role-expectations or in the superego structure of the personality.

Perhaps just as one can analyze the sociological dimension utilizing the central analytic elements of role-expectations, one can also focus on values as analytic elements of the cultural or anthropological dimension. The term value, like that of role, has been used in many different ways and in many different contexts.

An entirely new concept of values was suggested by Spindler when he said, "Conflicts between groups centering on issues of educational relevance, and confusions within the rank and file of educators, can be understood best, I believe, in the perspective of the transformation of American culture that proceeds without regard for personal fortune or institutional survival."[19] Spindler defines values as objects of possession, conditions of existence, personality or characterological features, and states of mind that are conceived as desirable and act as motivating determinants of behavior. He has characterized values as traditional or emergent.

The rationale of Spindler has been elaborated by Getzels to distinguish between *sacred* and *secular* values.[20] The sacred values— which we all tend to accept—were seen as democracy, individualism, equality, and human perfectability. The traditional secular values— the operating, down-to-earth beliefs—were seen as the work-success ethic, future-time orientation, independence or the autonomous self, and puritan morality. Getzels suggested that the sacred values have

[17] Jacob W. Getzels and Herbert A. Thelen, "The Classroom Group as a Unique Social System." In National Society for the Study of Education, *The Dynamics of Instructional Groups* (Chicago: The University of Chicago Press, 1960), Chap. 4.

[18] Parsons and Shils, *op. cit.*, p. 21.

[19] George Spindler, "Education in a Transforming American Culture," *Harvard Educational Review*, **XXV**, 3 (Summer, 1955), p. 156.

[20] Jacob W. Getzels, "Changing Values Challenge the Schools," *The School Review*, **LXV** (Spring, 1957), 92–102.

remained stable, but that the secular values are liable to the strains and cleavages of regionalism, rural-urban differences, social class, and social change. Encroaching upon the traditional secular values are the emergent values of sociability, conformity, relativism and present-time orientation.

In analyzing the relationship between the anthropological and the sociological dimensions, one must recognize that the two dimensions are not necessarily parallel to each other. However, the relationship may be represented schematically according to the diagram shown in Figure 8.4.

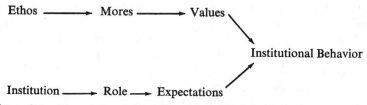

Figure 8.4   The relationship of the anthropological and social dimensions of social behavior (from Getzels and Thelen)

The model with three rather than two dimensions is shown in Figure 8.5.

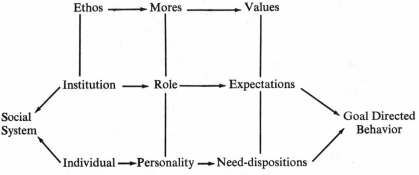

Figure 8.5   Extended model showing a third or cultural dimension of social behavior (from Getzels and Thelen)

This model permits one to posit some relationships between cultural values and institutional expectations, a possibility which stimulated Abbott to undertake a study of the influence of values upon the superintendent—school board relationships.[21] The central thesis of

[21] Max G. Abbott, "Values and Value-Perceptions in Superintendent-School Board Relationships," *Administrator's Notebook*, **9**, 4 (December, 1960).

the investigation was that difficulties in interpersonal relationships may be expected to arise, not so much from complexities and differences in values that are in the open and understood, as from complexities and differences that are underground and misunderstood.

Two hypotheses were formulated, based on prior theoretical and empirical work in the general area of values: first, an individual's own values were expected to influence his perceptions of the values held by others; second, both an individual's values and his value-perceptions were expected to influence his relationships with others. The following questions provided the focus for the investigation:

1. What is the relationship between superintendents' value-orientations and their perceptions of the values held by individual board members? Conversely, what is the relationship between board members' perceptions of superintendents' values and their own value-orientations?

2. What is the relationship between the confidence that board members evince in their superintendents' leadership and (a) congruence in value-orientations, (b) accuracy of perception of value-orientations, and (c) perceived similarity in value-orientations?

A values inventory was used to obtain from board members and superintendents responses to a series of items that represented a traditional—emergent value dichotomy. From the responses that were obtained, both self-scores of respondents and their perceptual scores of others were derived. A confidence-in-leadership scale was used to ascertain board members' confidence in their superintendents.

Thirty-seven superintendents and 213 board members from 27 elementary districts, 5 high school districts, and 8 unit districts, all located in the Midwest, made up the sample.

Interpersonal relationships were indeed influenced by the values people held and by the way in which those values were perceived. An individual's own values had an important influence upon his perceptions of the values held by others. Persons who held emergent values tended to view others as being emergent, while those who held traditional values tended to view others as being traditional. Moreover, these patterns of perception were unrelated to the actual values of those whose values were being perceived.

The values held by individuals had an important influence upon kinds of perceptual errors made. When the values of the perceiver and the perceived were similar, errors tended to be random. When the values of the perceiver and the perceived were dissimilar, errors followed a systematic pattern and tended to move in the direction of the perceiver's own value position with a frequency that was significantly greater than would have been expected to occur by chance.

The hypothesis concerning the relationship between confidence-in-leadership and agreement on values was substantiated. Board members whose values were most similar to those of their superintendents expressed slightly higher confidence to those superintendents than did board members whose values were least similar.

There was a relationship also between confidence-in-leadership and the accurate perception of values. Board members who were most accurate in perceiving their superintendents' values expressed significantly higher confidence in their superintendents than did board members who were least accurate.

A strong relationship was found between confidence-in-leadership and perceived similarity in values. Board members who perceived their superintendents to be most similar to themselves in values, regardless of actual similarity, expressed significantly higher confidence in their superintendents than did board members who perceived their superintendents to be least similar to themselves.

In general, it may be said that confidence was related positively to the accuracy with which board members understood their superintendents' value positions. Confidence was also related positively to the extent that board members assumed that they themselves were in agreement with their superintendents on basic issues. Whether or not this presumed agreement actually existed appeared to be relatively unimportant.

The concept of selective interpersonal perception is, therefore, important in understanding administrative relationships. In a sense, each person may be said to function in a world of his own making. His attitudes and values serve as a perceptual screen; he interprets his environment according to the way he perceives it; and he reacts to that environment in accordance with his interpretations. Thus, in analyzing the superintendent-school board relationship, it is not sufficient merely to determine whether or not superintendents and board members are in agreement on basic issues. It is necessary also to know how each member of the relationship perceives the positions of other members, since it is these perceptions which influence largely the action that will be taken. The findings of this investigation suggest that harmonious interpersonal relationships can be maintained despite differences in basic value positions, provided the differences are assessed accurately.

The extension of the social process model is dealt with more fully in recent work by Getzels and others.[22] This extension illustrates another characteristic of theory: it has within it the seeds of its own destruction and reconstitution. In other words, if the theory does not depict reality accurately, the testing of the hypotheses generated by the theory will reveal the shortage and will call for revision of the original formulation. With its new dimension the social process model describes a larger segment of administrative behavior—whether large enough remains to be seen.

IMPLICATIONS FOR PRACTICE

A theory of administration should suggest implications for practice as surely as it does hypotheses for research. Let us see if the social-process theory can meet such a demand.

IN-ORGANIZATION MEDIATOR

Within the organization it seems clear that the theory we have been discussing makes the administrator a mediator between the normative and the personal dimensions. At one point as organizational spokesman he will find it essential to explain, to reinforce, to emphasize the school's objectives and procedures. At another point he will find it desirable to listen to members of the organization, to ascertain their feelings about certain school practices, and to diagnose as best he can why they take the positions they do. When and under what circumstances he does either is part of the art of administration. Clearly, there are no recipes as to when the administrator behaves normatively or personally, but his judgment regarding such matters may be sharpened if he knows that both kinds of behavior are appropriate for the administrator. Some examples may help clarify this point.

The capacity of the administrator to be aware of both normative and personal roles is illustrated in the employment of personnel. Such a process is critical both for the school and the person, and thus the interests of both should be thoroughly explored in the employment process. The administrator should do his best to make clear the goals, program, and characteristics of the school and the expectations held

---

[22] Jacob W. Getzels, James M. Lipham, and Roald F. Campbell, *op. cit.*, pp. 89–102.

for the prospective staff member. At the same time, every effort should be made to understand the aspirations, the values, the motivations, and the strengths of the person being considered. Such a process can do much to insure some congruence between organizational expectations and personal dispositions should the candidate become a staff member, a condition necessary for best school operation.

A similar demand pertains in terms of the assignment of personnel. If the administrator emphasizes only his normative role, he will tend to look upon staff members as cogs in the organizational machine, each somewhat alike and replaceable by the other. On the other hand, if the administrator becomes completely personal he will strive to make assignments conform to individual whim with little or no regard for the total program of the organization. Clearly, neither extreme is acceptable; few administrators act completely one way or the other. It may help, however, to recognize that at times even unpopular assignments have to be made if the total program is to be served. At the same time, it should be clear that people tend to be more productive if at least part of the time they are doing those things they enjoy and for which they have competence.

Perhaps in the supervision of personnel the two dimensions of the model are even more suggestive. The aim of supervision is the improved performance of personnel, which in a school system means enhancement of the teaching-learning process. Both in the diagnosis of any difficulties a teacher may be having and in developing ways for overcoming such difficulties, the two dimensions of the model seem pertinent. The difficulty may lie, for instance, in a misunderstanding of what the school expects, or it may lie in unrealistic aspirations on the part of a teacher. Such diagnosis suggests the remedial measures: clarification of school goals in one instance, and modification of individual standards in the other.

Guba has extended the model by way of suggesting the actuating force or power of an administrator in an organization. His concept is shown in Figure 8.6. The administrator is seen as having two kinds of power: status and authority, which reside at the role or normative dimension; and prestige and influence, which reside at the person or idiographic dimension. The first kind of power resides in the office and is vested in the administrator. The second kind of power must be earned and is entrusted to the administrator. Clearly, an effective administrator has and exercises both kinds of power.

Conflict between institutional expectations and personal dispositions are seen as alienating forces in an organization. For instance, a

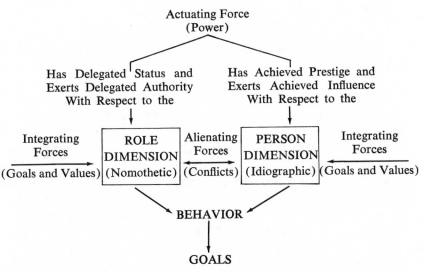

Figure 8.6   The power relationships of the administrator[23]

school may establish ability groups in mathematics or English. Some of these groups will be composed of slow learners but, even so, they must have teachers. If assigned to teach one of these groups, a teacher who has no patience with slow learners will probably resent the task and may actually sabotage the program. In any case, the lack of congruence between institutional expectations and personal dispositions is clear.

The alienating force of this conflict may be reduced by employing goals and values as integrating forces. Thus, in our illustration the forming of ability groups may be seen as one way of differentiating instruction for pupils who have a wide range of capacity. Moreover, the desirability of giving even slow learners an opportunity to do their best may be seen as consonant with the values of schools within a democratic society. This kind of exploration may make teaching a group of slow learners more rational and possibly more palatable. If at the same time such an assignment can be coupled with teaching a fast-learning group, more in keeping with the personal dispositions of the teacher, the total assignment may become quite acceptable.

[23] Egon G. Guba, "Research in Internal Administration—Is It Relevant?" in R. F. Campbell and J. M. Lipham, eds., *Administrative Theory as a Guide to Action* (Chicago: Midwest Administration Center, University of Chicago, 1960), Chap. 7.

THE ADMINISTRATOR IN THE MIDDLE

Another implication of the model, particularly when the cultural dimension is included, places the administrator squarely in the middle of a number of reference groups. There is the community with its many publics, the board of education with some lay and some professional understandings and convictions, the school system itself with its own set of social arrangements, and the impingement of the larger world at both lay and professional levels. Within this welter of forces there are many conflicting expectations and demands.

Conflicts within some of the reference groups have been very well documented. Ordinarily, the people of a community are not of one mind. One public, for instance, may wish the school to provide a program of released time for religious education, while another public opposes any such idea. One public may advocate extensive provisions for vocational education, while another public would leave all such efforts to industry. One public may place great stress upon the intellectual purposes of the school, while another public would give almost equal emphasis to social purposes.[24] These conflicts may become so sharp that they furnish the battleground for conflicts between competing leadership groups in the community.

Within the school itself there may also be sharp conflicts. In a study of 77 school administrators and 1065 teachers, Seeman found that teachers differ appreciably in their expectations of administrators.[25] For instance, teachers were almost evenly divided on the question of whether or not a superintendent should invite teachers to his home for social occasions.

In many school systems a number of other conflicts may be observed. Elementary and secondary school teachers differ in their viewpoints on many questions. Elementary school principals are seldom accorded the same status as secondary school principals. Some secondary school teachers believe that the high school should be a selective institution, whereas others think it should serve all youth. Although some teachers want almost complete freedom in

[24] Lawrence W. Downey, *The Task of Public Education* (Chicago: Midwest Administration Center, University of Chicago, 1960).

[25] Melvin Seeman, "Role Conflict and Ambivalence in Leadership," *American Sociological Review,* 18 (August, 1953), pp. 373–380.

their work, others have great need for direction from administrative and supervisory personnel.

Boards of education ordinarily talk out their conflicts until they reach agreement, but this should not obscure the fact that board members too have different expectations of administrators. One board member may think that the superintendent should be a "strong" leader, while another may believe he should consult freely with his staff. Still another may value above all else careful financial management and be opposed to all expansions of program regardless of need. Or current issues, such as changes in attendance area boundaries to further integrate schools or shared time between public and nonpublic schools, may divide board members just as they do citizens at large.

Even the influences of the larger world upon the administration of a school district are not of one voice. School practices in other communities may be quite diverse. Programs at the state or federal level may actually seem unacceptable to the people of a local school district. Witness, for instance, state programs of school district reorganization which are seen as undue meddling with local operation. Or note the number of school districts that have difficulty with the implementation of some of the federal programs.

Alas, even the professional voices heard by the administrator are not in complete unity. The teachers may be urging that since he knows good school practice, he should proceed to institute it in his school district. Some of his colleagues, on the other hand, perhaps as a result of bitter experience, urge caution. He may find in his professional magazines descriptions of opposing school practices, each of which is reputed to be professionally sanctioned.

Each of the reference groups to which we have alluded—the community, the board of education, the school system itself, and the larger environment—may have in a particular school community some common expectations for school administrators, but within each group there appear to be many real or potential conflicts. The administrator must chart a program despite these conflicts.

Perhaps even more significant to school administration than the differences within the various reference groups, as noted above, are the differences among these groups. Halpin found, for instance, that school staff members and board members usually agreed within their respective groups in describing the leadership behavior of superintendents, but that the two groups did not agree with each other.[26] In

[26] Andrew W. Halpin, *The Leadership Behavior of School Superintendents,* 2nd ed. (Chicago: Midwest Administration Center, University of Chicago, 1959).

companion studies Buffington[27] and Medsker[28] attempted to identify the job of the elementary principal from the standpoint of the parents and teachers, respectively. In many respects the perceptions of these two groups were far apart. For example, the parents tended to see the principal's first duty as that of developing relationships with parents and other groups in the community. The teachers, on the other hand, perceived the principal's first duty as that of providing leadership for them.

In a sense these conflicting expectations among reference groups place the school administrator squarely in the middle. In order for the principal to meet the expectations of the parents, he may not be able to meet the expectations of the teachers, or vice versa. In like manner a superintendent may find his board of education holds one set of expectations for him, while his staff holds another. This is not merely a theoretical matter; it is one which has been documented time and again in practice. Consider the expectations each group holds for the superintendent on the question of salary negotiations. Or reflect upon the superintendent's dilemma when a board of education is anxious to improve the physical plant of the district and the teachers are in great need of an improved salary scale. Or think of the school administrator who gets caught in a school district reorganization hassle, with his local community resisting any change and the state department of education and other professionals urging a larger district and combination of high schools.

The dilemma of the administrator as the man in the middle is shown in Figure 8.7. Each major group holds expectations for the

Figure 8.7   The administrator and some of his major reference groups

[27] Reed L. Buffington, "The Job of the Elementary School Principal as Viewed by Parents," Stanford University *Dissertation Abstracts,* **14** (1954), pp. 943–944.

[28] Leland L. Medsker, "The Job of the Elementary Principal as Viewed by Teachers," Stanford University *Dissertation Abstracts,* **14** (1954), pp. 946–947.

administrator, and there is often conflict among these expectations. Within each of these groups there may also be conflict in terms of what is expected of the administrator. We might conclude, after noting the conflicting expectations facing administrators both within and among the various reference groups, that the only alternative is to do nothing. Actually, it is not that simple; to do nothing is in a sense a program and some groups will, after a time, object even to that program. The administrator is thus faced with the development of the best program that can be devised within the limits of the situation.

Despite the many limitations which characterize most situations, there is on most questions some flexibility, or an "area of tolerance." Although the board of education, for instance, may not believe in citizens' advisory committees in general, it may be willing to try out a citizens' advisory committee organized around a particular task, such as a bond campaign. Or teachers may be dead set against a merit factor in a salary schedule, but they may be willing that a program designed to evaluate teaching be developed for instructional improvement purposes only. It is within these areas of tolerance that a school administrator may be able to resolve at least some of the conflicts which seem to exist both within and among major reference groups.

The limits discussed above also suggest the real challenge to educational administration; most of the limits have a time dimension. A position taken by a community, a board, or a faculty today need not hold forever. We have only to look at a few of the positions taken by such groups a decade or two ago to find how true this is.

But the administrator cannot be content merely to wait in hopes that time will alter the situation. He needs some way of getting at the dynamics of the situation. The questions become: Under what circumstances do people have a chance of changing their minds? How and to what extent may I bring these circumstances about?

While the answers to these questions are by no means complete, one prerequisite to bringing some harmony out of disagreement seems to be face-to-face communication. School boards and faculties usually find more in common when they have many opportunities to talk together. In like manner teachers and parents find the grounds of agreement broader when they confer frequently with each other. The administrator can facilitate the kinds of communication alluded to above.

Another element in the process of change appears to be complete information. To be sure, some people are like the chap who said, "My mind is made up; don't confuse me with the facts," but most people are willing to give some attention to the facts that are relevant to a problem. Often these facts include a description of what is being done elsewhere. While this proves nothing, the example of others is a powerful argument to many people. Again an administrator can facilitate the processes of fact-gathering and presentation.

Complete integrity on the part of the administrator is also necessary if people are to be willing to make compromises or arrive at new positions. This situation may mean that no group comes to love the administrator, but all groups come to respect him. Seldom can the educational leader take a position completely to the liking of a particular reference group, but his reasons for not doing so should be clear, and he should be seen as serving a larger constituency. Difficult as this role may appear, it is only leadership of this kind which will help the school fill its unique place in our society.

In the great dilemma about which we have been speaking lies the real challenge to administrative leadership. If areas of tolerance are to be extended, if members of reference groups are to understand how the school must stand above the welfare of a particular group in order to serve all groups, if change is to be seen as a way of life, the leadership of the administrator must help all groups understand the viewpoints of other groups and the administrator's position as a competent adjudicator.

SUGGESTED ACTIVITIES

1. Describe the similarities and differences between the initial Getzels-Guba model and the major concept of Argyris or the two dimensions suggested by Cartwright and Zander.

2. Formulate a few simple questions pertaining to some issues affecting the public schools of your community, and use these questions to interview a number of citizens. Note the similarity and diversity of their opinions.

3. As one of your questions above, ask each citizen to name the three most influential people in the community. To what extent do you get a duplication of names? Determine to what extent incumbent school board members are numbered among the community leaders named by citizens.

4. Interview a number of teachers, a number of pupils, and a number of parents in a particular school or school system, and ask them what they consider the important duties of the school principal to be. Note similarities and differences in the responses.

SELECTED READINGS

ARGYRIS, CHRIS. *Integrating the Individual and the Organization.* (New York: Wiley, 1964).

CAMPBELL, ROALD F. and GREGG, RUSSELL T., eds. *Administrative Behavior in Education.* (New York: Harper & Brothers, 1957), Chap. 7.

CARTWRIGHT, DORWIN and ZANDER, ALVIN *Group Dynamics: Research and Theory.* 3rd ed. (New York: Harper & Row, 1968).

DOWNEY, LAWRENCE W. *The Task of Public Education.* (Chicago: Midwest Administration Center, University of Chicago, 1960).

GETZELS, J. W., LIPHAM, J. M., and CAMPBELL, R. F. *Educational Administration as a Social Process.* (New York: Harper & Row, 1968).

GROSS, NEAL, MASON, WARD S., and McEACHERN, ALEXANDER W. *Explorations in Role Analysis: Studies of the School Superintendent Role.* (New York: Wiley, 1958).

GUBA, EGON G. "Research in Internal Administration—What Do We Know?" In R. F. Campbell and J. M. Lipham, eds., *Administrative Theory as a Guide to Action.* (Chicago: Midwest Administration Center, University of Chicago, 1960), Chap. 7.

HALPIN, ANDREW W. *Theory and Research in Administration.* (New York: The Macmillan Co., 1966).

KATZ, DANIEL and KAHN, ROBERT L., *The Social Psychology of Organizations.* (New York: Wiley, 1966).

9

Roles Of School Personnel
In Administration

If, indeed, the school administrator is a leader among the various reference groups with which he works, and if the school operates as a social system in the manner previously described, many people participate in the educational enterprise, with the administrative head giving direction to and co-ordinating their involvement. This chapter deals with the implications of theory and experience for a co-operative working relationship among school employees. For the most part, this discussion will be confined to the internal operation of the school. We shall not attempt to give a comprehensive list here of all the duties of all school personnel. Rather, our purpose in this chapter is to highlight those roles of superintendents, members of the central office staff, principals, teachers, and other school employees which are synchronized to provide a co-ordinated organizational effort.

THE ROLE OF THE SUPERINTENDENT

The superintendent of schools accepts final responsibility for the operation of the schools. The accountability of the total staff to the public is usually marked by pressure upon the superintendent. While in many school systems the superintendent delegates authority and some degree of responsibility to assistant superintendents, business managers, directors, co-ordinators and supervisors, principals, teachers, and other personnel, he cannot delegate final accountability for the tasks which they perform. This dilemma in delegation may govern the degree of the superintendent's direct involvement in the activity assigned to other persons, and his understanding and perception of his and others' roles in the performances of administrative tasks. Delegation is also dependent upon the understanding which other staff members have of their roles, and their readiness to accept the roles.

266

We spoke previously of various leader behavior styles or patterns. These patterns are observable in the working relationships between the superintendent and his staff members. One superintendent may delegate so completely that he participates very little in the proposing, planning, conducting, and evaluating of programs. Another superintendent may work with members of his staff in such a way as to enhance the leadership performance of those individuals directly responsible to him. Still another superintendent might keep a tight rein on all activities conducted by his associates.

While, conceivably, in the variety of situations that exist, superintendents may operate successfully at any point within the range of practices just described, the latter practice of "being in on everything" becomes less and less tenable as the size of school districts becomes larger. One fact is clearly established: the course of action that the superintendent chooses to take must be generally acceptable to the board of education and to his staff. The wise superintendent makes clear his perception of his role and seeks general agreement from these two important reference groups to operate in accordance with this perception.

A GENERALIST

As the number of school districts is reduced and the size of many is increased, it seems reasonable to expect that the superintendent will, more and more, assume the role of a generalist rather than that of a specialist in a particular phase of school operation. That is, the trend is in the direction of establishing an administrative team, including a number of specialists whose work he must co-ordinate. It is the superintendent whose responsibility it is to view the entire enterprise in broad perspective.

Miller describes the superintendent as a perceptive generalist:

The perceptive generalist must know enough of the general field and enough of the nature and problems of the specialists so that he can communicate with them with understanding, comprehensible among the specialists as a collective group and meaningful between specialists and the general public. He will miss the detail of many of the specialties but he sees all of them in wider configuration than do the specialists.[1]

[1] Van Miller, "The Superintendent of Schools." In D. J. Leu and H. C. Rudman, eds., *Preparation Programs for School Administrators* (East Lansing, Mich.: Michigan State University, 1963), Chap. 5.

The superintendent's expertness lies in his conceptualization of the tasks to be performed, in his inventiveness and genius in organization, and in his ability to work with people. His is an overall or *general* perspective, which he utilizes in charting the course that the school is to take. Although his staff assists him in achieving this perspective, he must articulate it, and he must have the power to use it as a guide for action.

A Staff Leader

It is often said that the strength of a superintendent can be measured by the competence of his staff—a statement which does not mean that a strong staff has no need of a strong superintendent. We hope that we have made it clear that staff strength is dependent upon leadership strength. The leader and his staff are dependent upon one another; the strength of one enhances the strength of the other.

As a consequence of the acceptance of this point of view, much is done to build up staff strength. Assessment and appraisal are common activities used to find the most competent teachers. Recruitment, selection, and orientation of new teachers have taken on added importance as administrative functions in recent years. In-service education and individualized help in instruction have become increasingly important.

Griffiths and his co-authors describe the growing importance and complexity of the superintendent's staff leadership role as follows:

> The personnel function of the superintendent is assuming larger and larger proportions. Due to such factors as increased size of school districts, increased professional preparation of teachers, the teacher shortage, increases in salaries of professional educators, and the general change in employer-employee relationships in the country, the superintendent of today faces many more problems than did his predecessors. Some of these factors are of the superintendent's own making. He exercises no control, however, over most of the factors, but must cope with them nevertheless.[2]

Not only are the better superintendents of schools alert to the sources of competent personnel; they devise ways of improving the competence of the personnel already on the job. They find ways of

[2] Daniel E. Griffiths, *et al., Organizing Schools for Effective Education* (Danville, Ill.: Interstate Printers & Publishers, 1962), p. 165.

deploying the services of their staff members to accomplish the tasks of the school as effectively and efficiently as possible. If necessary, they separate the incompetents from the school system. The tasks involved in personnel deveolpment have become so important and so complicated that specialists in personnel and instruction have been employed with assignments in their particular fields.

A Symbol

In spite of much talk in our society about equalizing the status of the leader and the members of his group, it is still a fact that in schools the status of the superintendent permits him to establish, in marked degree, the behavior pattern of the staff. "Businesslike procedures," "good communication," "courage to act," "kindness with firmness," "vision and foresight," "a good organizer" are typical of terms used by staff members to denote the tone set by superintendents whom they respect. On the other hand, lack of respect for superintendents is shown by such terms as "careless business practices," "lack of integrity," "favoritism among staff members," "failure to communicate," "poor organization," and "lack of vision."

Reference has been made to the fact that students of leadership and of administrative behavior agree that staff morale is as much a function of staff accomplishment as of warm human relationships. Whether the superintendent wishes it or not, he becomes the symbol of his school; in turn, perhaps to a somewhat lesser degree, the school tends to be described in the same terms as those applied to the superintendent. Therefore, regardless of the number of helpers he has or their disposition toward the tasks to which they have been assigned, the superintendent is the head of the school system and cannot escape the role of setting the stage for staff participation.

The superintendent may also be a symbol in the eyes of the community. It has not been uncommon for groups of citizens who were unhappy about the schools to view the superintendent as the cause and, in a way, the symbol of all school problems and demand his ouster as a first step to school improvement. Conversely, a number of outstanding educators have achieved local and national prominence as the symbols of fine school systems. Much of the superintendent's image in the community depends upon the ways he interacts with the public. As in matters of staff participation, people look to the behavior of the superintendent as a model to follow in school-community relationships.

THE ROLES OF CENTRAL OFFICE PERSONNEL

With the growth in the size and complexity of school systems, we witness a corresponding growth in the number and complexity of the functions of the central administrative office. These new demands upon the central office have created a need for the development of new and more efficient ways of conceptualizing school district organization and structure. Systems analysis and research as it is applied to educational institutions seems to offer a powerful means by which educational leaders can analyze, and adapt to, the changing role which the central office must play.[3] Hencley uses a form of systems analysis when he writes:

> The need for developing goal-centered and implementation-centered policies, and the parallel need for integrating, formalizing, and unifying workflow patterns in organizations requires members of administrative performance systems to be sophisticated in various administrative processes. Functional order in organization, adjustments in organizational workflow patterns, and maintenance and improvement of the organizational environmental exchange system are achieved through administrative processes such as communication, decision-making, change, and morale maintenance. The need for competence in such processes is not restricted to intraorganizational settings. As figure 10 indicates, the ad-

Figure 10   The administrative performance system as an open system (from Leu and Rudman)[4]

---

[3] See D. E. Griffiths, "The Nature and Meaning of Theory." In National Society for the Study of Education *Behavioral Science and Educational Administration,* 63rd Yearbook, Part II (1964), pp. 116–118.

[4] S. P. Hencley, "Functional Interrelationships Within Administrative Performance Systems." In D. J. Leu and H. C. Rudman, eds., *Preparation Programs for School Administrators* (East Lansing, Mich.: Michigan State University, 1963), p. 82.

ministrative performance sy em is an open system which interacts and exchanges information with its environment. Thus sophistication in the use of administrative processes is necessary in several kinds of settings: intraorganizational, extraorganizational and interstitial.

. . . Perhaps the most important point b ught out by study of figure 10 is that all members of the administra ve performance system require some sophistication in the process are oi administration. However, the degree of sophistication required is determined by the level and function of the various positions and by the number, type, and complexity of social and organizational variables confronting administrators in these positions.[5]

While it is not our purpose here to elaborate on all of these functions and processes, we call attention to the fact that the growth of the central office staff of a school system comes about, in general, in response t' the need for greater specialization in various aspects of school administration, better co-ordination of the separate but related phases of the school program, and increased services to the several operating units of the systems. We shall discuss the roles of central office personnel in terms of these functions.

Specialization

The role of some persons on the central office staff is that of providing special expertness in certain phases of school operation. Assistant superintendents are examples of people who assume such a role. They may be placed in charge of instruction, staff personnel, pupil personnel, business or other functions. While each assistant superintendent is responsible to the superintendent, he has been employed because of his expertness in his particular field of specialization. The employment of an assistant superintendent of schools is based upon the assumption that his special expertness will be directed to that limited sphere of school operation designated by his assignment.

Other specialists are often needed in the school. They may have various titles depending upon where they work and the manner in which their specialty is used. The title of administrative assistant or assistant to another administrator connotes a *staff* rather than a *line* responsibility. *Staff* personnel carry out specific assignments for their superior officer, while *line* officers direct the work of a number of

[5] *Ibid.*, p. 89.

other people. The superintendent may employ a *general* administrative assistant who performs a variety of tasks assigned to him. In contrast to this, a research assistant or an assistant in communications may have a *specific* function.

Specialists may be assigned to work at almost any level of the administrative hierarchy and with either staff or line responsibilities. To bring special expertness to the instructional program, for example, an assistant superintendent in this area may decide that he needs *directors* of elementary and secondary education, each of whom can center attention upon that part of the program for which he is responsible. In turn, the director of elementary education may assign a specialist in reading to serve as a supervisor, consultant, advisor, or teacher helper in the several elementary schools of the system.

Griffiths has made an interesting distinction between various kinds of staff officers. He writes that:

> Staff officers may be classified as either coordinative or advisory. Coordinative staff officers assist the chief administrator in the discharge of many detailed functions of his position and aid him in the general coordination of school affairs. Any authority they may exercise is derived from the chief school administrator and exercised in a specific situation. For example, staff officers are not assigned authority to handle an area of school operation or given responsibility for that area. This type of staff officer must, however, be a generalist skilled in working with people.
>
> . . . .
>
> Advisory staff officers are specialists who supply expert assistance upon request. They have no authority except that which comes from their specialized knowledge in an area. An example of such a position in the public schools would be the subject-matter consultant or helping teacher. On a higher authority level, an assistant superintendent for business affairs or instruction might be placed in such a position. He would have hierarchical authority over those persons connected directly with his central office staff, but none over building principals or teachers.[6]

There is a growing trend in larger school systems toward a decentralized organizational structure. Decentralization in a school system requires, in most cases, the assumption of greater line authority by building heads, or principals, or area administrators, and the increased specialization of staff personnel at the central office. Under

---

[6] Daniel E. Griffiths, *et al., Organizing Schools for Effective Education* (Danville, Ill.: Interstate Printers & Publishers, 1962), pp. 23–24.

a decentralized arrangement most of the central office personnel will be either coordinative or advisory staff officers.

The increased size and complexity of many modern school systems have created a need for the central office to make proper use of innovations such as data processing systems, computer information systems, and centralized purchasing-accounting systems. These innovations have created the need for a different breed of specialization. For example, a school system utilizing computer-based data processing will need both technicians to operate and program the machines, and research-oriented analysts to provide questions and research frameworks for the machines.

The reader should recognize that the practice of discussing organization in terms of line and staff positions has some limitations. A clear dichotomy between *line* (denoting authority) and *staff* (denoting a consultive or co-ordinating role) should not be made. Experience has shown that such a dichotomy is inadequate for describing precisely how people function in a school system and how jobs get done.

Thus, the function of providing greater expertness through specialization can be accomplished through the services of a number of different kinds of personnel working at different levels and in various ways throughout the school system. Their competence supplements and complements that of other specialists—the superintendent, the principal, and the teacher. Increased specialization in the central office should make it possible both to intensify and diversify the educational effort of the school system.

CO-ORDINATION

The assistant superintendent of instruction must give his attention to planning and co-ordinating instruction throughout the school system. Thus, while he serves as a specialist in instruction, in contrast to specialists in staff personnel and business, he also serves the school in the capacity of a co-ordinator. Assistant superintendents must view their co-ordinating role in at least two ways. One of these we have just mentioned, namely the system-wide co-ordination within his sphere of school operation. Another essential view, however, concerns the co-ordination of efforts among the several task areas of administration. That is, business, staff personnel, instruction, and other functions must be worked out together.

There are other levels at which co-ordination plays an important part in the operation of the school. Co-ordinators of elementary education, of pupil personnel, and of audio-visual education all have responsibilities for system-wide co-ordination within their functional areas as well as for seeing that pupil personnel services and the facilities of the audio-visual instructional department are used to facilitate instruction in the various elementary schools of the system. This example clearly illustrates our point that personnel in the central office do have a co-ordinating role and that co-ordination is important both within and among divisions of school operation.

SERVICE

Many schools employ a number of persons whose primary function is that of service to the several building units.

Resource people. Supervisors, consultants, and resource persons may be classed primarily as service personnel. Their function is to help teachers or other school workers carry out their specific assignments. True, they are specialists who may have particular competence in diagnosing difficulties and improving upon the means generally used to overcome them. However, their usefulness to the school system is demonstrated by their acceptance as helpers rather than by the authority of the status position that they hold.

In a certain sense all central office personnel perform a service role. They are employed to carry out those functions that facilitate teaching and learning. The effectiveness of the central office operation depends, in large measure, upon the acceptance and utilization of its services in the several school units in the system.

Other service personnel. In addition to the members of the professional staff, there are other employees whose work contributes to the system-wide effort. Many of them are associated in some way with school management. Among such employees are the school clerk who keeps the official records of the board of education; various clerical workers, such as secretaries, filing clerks, typists and stenographers, and bookkeepers; custodians, bus drivers, cafeteria managers and cooks.

Although most of these people do not expect to take an active part in making the professional decisions with which our previous discussion has been concerned, they are an integral part of the school system. Their effectiveness is dependent both upon how well they understand the roles they play and the degree to which they feel that they truly belong to the school system.

Job descriptions are often useful in clarifying assignments. In-service education meetings to discuss improvements in procedures and the improvement of skills can also be very helpful. Often, training programs are provided at the state, regional, or university level for up-grading the services of such personnel. The advantage of the utilization of such means to the improvement of services cannot be overstressed.

THE ROLE OF THE PRINCIPAL

The individual school is the center for all teaching and learning. In any given neighborhood the effectiveness of the local school may be the criterion by which people judge the effectiveness of the entire school system. Hence the principal is a key person in the administrative organization. He performs administrative tasks similar to those of a superintendent of schools, but he does so within the policy limits of the system. Instructional leadership, community relationships, staff personnel, pupil personnel, facilities, finance and business management, and organization are all areas in which tasks must be performed at the school-building level as well as the level of central-office administration. Public pressure for community control has accentuated the importance of the principal in many areas.

The nature of the responsibilities differs somewhat among elementary schools and junior and senior high schools. High schools, for example, tend to recognize more managerial responsibilities than do elementary schools. The size and complexity of the schools are factors that affect the nature of these responsibilities also. Ordinarily we transport high school youth greater distances than we do elementary school children. Enrollments in high schools are usually larger than in elementary schools. The curriculum of the comprehensive high school is extensive and complex. The role of the middle school or junior high school in the American school system is not as clear as that of the elementary and high schools. Thus, not only are the functions of administration at the building level as varied as those for the entire system, but in addition they are complicated by circumstances that require treatment unique to each school.

An Organizer

While principals in smaller school systems are expected to perform all of the tasks associated with the office, this expectation results from a lack of appreciation for the scope and comprehension of the job. In larger school systems, where the complexity of the work of the principal is more apparent, specialized personnel either are assigned as regular assistants to the principal or are supplied by the central office. Both practices are common in school systems.

Whether or not the principal himself performs all of the tasks associated with his office, he must organize his school in such a way that the tasks are accomplished. True, the basic administrative unit of which the principal's school is a part determines the financial structure for the system. It provides the building and furnishings. The financial resources of the total school system provide for the operating expenses of the school, including the teachers' salaries. As indicated previously, the central office provides for many resources. But these provisions supplied in such manner do not make a school. The principal must understand how to weld these resources—those of his teachers, of the neighborhood which his school serves, of special personnel, and of the students—into a school community that has a character of its own.

A Communicator

Another reason why the principal holds such a key position in the organizational structure of a school system is that he stands in an intermediate position between the central office and his teachers, and between the people of his local school neighborhood and the citizens of the entire attendance unit. It is not enough that his school take on a unique character indigenous to the particular circumstances immediately surrounding it. The individual school is also a part of a system. The principal is the chief interpreter of official policy of the system for his staff and for the school community. It is also largely through him that certain special contributions of the individual school become incorporated as integral parts of the total system. Thus, his understanding of the decision-making process and his ability to communicate to staff and community and to central administrative officers are one measure of his competence.

An Instructional Leader

Important as it is for the principal to play the roles of organizer and communicator well, they are inadequate to explain the common reference to him as a *key* administrator. Like the superintendent of schools, he holds a position of high visibility in his community. He must not only be articulate about the purposes which his school is to serve, but he must demonstrate that under his leadership the school is achieving them in reasonable degree. He is at once a diagnostician of the problems that this school needs to solve and a synthesizer of the forces that must be brought together to solve them. If he fulfills this expectation, he develops a congenial working relationship among his staff members; he encourages their creativity by seeking out the special talents of individual members and encouraging their innovation and experimentation.

It should be noted that the contemporary role of instructional leader is not that of a "super-teacher"[7] who directs teachers in the specifics of teaching. Given the complexity and variety of the school curriculum as well as the increasing preparation and sophistication of teachers, such a role is no longer realistic. However the principal can assist teachers by sharing his impressions of their work and encouraging them to do the same for each other. Working with his staff, he assesses the need for the use of resource personnel and deploys them to spots where they may be effective. He also works with them to appraise the effectiveness of the instructional program and to take the steps necessary to improve it.

A Line Officer

The principal is, in most forms of administrative organization, the line authority in his building. His authority devolves from the laws of the state and, through the superintendent, from the board of education and the people of the community. This vested authority is the principal's legal-traditional source of power. However, to operate suc-

---

[7] For a review of research which notes this perspective, see Donald A. Erickson, "The School Administrator," *Review of Educational Research* **XXXVII** (October, 1967) 417–431.

cessfully within his school, the principal must possess entrusted authority—authority based on *competence,* as noted in Chapter 8.

Griffiths has recognized four types of functions in which all principals must be competent:

1. Improving the educational program.
2. Selecting and developing personnel.
3. Working with the community.
4. Managing the school.[8]

THE TEACHER'S PLACE IN THE ORGANIZATION

The teacher derives considerable satisfaction from the recognition of the importance of his task. The satisfactions resulting from a successful experience in the classroom are among the enduring benefits of the teaching profession. Lortie[9] has shown that the job rewards which teachers consider most meaningful are those achieved through interaction with students. However, as schools have become larger and an organizational effort is required to do the total job of the school, the need for identification with the total organization has increased. The teacher of the one-room school knew how he fared in the school enterprise, because there were no intermediaries between him and the school board on the one hand, and the children and the parents on the other. Furthermore, this teacher taught all of the children in all grades. He determined the standard of achievement at all grade levels.

INTERDEPENDENCE OF TEACHERS

In the school of today each teacher is a contributor to the total educational endeavor; he cannot carry out his assignment alone. He works in a co-operative enterprise in which the educational process is a team affair. This interdependence among contributors to the educational process is a phenomenon of the multiple-teacher school. The larger and more complex the school or school system, the more

---

[8] Griffiths, *op. cit.,* p. 172.

[9] Dan C. Lortie, "The Balance of Control and Autonomy in Elementary School Teaching." In Amitai Etzioni, ed., *The Semi-Professions* (New York: The Free Press, 1969), pp. 1–53.

important this phenomenon becomes as a factor in organization and administration.

It is now common to speak of the ungraded primary divisions of the elementary school, team teaching, the utilization of master teachers either within the school system or by television, and various forms of grouping of pupils; and of teaching machines, the teacher's helper, and other novel ways of organizing the school and combining various forms of instruction to meet differentiated learning needs of pupils. In addition to distinguishing various faculty roles, differentiated staffing proposals call for enlarged faculty responsibility in planning and co-ordinating the instructional program.[10] Implementation of such plans will increase faculty interdependence.

The modern school system is an intricate network of varied activities and services carried on by personnel who assume a variety of responsibilities for the teaching-learning process. Teachers are aware that the organizational achievement is more than the sum of their individual efforts. Their satisfaction must be derived from the knowledge that their individual and collective efforts have contributed both to the formulation and to the achievement of the school's goals. Teachers who gain these satisfactions feel an identification with the organization, its purposes, and its methods of achieving these purposes.

THE TEACHER'S POSITION IN THE HIERARCHY

Teachers and administrators should strive to understand the working relationship among those who have responsibility for the day-by-day operation of the school. One method of accomplishing this purpose is to supply school personnel with a handbook of policies, regulations, job specifications, and diagrams showing working relationships thought to be instrumental in achieving the goals of the school. Organization charts shown in such handbooks describe line and staff organizations which illustrate the functional relationship between citizens of the community, the board of education, the superintendent of schools and the central office staff, the principals, the teachers, and the pupils.

A very careful explanation of such a chart should contribute to the teachers' understanding of their places in the total organization. The

---

[10] For an example and discussion of such a plan, see M. John Rand and Fenwick English, "Towards a Differentiated Teaching Staff," 44, *Phi Delta Kappan* (January, 1968), 264–268.

diagram shows that the teachers are members of the organization. It suggests, too, that the teachers are responsible *to* the principal and *for* the pupils. It identifies a line of authority. It indicates that there is a functional relationship between certain staff and line personnel. All of the variations in the understandings and the misunderstandings of the faculty concerning the administration of a school cannot be diagrammed, however. Administrative organization will actually be understood only when it becomes a legitimate subject for study by the faculty.

An administrative problem of particular concern to teachers involves the hierarchical levels on which personnel are classified. Some administrators fear that teacher participation in decision-making jeopardizes the exercise of their authority. Teachers, on the other hand, accuse administrators of being too authoritarian. Is there a master-servant relationship that must be maintained? Does the administrator have more or less authority than the teacher? What is the source of authority? Does authority flow down from the top through the administrative line? Or could it flow in the opposite direction also?

These are difficult questions to answer, and the administrator who attempts to be democratic by including the faculty and other reference groups in decision-making often becomes discouraged when he finds that he must accept responsibility for a decision with which he does not agree. The obvious consequence is that, losing faith in broad participation in the making of decisions, he resorts to the more comfortable autocratic procedure which he previously abandoned. With this reversal of action the teachers see the administrator becoming more dictatorial and their own importance in the organization diminishing.

Cabot and Kahl, in discussing the social theory of organization, describe the problem this way:

> The existence of hierarchy within an organization implies that those with lower status in the organization will not completely share the values of those with higher status. Hence, the lower-status individuals are "under-privileged" in terms of the values of those of higher status, since these latter values are mostly related to the over-all purpose of the organization.[11]

The administrator of a school system has a responsibility to see that the decisions which are made contribute to the accomplishment

[11] Hugh Cabot and Joseph A. Kahl, *Human Relations* (Cambridge, Mass.: Harvard University Press, 1953), Vol. I, p. 232.

of the overall purpose of the organization. He may feel that teachers or any other single group of people associated with the school are not in a position to see this total purpose. He may think that their participation in decision-making reflects the bias that results from the limited perspective with which they view the problem.

On the other hand, teachers who would like to participate in making important decisions about school practices must find a way to gain the perspective of other groups which have a stake in the decisions that are made. The opportunity to make decisions also carries with it the responsibility for them. Neither teachers nor administrators have found a satisfactory means for sharing the responsibility for many decisions which they have made together. It must be remembered that even though an administrative procedure has been developed from faculty thinking, it is often the administrator whom the board of education and the people of the community hold responsible for the decision.

While we would not argue that the administrator's judgment and wisdom are necessarily any better than the judgment and wisdom of his teachers, the administrator does occupy a position that requires him to look at problems in terms of the interests of all groups affected by the school—the pupils, the citizens of the local community, the teachers and other school employees, the board of education, the state, the schools and education at large, and the total profession. This is what makes the participation of special-interest groups so very difficult. If administrators have been wary of teacher participation in the past, it may have been largely because they had not yet found a satisfactory means by which teachers could perceive the total problem without spending so much of their time on it that their effectiveness in the classroom was jeopardized.

The problem with which we are faced is one of reducing the master-servant feeling while at the same time maintaining such an organizational arrangement as permits an efficient system of decision-making, respected by all for its fair treatment of everyone's interests. The method of solving the problem has been to increase the amount of participation of those groups concerned. The solution has not been easy. Parsey and Chase, reporting on studies of teacher participation, comment, "Some people talk as if it were easy for all teachers in the system to share in the making of all kinds of policies. Yet, even the best school systems have had only partial success in enabling teachers to take an active part in educational planning."[12]

---

[12] John M. Parsey and Francis S. Chase, "The Teacher and Policy Making," *The Administrator's Notebook,* 1 (May, 1952), 1.

The modern concept of administration rejects the idea that the administrator is "the boss" who makes decisions for the group, and it will not condone the paternalistic attitude of the administrator who, through his kindly and fatherly wisdom and maturity, makes decisions for the welfare of the group. But this modern viewpoint rejects also the notion that the administrator simply leaves decisions up to the group. It espouses a participative structure that recognizes the administrator as the person who, through his leadership or by the authority granted him by the group, leads his teachers toward the achievement of a goal that has come to be accepted as desirable. The realization of such a concept will be achieved neither by teacher demand nor by administrative compromise. Both teachers and administrators need to work at the problem together. A little success from small beginnings will open the door to new ventures in co-operative decision-making.

THE TEACHER AND ADMINISTRATIVE AUTHORITY

A second factor that has in many instances served as a serious deterrent to good working relationships among teachers and administrators has been confusion concerning the nature and the extent of the authority of the administrator. Here again, although there is considerable precedent upon which we may draw in arriving at a satisfactory understanding, teachers and administrators within a given school system need to arrive at their own understandings of how and where authority is to operate in the organization that has been built to accomplish their purposes.

Actually, there may be a number of sources of authority. Certainly the state, charged with the responsibility for the public school system, has powers that are vested in it by the authority of law. The community has certain authority which it exercises through local option. The teachers have authority in their own classrooms. Much of this kind of authority is legal in character. It can be tested in the courts. It can be described by a chain of relationships leading from the state, through the local school organization, to the pupil.

The state has delegated certain of its powers to the board of education of the local school district. This delegation of powers gives the board the authority to exercise these powers. The citizens of the school district by vote and moral support add to the authority of the local school board. In turn, an administrative organization is developed to execute those functions of the board which deal with school operation. The administrator of the school is charged with responsibility for the effective operation of this organization to accomplish the purposes for which the school exists. Administrators differ in the manner in which they carry out this responsibility. Those who abuse their authority in discharging their responsibilities are misusing the powers of their office.

There is another kind of authority that must be recognized if the school is to accomplish its purposes. This is the authority derived from the philosophy and science of education. It emanates from the theory of how children learn and from the values that people hold for education. This source of authority, while alluded to in the professional literature and in our professional associations, has not been given consideration equal to that of legal authority in designing administrative organization. In reality, this source of authority cannot be used effectively in determining organizational structure unless the teachers play an active role both in the accumulation of new knowledge about education and in the assessment of values which people hold for education. The teachers have very real responsibility for the interpretation of the implications of this knowledge and these values for organizational structure. By virtue of their knowledge and competency, teachers have a right to some degree of authority in the administration of schools. However, the teaching profession seems to have encountered a major problem in getting its right to authority recognized and legitimatized in the legal-traditional channels of the American educational system. The existence of this "problem" may explain, in part, the trend toward increased formal professional organization of teachers into teachers' unions or associations.[13]

Many attempts have been made to picture a type of organization built out of a consideration of these two kinds of authority. The object of such a representation is to show that important considerations flow in both directions along the line—from the bottom to the top as well as from the top down. As one administrator has so aptly stated, "Authority bubbles up as well as trickles down." The two-way flow of authority in the line concept of administration may be pictured as follows:

[13] See Ronald G. Corwin, "Professional Persons in Public Organizations," *Educational Administration Quarterly* 1:1–22 (Autumn, 1965).

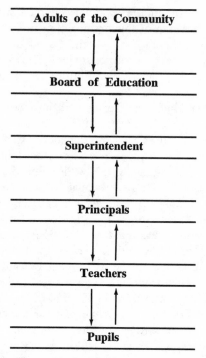

Figure 9.1   A flow chart on policy formation in education

In deciding matters of some consequence to the school, the administrator, before exercising the authority vested in him by the board of education, usually seeks the counsel of those who are most directly affected by the decision. Often he asks that a study be made by professional people whose competence in such matters can be respected. The administrator's recommendation to the board of education is based upon this study. Most school systems, for example, accept the judgment of teachers as the most authoritative source of information on the selection of textbooks and other instructional materials. For all practical purposes the teachers make the decision, even though their decision must be acted upon by the board of education.

This means, then, that the functions of the participants in the organization are established on a rational basis, giving due consideration to the kinds of influences that have a bearing on these functions. The effective educational administrator knows that the organization succeeds insofar as there is mutual acceptance of these functions and the relationships that are established and maintained between the participants who must carry out these functions. This mutual understanding and acceptance of the working arrangement that is to exist is what we have chosen to call *organizational* or *normative authority*. It is that type of authority which Dubin says is "based on rational grounds."[14]

According to this concept, it is conceivable that an administrator may make decisions for the organization because it makes sense for him to do so, rather than because he has traditionally been given the power to do so, or because he possesses an unusual or superior wisdom. He simply occupies a position where, if he is competent, the purposes of the organization are best achieved this way. The rules established for the operation of the organization determine the authority structure. The administrator derives his authority from them. It is from this same set of rules that the teacher, too, obtains organizational authority, and thus group approval, to carry on those functions assigned to him. We hope, of course, that a process of interaction can be established whereby the mutuality of understanding of the organizational structure is maintained among the administrators and the reference groups who have a stake in the educational enterprise.

THE TEACHER'S PART IN DECISION-MAKING

Teachers do not want to participate in all decisions that administrators need to make; in fact, they chafe at some of the decision-making in which they are asked to take part. Sometimes their reluctance is justified, because the decisions are of so little consequence that the time used on them is an utter waste of human resources. Faculty meetings often deal with routine matters that were previously settled and are being announced in a group meeting. Such administrative behavior is not conducive to further staff participation. On the other hand, administrators have a justifiable criticism of teachers who are unwilling to spend the time or accept the responsibility for shared decisions. Since in the great majority of our schools both administrators and teachers have to learn how to share in decision-making, it seems appropriate at this time to discuss those areas in which teacher participation has the most promise of success.

[14] Robert Dubin, ed., *Human Relations in Administration* (Englewood Cliffs, N.J.: Prentice-Hall, 1951), pp. 196–197.

DETERMINING GOALS AND OBJECTIVES

While cultural values and the community's interpretation of the implications of these values have much to do with the determination of goals and objectives to be achieved by the schools, the teacher feels that he has a stake in this important decision-making process. Certainly there is no group in the school community that has had more opportunity than the professional staff to study the role of the school in American society. If we accept the proposition that the professional knowledge of the staff is essential to intelligent decision-making in this area, we have established a very important responsibility for the teachers in the school. According to this proposition, the teachers of the school, because of their insight into the educational alternatives open and the implications of each alternative for society, should take positions of leadership in helping the citizens determine the kind of educational program which they can actively support.

It is a mistake for the administrator, either superintendent or principal, to assume that he can obtain an effective community understanding of the purposes of the schools by "going it alone." Kimbrough's work on the power structure of communities provides evidence to support the position that lay leadership is effective in influencing people's decisions about school and other important matters.[15] A more recent set of case studies indicated that citizens with widely varying backgrounds are interested in helping to shape school policies and programs.[16] *How* decisions are made seems to be just as important as a determiner of group action as *what* decisions are made. For purposes of this discussion, then, the people involved in determining goals and the way goals are set are crucial factors in bringing about their achievement. A mutual understanding of goals derived by faculty and citizen co-operation is urged as the really effective means by which community support for the school is derived and maintained.

[15] Ralph B. Kimbrough, *Political Power and Educational Decision-Making* (Chicago: Rand McNally, 1964).

[16] Luvern L. Cunningham and Raphael O. Nystrand, *Citizen Participation in School Affairs* (Washington, D.C.: The Urban Coalition, 1969).

POLICY-MAKING

As suggested above, another kind of decision-making in which teachers can participate effectively is in the area of policy-making at both the school building and the system levels. Teacher organizations have worked hard in recent years to legitimatize this kind of participation through collective negotiations agreements. Such agreements are policy statements in themselves and often specify conditions for involving teachers in certain other policy decisions (the selection of textbooks or acceptance of curriculum guides). There is some evidence that teacher organizations are expanding their previously dominant concern with "bread and butter issues" to curriculum and other policy matters of educational substance.

A policy statement is a working agreement. Once understood and accepted, it clarifies the manner in which school employees, the board of education, the administrators, the pupils, and the citizens of the community relate themselves to each other to meet the goals and objectives to which they have subscribed. The problem in the incident related in Chapter 1, entitled "Jimmy Is Promoted," centers in the school. It appears from the facts presented that the policy in operation, which as a written policy had the official approval of the board of education, had, in part, been formulated by personnel who had left the school. Even the superintendent of schools was not fully committed to the policy and thus supported it halfheartedly. Making, maintaining, and improving policy are parts of a continuous process. Staff changes, changes in point of view, and the assessment of the effectiveness of certain policies are factors that constantly affect policy.

Teachers are interested not only in those policies which affect teacher personnel practices, but they have much to do—and, hence, to say—about daily school procedures relating to marks, promotion, reporting to parents, attendance, the punctuality of pupils, discipline, grade placement of pupils, use and distribution of resources, selection of textbooks, standards of achievement, and many other school operations. However, some administrators and teachers act as if they must actively participate in each of the myriad *decisions* that must be made about matters of every kind in the course of a school year even if the matters do not directly concern them. How much better it is to arrive at *policy* agreements, which give to the individuals most directly concerned the *authority of the organization* to act without having to get a decision from an entire staff each time an action becomes necessary.

APPRAISING THE EDUCATIONAL PROGRAM

Much of the responsibility for achieving the objectives of the school rests with the teachers. Both their individual efforts as classroom teachers and the total organizational effort to which they contribute are important factors in the school's achievement. Hence the school cannot really take stock of its efforts without involving its teachers. But what are the measures of a good school program? How should these measures be applied and by whom?

The critics who decry the ineffectiveness of our schools on the basis that our young people have not mastered the 3 R's suggest one criterion for appraisal. Those who think that the schools should prepare youth to meet successfully the highly competitive challenges of industrialized society suggest more emphasis on a program designed to meet the needs of the gifted child. Some people are concerned about the youth who leave school earlier than is normal. Does a high drop-out rate in a school suggest that the program is not meeting the needs of students? What is the meaning of low test scores on a school-wide basis? What are the students' needs, and what are the needs of society that the schools must try to meet? These and other questions that could be raised relate to the objectives of the school. Even these are difficult to answer. A school has established some basis for an appraisal program when it has answered for itself these and similar questions that have been at issue in the district in which it operates. The co-operation of the teachers is essential in creating such understanding in the community.

Measurement of the effectiveness of the school in achieving these objectives is still a problem. Available measuring instruments are crude. If their limitations are recognized, however, they can serve a useful purpose. It is not the measure of the pupils' achievement that causes the great difficulty. Crude as the instruments may be, they do provide us with meaningful information concerning the pupils' growth. However, once we know that pupils are or are not achieving, how do we establish the positive and negative influences of the school? Can these be traced to the influences of poor, average, or superior teachers?

PROVIDING FOR IN-SERVICE EDUCATION

The need for the professional improvement of school personnel is practically taken for granted as an essential part of a staff personnel program. The rapidly increasing school enrollment; the increase in the numbers of teachers needed; the rapid turnover of school personnel; the large number of temporarily certificated teachers; the new knowledge that is accumulating concerning the learning process, human relations, and administrative behavior; and the rapidly changing industrial, political, and social character of our society amply prove that acquiring the knowledge necessary to become and continue to be a good teacher or educational leader is a lifetime endeavor. Four- and five-year teacher education programs do not adequately prepare prospective teachers for their careers. All that can be claimed for them is that they provide the prospective teacher with the basic knowledge and skill which he must use to continue to develop his competence throughout his career. Part of the continuance takes place in graduate programs of education. Much of it is done through in-service education.

In those schools where in-service education programs are proving to be successful, teachers participate in planning, organizing, and evaluating them. Programs planned for the teachers solely by the administrators are doomed to failure before they begin. Teachers as well as administrators must be in on the process of growing. An adequate program provides growth opportunities for both.

The American Association of School Administrators and the National Society for the Study of Education thought this subject so important that they devoted their 1957 yearbooks to an extensive treatment of it.[17, 18] Both publications stress the importance of the involvement of personnel affected at all stages in the program from planning to evaluation. Both recognize the importance of the status leader in creating an appropriate climate for growth. Together they give credence to the concept that in a growth situation, leadership from within the group emerges, and that when this happens the opportunity for shared responsibility is enhanced. Parker, writing in

[17] American Association of School Administrators, *The Superintendent as Instructional Leader* (Washington, D.C.: AASA, 1957).

[18] National Society for the Study of Education, *In-Service Education,* Part I (Chicago: University of Chicago Press, 1957).

the NSSE Yearbook, discusses twelve guidelines that he recommends for in-service education programs. They are listed here because they continue to have relevance concerning the participative structure that should characterize in-service education of school personnel:

1. People work as individuals and as members of groups on problems that are significant to them.
2. The same people who work on problems formulate goals and plan how they will work.
3. Many opportunities are developed for people to relate themselves to each other.
4. Continuous attention is given to individual and to group problem-solving processes.
5. Atmosphere is created that is conducive to building mutual respect, support, permissiveness, and creativeness.
6. Multiple and rich resources are made available and are used.
7. The simplest possible means are developed to move through decisions to actions.
8. Constant encouragement is present to test and to try new ideas and plans in real situations.
9. Appraisal is made an integral part of in-service activities.
10. Continuous attention is given to the interrelationship of different groups.
11. The facts of individual differences among members of each group are accepted and utilized.
12. Activities are related to pertinent aspects of the current educational, cultural, political, and economic scene.[19]

CHANGING THE CURRICULUM

The dynamics of curriculum change have been suggested in the previous discussion of teacher responsibility in decision-making. If teachers participate in the determination of goals and objectives, policy-making, the appraisal of effectiveness, and in-service growth activities, they have gone a long way toward curriculum planning and change. The important principle to keep in mind here is that curriculum change is dependent upon the changes that take place in people. For purposes of this discussion, the changes in teachers' beliefs about the role of education in our society, their understandings about how

[19] J. Cecil Parker, "Guidelines for In-Service Education," *ibid.*, pp. 103–128.

learning takes place, their interpretations of the needs of children and youth, their interpretation of the impact which the demands of society should make upon the program, their increased knowledge about the world in which we live, and their development of skills in working with pupils, parents, and others who have an effect upon learning are some of the factors that change the learning activities provided and the way teachers relate themselves to the teaching-learning process.

Change, however, must be of two kinds—change in individual staff members and institutional change. The teachers' changing conceptions of what and how to teach must add up to orderly program changes. Some program decisions must be made for the school, the school district of which each school is a part, and for the state. The suggestion made here is that program changes for the total institution emanate from changes in individuals, largely changes in the understandings of teachers; but some effort needs to be made to group these changes in meaningful and related learning experiences for pupils. Leadership and co-ordination on the part of administrators should provide not only the climate for change to occur, but the procedures by which changes in individuals can add up to system-wide or institutional changes.

What the teacher wants to accomplish through his participation in decision-making is to exert an influence on the educational program. He is not satisfied with his own individual growth nor the improvements that he makes in his own teaching. He wants to have a part in molding the educational program. This is his *professional* stake in the business of education. The teacher's competence as a professional educator, as contrasted to that of a skilled craftsman, comes to fruition when this competence is used to make improvements in what is being taught, in the services the schools render, in the size of classes, the grouping of pupils, the instructional materials to be used, the classroom environment and the resources to be used in teaching, and in the nature of the agreements among the schools within the system on these and related matters.

Teachers and administrators must keep in mind that the major purpose of this participation is not merely the maintenance of good morale, however necessary that may be. Staff participation in decision-making must be justified not merely because of what it does for teachers, but because experience and research show it to be the most effective means available to accomplish the purposes for which the schools are organized. The challenge for the administrators is to get and maintain the kinds of participation discussed here among an increasing number of teachers in the kind of organization that leads to accomplishments mutually satisfying to school personnel and their clients—the children and the adults of the community. The challenge to teachers is to keep the objectives of the school foremost, to improve their own teaching, and to build those team relationships which enhance the effectiveness of the organization of which they are a part.

PLANNED STAFF PARTICIPATION

Effective staff participation does not just happen. It must be nurtured. The assumption that there is a democratic working relationship when each employee is permitted to go his own way has led not only to individual stagnation but to lack of organizational achievement as well. Fortunately, studies of teacher participation indicate that both teachers and administrators desire an organizational pattern in which there is some structure to guide their behavior. The most effective teacher-administrator relationship, from the standpoint of both morale and productivity, is a participative one. That is, a condition must exist whereby both administrators and teachers call upon each other to define the structure that increases their productivity in achieving the ends desired by their organization, the school. Teachers need to know that, with the help of their administrative leaders, they are working on vital educational matters. They need to know that when they give time, energy, and interest to the consideration of crucial matters, their ideas or proposals for action make a difference to those who have the power to make final decisions.

In developing an organizational structure which optimizes staff participation in decision-making, the administrator must remember that his purpose is not one of concession to others. The school is operated to educate effectively its children and youth. The wise administrator knows that he must capitalize on the creativity of all his staff members in building a structure that places a premium upon the co-operative effort required to do this job. In other words, the co-operative method is better than any other yet devised.

Building Sound Personnel Policy

The interests of staff members in personnel policy are broad and varied. Sometimes they are criticized because their interests in what appear to be matters of their personal welfare overshadow their concern for the solution of other professional problems. Those who are active in programs for the welfare improvement of staff personnel take the position, however, that this is an integral part of a broad program of professional improvement. In other words, sound personnel policies form a foundation upon which to build sound programs for professional advancement.

Personnel policy statements with which we are familiar include such topics as these:

1. Absence
2. Assignments and transfers
3. Benefits and services
4. Contractual status
5. Discharge
6. Suspension
7. Employee–group relationship
8. Ethics
9. Evaluation
10. Exchange teaching
11. Extra duties and compensation
12. Grievances
13. Health and safety
14. In-service growth
15. Leave of absence
16. Official communications
17. Orientation
18. Outside employment
19. Overtime
20. Pay procedures
21. Probation
22. Professional meetings
23. Promotions and demotions
24. Re-employment
25. Resignations
26. Responsibilities
27. Definition of positions
28. Retirement
29. Salary schedules
30. Selection
31. Seniority
32. Sick leave
33. Substitute teachers
34. Vacations
35. Workmen's compensation
36. Work schedules, daily and yearly

Any complete textbook on staff personnel gives an even more comprehensive list of personnel concerns with which the school administrator must deal. His problem is to provide leadership in determining who should make what decisions. It is generally agreed that to develop satisfactory personnel policies for a school system, it is necessary to involve those who are affected by such policies. We know, also, that all school employees respect the fact that their welfare is conditioned by organizational agreements other than their own personal interests. Studies of teacher participation have shown that teachers differ widely in their opinions about the degree to which they should participate in decisions concerning themselves and those who are soon to join their ranks. For example, not all of them are agreed that they should participate in the actual selection of new teachers, in promotions, or in the evaluation of the effectiveness of their colleagues. On the other hand, a great many teachers do have definite opinions concerning the criteria to be used for their selection, promotion, and evaluation.

In some schools, teachers are ready to assist in the formulation of procedures to be applied in carrying out a given policy. In most school systems teachers insist on having some voice in the determination of salary schedules, teaching assignments, work schedules, and benefits to be derived in the form of compensation for extra duties and extra preparation for teaching. Some schools are finding teachers willing to consider salary schedules based upon a rating of teaching effectiveness.

Bridges[20] has discussed the conditions under which principals can share decision-making most effectively. He noted that teachers do not want to participate in all decisions but have greatest interest in those which bear directly upon classroom affairs. The first task for the principal who wishes to extend participation is to determine which matters fall within the range of teacher interests and expertise. A second step is to decide exactly what teachers should help do (define the problem, suggest alternative courses of action, or select one of the alternatives). It is important that these decision-making boundaries be made absolutely clear.

Bridges[21] noted that the third step is to determine the mode in which the decision-making group will operate. One mode is participant-determining, in which it is agreed that a decision is reached only when all members of the group achieve consensus. A second is the parliamentarian mode where a decision is achieved when a majority of the group agree. The third mode is the democratic-centralist, in which one member retains the authority to decide after considering the views of others in the group. The role of the administrator will vary in each instance. In the first, he must help to build consensus. In the second, his task is to encourage the full expression of minority views and to maintain group strength in the face of divided opinion. As the person who probably reserves the right to decide in the third

---

20 Edwin M. Bridges, "A Model for Shared Decision-Making in the Principalship," *Educational Administration Quarterly* 3, (Winter, 1967), 49–61.

21 *Ibid.* This part of Bridges' discussion is based upon Guy E. Swanson, "The Effectiveness of Decision-Making Groups," *Adult Leadership* 8, (June, 1959), 48–52.

instance, he must help the group explore all relevant aspects of the problem and encourage the discussions of varying alternatives and their consequences.

While Bridges' article focused upon the role of the principal in facilitating group decisions, it applies to other administrators as well. The following section describes some patterns of staff participation in which these suggestions for administrators can be applied.

PATTERNS OF STAFF PARTICIPATION

Various attempts have been made to involve the staff of the school in decision-making. Not all of them are successful; examples of unsuccessful faculty meetings are legion. Yet we suspect that the faculty meeting called by the superintendent of the district or by the principal of the building is the only formal means by which many teachers have an opportunity to participate, even passively, in matters pertaining to the entire school. Often these meetings are nonparticipative; their agenda are not planned with the purpose of engaging the faculty in a consideration of matters that make a difference in the operation of the school. The following organizational patterns, which have been tried for the purpose of improving instruction, show promise for improvement in other aspects of the school also.

Central office planned participation. Some school systems, in an effort to improve the education of children and youth, have greatly enlarged their central office staff to include personnel to plan teacher involvement, particularly in the area of improvement of instruction. With the increasingly large numbers of temporarily certificated teachers and the mobility of teachers from one school system to another, the need for acquainting them with procedures employed in the local system has been greatly emphasized. Conferences and workshops are planned to assist in instructional improvement. Orientation programs are planned to acquaint new teachers with the local school program. Committees of teachers assist in selecting textbooks, in planning courses of study for each of the several grade levels, and in solving a number of problems which are defined by the central office personnel.

This pattern of organization is based on the belief that improvement programs should be determined, planned, initiated, and carried out by central office personnel who call upon the teachers for assistance and advice. Often it is a program organized *for* the teachers rather than *by* the teachers.

It has the advantage of being easily controlled. Originating in the central office, it can be as narrow or as broad in scope as the central staff wishes. Plans can be put into operation quickly. New techniques or methods to be employed can be defined by relatively few people and brought to the attention of teachers by direct communication from the central office. There can be little question about the fact that recommendations have the support of the administration and therefore carry the weight of administrative authority. Its greatest advantage is that it focuses upon the problems of the entire school system rather than upon those which seem important in a particular school only or to a few individuals.

In recent years, schools that operate in this pattern of organization have greatly broadened their opportunity for teacher participation. Many teachers become involved in getting the work done. Often a wide range of resources is used in meaningful ways to solve school problems. Curriculum leaders, special supervisors, and special service personnel have been added to the central office staff to assist teachers in improving learning.

In some situations, however, participation planned and conducted by central office people does not accomplish its purpose. Teachers participate, but fail to identify themselves with the problems on which they are working. There is no real involvement, because teachers are called upon to work on problems that were originally identified not by them but by their superiors. No matter how sincere administrators may be in wanting to serve the school's purpose through such an organizational pattern, those who fail in its application do so largely because they have not succeeded in imbuing the entire staff with their own faith in the co-operative process.

School-building autonomy in planning. In contrast to this highly centralized system, some school administrators, community leaders, and educational theorists have advocated decentralization in programs for school improvement. Under such a system, the building principal becomes the administrator who is charged with the responsibility of giving leadership to the improvement of the educational program in his building.

The effectiveness of this plan depends to a great extent upon the ability of the individual principals to work with their teachers. Some principals are prepared neither to institute an improvement program of their own design nor to involve their teachers in building a co-operative plan for improvement. But where principals are capable of good leadership, effective results are obtained from improvement programs in individual buildings.

It is obvious that one of the purposes to be achieved by the decision to use a decentralized plan of attack on the problems of the school system is to obtain greater involvement of school personnel. Hence, the principal who is autocratic in his dealings with faculty, or who is inept in teacher involvement, defeats the plan at its inception.

An advantage of the decentralized system is that the focus is upon the work to be done at the place where the need is felt most keenly. If the teachers are given an opportunity to define the problems of the school, and if the principal is authorized to take action upon the recommendations that they make for solving these problems, much can be accomplished. Thus, school programs can be adjusted to the particular needs of the residential area which the school serves. Often such an adjustment causes no system-wide problem. On the other hand, where the instructional problem is complex, where services in the several schools of the district differ, or where practices in dealing with the public vary from school to school, questions may be raised concerning the equality of the educational opportunity afforded by the several schools.

The flexibility of decentralized planning lends itself to adaptation to the needs of particular schools. The planning and the program for improvement, however, may be as different as the several staffs who engage in it. Without some leadership from the central office, there is no guarantee that individual schools within a school district will continue to improve simply upon the initiative of the local staff. It is important to raise the questions of how much and what kind of flexibility or uniformity is necessary in a school system to provide equal educational opportunity.

Central office co-ordinated planning. This plan incorporates certain features of both the centralized and decentralized plans described above. Both the faculty of each building and the personnel of the central office are involved in the planning. Ideas for improvement originate with the teachers, the principals, and the central office personnel. (Sometimes this includes pupils, parents, and other community representatives, also. It is not implied that these groups are unimportant; since this chapter deals with teacher participation, these groups are omitted.) By a system of representation from each of the several groups involved, a co-ordinating council is organized. This body receives ideas, sorts them in terms of urgency or need, establishes its best judgment concerning the wishes of the people whom it represents, and finally emerges with recommendations for administrative action.

After receiving administrative approval, the plan of action is generally executed through the usual line and staff organization. To the extent that the plan involves individual buildings, the principals are called upon for leadership. Teacher representatives who have been active on the co-ordinating council furnish excellent assistance. However, the major interest of teachers is that their ideas get to the administration and that they have some voice in determining what should be done about them. They are not vitally concerned that they have an active role in executing these ideas. If, on the other hand, the administration fails to take any action, the co-ordinating council reports this matter to its group members, who may decide to use the force of their numbers to apply pressure on the administration. The employment of the centrally co-ordinated plan of participation implies that the chief administrator believes in action and that this action is most effective when it grows out of the intelligent thinking of the groups who are affected by it.

One school system that has been using central office co-ordination with real success began by asking the teachers, the officers of the Parent-Teachers Association, and the members of the board of education to list the major needs of the school. The superintendent of schools enlisted the co-operation of each of the building principals in securing the initial list of these needs which, incidentally, contained more than 500 items. A temporary committee consisting of three teachers, a principal, a P.T.A. officer, and a representative of the central office staff sorted the items and ranked them according to the frequency with which each was mentioned. The committee also suggested a classification of items which made possible the grouping of related problems.

The next step taken by the committee was to check this classification and ranking of items with all of the groups that had participated in preparing the original list. With this portion of the work approved, the committee then suggested immediate action for certain improvements which the responses to the check list showed to be the most urgent. This suggestion was accepted by the superintendent of schools. From his study of the list of needs, the superintendent discovered several problems that he believed could be solved almost immediately with a minimum of study, time, materials, and expense. He informed the members of the committee that he was ready to act on these matters. He further instructed them to devise a plan for studying some of the more intricate problems to which the teachers, parents, and board members had given a high priority.

This administrative act proved to be a great morale builder for the teachers. In fact, a number of teachers who had expressed a lack of enthusiasm for the project originally were pleasantly surprised to find that the administrator meant business. This was not a "talking game," an expression they used to describe previous in-service and improvement projects.

In the course of the two years during which this project was observed, it was not possible to make changes as rapidly as some people would have liked. What was evident, however, was that during this brief period there was a growing confidence in the leadership of the superintendent of schools; the co-ordinating council (an outgrowth of the temporary committee that acted in this capacity) had gained in status; and the morale and productivity of the teachers had steadily improved. Many of the little annoyances—such as leaking faucets in the rest rooms, failure of janitors to sweep adequately, and torn window shades—were quickly corrected. Program changes came more slowly. Differences in points of view among teachers concerning standards of achievement at the several grade levels were still apparent, but one observable accomplishment was that even the teachers agreed that there was no simple answer to this problem. Teachers found that they could discuss the matter calmly as a problem to be solved rather than in terms of emotionally charged biases. Furthermore, after two years of co-operative effort, the staff showed a readiness to agree that many of the most important problems which they listed required intensive study before action should be taken. Many of these problems have become subjects for study by faculty and community groups, to whom resource persons from neighboring schools and universities have been found to be of great assistance.

In a discussion with the members of the co-ordinating council, at least two principles of action emerged as being of real importance for administration. They are (1) that teachers (and representatives of all participating groups) must believe that their ideas are wanted by the administrator and that their ideas will have an effect upon the actions that the administrator recommends, sanctions, or makes himself; and (2) that some action on matters of prime importance to teachers should be initiated by the administrator and vigorously supported on the basis of the evidence available. The members of this particular co-ordinating council did not feel that the administrator needed to be always in agreement with his teachers. It was their judgment, however, that if an administrator fails to approve a group decision or if he recommends an action contrary to that approved by the group, he should report the same and give his reasons.

No generalizations concerning the relative merits of these three patterns of organization can be drawn from one incident. It merely illustrates that teacher participation can be meaningful or not according to the insight and skill of the administrator. There is no gainsaying the fact that teachers need to grow, that they learn by doing just as surely as do the pupils, and that helping to solve the problems of the school is probably more meaningful to them than many simulated growing experiences that are created for them.

COLLECTIVE NEGOTIATIONS

Teacher participation in policy development has, in the past, resulted from the board of education's voluntary co-operation with the teachers involved. Behind this action has been the belief that those who would be affected by changes of policy should, after all, have some voice in these changes. However, since boards of education have had the legal right to control their relationships with teachers, it cannot be said that these relationships were fully bilateral.

Now as the result of many complicated, frequently misunderstood, and interrelated forces, American teachers are requesting or, in some instances, demanding the right to play a stronger role in the formulation of educational policy. The emergence of teacher militancy was discussed in Chapter 3. A comprehensive discussion of collective negotiations is not appropriate here, but it is important to note certain aspects of the phenomenon as they relate to teacher and administrator participation in decision-making.

The initial step in collective negotiations is the recognition of a bargaining agent. To some extent, this is a matter of statute. Several states have enacted laws which permit or in some instances require boards of education to negotiate with teacher organizations.[22] These statutes typically specify conditions for selecting a bargaining agent and the general conditions which may be negotiated. They often contain a formula for resolving impasses which develop in bargaining and frequently contain a section which prohibits work stoppages. In

[22] For review of such legislation, see John Phillip Linn and M. Chester Nolte, "Collective Bargaining Legislation in Education." In Patrick W. Carlton and Harold I. Goodwin (eds.), *The Collective Dilemma: Negotiations in Education* (Worthington, Ohio: Charles A. Jones Publishing Co., 1969), pp. 3–22.

the absence of statutes in several other states, bargaining agents have been selected and negotiations taken place in numerous instances.

Both the AFT and NEA seek exclusive bargaining rights for teachers at the local level. The logic of such a position is that it enables the teachers to speak with one voice and also encourages the development of organizational strength. Common methods for selecting a bargaining agent are examination of organizational membership rolls and employee elections. NEA and AFT locals have waged some strongly contested campaigns in such elections.

The selection of bargaining agents can pose a problem for middle-echelon administrators, whether they are or are not included in the same bargaining unit with teachers. In the first instance, they may find it difficult as outnumbered representatives of "management" to have their views about some items given the emphasis they desire in negotiations. In the second case, they may find themselves entirely without representation in dealing with the board of education. Two courses of action have been taken to achieve greater role clarity for principals and other middle-management personnel. The first has been to identify them as part of the management team and incorporate their views with those of the board of education in negotiations. The second has been the organization of independent administrator groups which also seek to negotiate with the board of education. While such groups have often been relatively weak in negotiations, their entry to the arena has added to the complexities of the process.

The principal parties in collective negotiations are the board of education which has the legal authority to make policy decisions and the teachers' association which seeks to influence those decisions. In some school districts, members of the board conduct face to face negotiations with officers of the teachers' organization. As the process of negotiations has become more time-consuming and complex, both of these bodies have shown a tendency to delegate this responsibility. The board often delegates it to the superintendent and/or a committee of administrators. Some school districts following the pattern established by industry have employed specialists to work full time on negotiations and related matters. Others employ such persons on a part-time, consulting basis to negotiate for them or to advise their own local team. Teacher organizations have acted similarly; local affiliates often receive assistance from negotiations experts employed by state or national parent organizations. When the representatives of the two bodies reach an agreement, they present it to the board and often the membership of the teacher organization for their approval. Of course, the board and at least the officers of the teachers' group generally consult with their negotiators about respective offers and counter-offers as the process goes on.

The objective of negotiations is to reach agreement, usually in the form of a written contract, about matters of interest to one party or the other. In the early stages of collective negotiations in education, the process was generally one in which the teachers submitted a set of demands to which the board responded. Now it is common for both parties to submit a set of demands, and for negotiations to involve board expectations for teachers as well as matters introduced by the teachers.

The actual negotiations process is the culmination of much research and discussion by all who are involved. It requires parties on both sides to identify problems from their own perspective, to determine the amount of resources available, and to establish priorities for the allocation of these resources. From this perspective, bargaining is a rational process which forces attention to organizational problems and priorities. It provides an opportunity for both sides to agree and act upon priority items and to bring items of disagreement to public attention.

However, the process is also based upon an adversary concept. Resources are limited and each side has a constituency to which it feels responsible. Their priorities may differ. This is perhaps most clearcut when the issue is one of salaries or other benefits, but it is applicable in other areas as well. Considering the matter of salaries, negotiators for the teachers will clearly win more support from their constitutents as they win larger salary increments at the bargaining table. Board members, on the other hand, while perhaps desirous of raising salaries somewhat, may also be mindful of citizen pressures to keep taxes down. Thus, negotiators for each side feel a need to "win."

The adversary nature of the process gives rise to some informal rules which often govern the bargaining process. For example, neither party is likely to yield to the other at the outset lest their constituents accuse them of "giving in without a fight." Both sides are likely to present an inflated set of demands at the beginning. This has the dual effect of providing interested outside parties with an image that emphasizes willingness to seek the maximum while simultaneously providing some "throwaway items" which can be surrendered in return for concessions on matters considered more important. The resulting agreement can then be termed a "compromise"—a very acceptable word in American ideology, in which both parties came to agreement upon what is best for the total school program.

Agreement is not always reached easily, however. Sometimes, the respective parties are unable to persuade each other of the accuracy of their facts or the validity of their claims. This condition is termed an impasse.[23] There are several ways to resolve an impasse. One is to rely upon the power of one side or another to force a settlement. This means is most common in industrial settings, and strikes and lockouts are the principal techniques associated with it. A second method is fact-finding, in which both sides agree upon a reputable outside party to study the situation and make a public declaration of the facts inherent in it. The theory here is that public disclosure of the facts as determined by such a party will encourage both sides to reach agreement. A third process is mediation, in which an outside party is invited to work with both sides, privately and together, in an effort to find basis for agreement. A fourth means of resolving impasse is submission of issues to binding arbitration. Under this procedure, both parties agree upon an arbitrator and consent to abide by the decision he renders after examining the case presented by each of them. All of these means have been employed at one time or another to resolve differences between school boards and teacher organizations.

One other aspect of collective negotiations which has particular relevance to administrators is that of administering the resulting contract. As noted earlier, there is a tendency for contracts to include provisions which deal with many aspects of the teachers' working day besides salaries and fringe benefits. The administrator must be knowledgeable about these provisions and how they affect his formal role vis-à-vis his staff. It is also important that he understand the leadership role of the teacher organization representative in his building or unit. Progress in many instances may depend upon the ability of these two persons to co-operate in their relations with each other and the total staff. From time to time, instances will arise in which a teacher or administrator will feel that the other has violated some provision of the contract. Such matters can often be settled through discussion by the parties involved. Sometimes the teacher-organization representative at the building level can serve as an informal mediator. In the event that such disputes cannot be resolved informally, many school systems with negotiated teacher contracts have formal grievance procedures included in them. These procedures vary, but gen-

---

[23] The dynamics of negotiations and impasse procedures are discussed by Myron Lieberman and Michael H. Moskow, *Collective Negotiations for Teachers* (Chicago: Rand McNally, 1966), pp. 248–324.

erally include a number of levels of appeal including the board of education and, in some cases, an outside source if the grievant is not satisfied by the board.

No Plan Is a Panacea

In developing the teamwork approach to the solution of problems in the school, the administrator must remember that no plan is a panacea. Possible approaches have been explained very briefly to provide the administrator with suggestions upon which he may build a program suited to the needs of the school in which he has such a responsibility. Other writers have pointed out advantages and disadvantages of these plans.[24]

None of the approaches discussed in the first part of this section included suggestions on handling the changes brought about by the introduction of formal negotiation procedures into the school's organizational structure. Certainly the introduction of such procedures will create different conditions in the internal organization of school districts, but they need not obviate the possibility of co-operative planning. The administrator should recognize that most of the policies and practices that serve to increase staff participation in planning and administration are viable in school districts with formal provisions for staff representation as well as in those which do not have such provisions.

The implication is clear that the administrator of the modern school should be more a leader of people than a manipulator of things. The accomplishment of the school's task requires a teamwork approach. Teachers and other school employees are a significant part of this team. It is essential, therefore, that an administrator be able to understand and work with his staff. The plan he will use must be built upon a profound insight into human relations and a sound set of principles of co-operative action.

TREND TOWARD FUNCTIONAL STAFF PARTICIPATION

There is a definite trend toward more functional staff participation in making important decisions for the school. Much of this trend is evidenced by the emergence of an organizational structure that

---

[24] Ronald C. Doll, *et al., Organizing for Curriculum Improvement* (New York: Teachers College, Columbia University, 1953).

encourages teamwork among all employees. The roles of various staff members are being defined in terms of the kinds of expertness which they can bring to bear in facilitating the teaching-learning process.

To obtain meaningful involvement of the staff, an organizational structure is needed, and staff participation must be planned. Teachers do not expect to participate in all decisions, but they believe they have a professional stake in the decisions that involve program planning and execution. Means have been found to involve central office personnel, principals, and teachers so that all groups can make meaningful contributions in crucial decision-making areas. Such practices are not universal, but the trend is definitely in this direction. The administrator should note that this trend may be leading toward a seeming paradox. According to Wildman:

> . . . there may be a seeming paradox in the fact that widespread adoption of the current best thinking and practice regarding democratic or consultative administration has been accompanied by an apparent increase in the desire of teachers to organize. On this interesting subject, let me simply observe that to consult with subordinates and to encourage them, in the best of faith, to formulate opinions and judgments outside their sphere of ultimate responsibility and control, and to encourage them to voice dissatisfaction when it is felt, may lead inevitably to a desire to have some actual power over the decision making process, and may give rise to a desire for an impartial adjudication of disputes. It appears at least conceivable that in some situations democratic administration of any enterprise may actually hasten the process of organization and power accumulation. There are indications that where democratic administration is practiced, participation of subordinates is often an uncertain privilege and that unless the right is guaranteed, it tends to be withdrawn; strong desire may exist within homogeneous employee groups to convert privilege to right.[25]

Neither theory, practice, nor the opinions of staff members suggest that all staff personnel should participate in making all important decisions. The problem to be solved in educational administration, as in the administration of other institutions, is to bring expertness, wherever it is to be found, to bear on the making of crucial decisions at the time and place where such decisions will be to the benefit of the greatest number of people.

---

[25] Wesley A. Wildman, "Implications of Teacher Bargaining for School Administration," *Phi Delta Kappan,* **XLVI**, 4. (December, 1964), pp. 152–158.

SUGGESTED ACTIVITIES

1. Study the organizational structure of the school in which you work. Describe the role of teachers in this organizational pattern.
2. Visit a neighboring school system and, by observation and interview, determine the organizational structure. Draw a diagram of the administrative organization, and describe briefly how it works in making curriculum changes. Check your description with the superintendent, the principal, and a group of teachers.
3. Obtain a copy of a formal agreement between a board of education and a teachers' organization. Apply the agreement to your school system, or to a system with which you are familiar. Acting under the terms of this agreement, how would the role of teachers differ from that which they now play in decision-making? What are the potential advantages and disadvantages of operating under the terms of a formal agreement with the board of education?
4. Attend a state meeting of a professional organization. Prior to your attendance set up criteria for effectiveness. After attendance write your evaluation of the meeting based on your established criteria.
5. Write a critique of the chapter on "The Faculty Meeting" in Griffiths' *Human Relations in School Administration*.
6. Examine the minutes of the board of education in your school district. List the personnel policies which you find recorded there. Add to this list the areas in which you think there is further need for policy.

SELECTED READINGS

Administrator's Notebook, "The Teacher and Policy Making" 1 (May, 1952); "Who Should Make What Decisions?" 3 (April, 1955); "Some Causes of Conflict and Tensions Among Teachers," 4 (March, 1956); "Administrative Procedure in Curriculum Revision," 5 (February, 1957); "The Leadership Patterns of School Superintendents and School Principals," 6 (September, 1957); "Administrative Behavior and Staff Relations," 6 (October, 1957); "The Superintendent of Schools: Officer or Employee?" 6 (November, 1957); "A New Concept of Staff Relations," 8 (March, 1960); "Bureaucracy and Teachers' Sense of Power," 11 (November, 1962); "The Alberta Teachers' Association: A Prototype for the American Scene?" 12 (October, 1963); "Major Communication Problems in the Schools," 14 (March, 1966); "The Principal: Forgotten Man in Negotiations," 15 (October, 1966); "A New Approach to Merit Rating of Teachers," 17 (September, 1968); "Alternative State Models for the Regulation of Teacher-School Board Negotiations," 17 (November, 1968).

American Association of School Administrators, *Roles, Responsibilities, Relationships of the School Board, Superintendent, and Staff.* (Washington, D.C.: The Association, 1963).

CARLTON, PATRICK W., and GOODWIN, HAROLD I., *The Collective Dilemma: Negotiations in Education.* (Worthington, Ohio: Charles A. Jones Publishing Co., 1969).

CASTETTER, WM. B. *Administering the School Personnel Program.* (New York: The Macmillan Co., 1962).

CORBALLY, JOHN E., JR., JENSON, T. J., and STAUB, W. FREDERICK. *Educational Administration: The Secondary School.* Second Edition. (Boston: Allyn & Bacon, 1965).

GRIFFITHS, DANIEL E. *Human Relations in School Administration.* (New York: Appleton-Century-Crofts, 1956).

LEU, D. J. and RUDMAN, H. C. *Preparation Programs for School Administrators: Common and Specialized Learnings.* (East Lansing, Mich.: Michigan State University Press, 1963).

LIEBERMAN, MYRON, and MOSKOW, MICHAEL H. *Collective Negotiations for Teachers: An Approach to School Administration.* (Chicago: Rand McNally, 1966).

MILLER, VAN. *The Public Administration of American School Systems.* (New York: The Macmillan Co., 1965).

National Society for the Study of Education, *In-Service Education,* Part I. (Chicago: University of Chicago Press, 1957).

10

Policy Formation In Education

Many views of educational administration, including some presented in this book, deal inadequately with the policy-making aspects of education. While some hold that policy evolves from the practices and procedures followed in an institution, such an approach leads to inconsistent practices and procedures and to an inability to evaluate the effectiveness of the institution. Policy must underlie practices and procedures. We are using the term policy to mean the expression of the broad goals or purposes of education. We look upon policy decisions as essentially lay decisions, made, we hope, after information and judgments have been provided by the professionals. We suspect that many laymen and a fair proportion of their professional advisers do not appreciate the complexities of the policy-making process in a free society, and we hope to help clarify that process in this chapter.

Parsons, as we have noted in Chapter 4, does give a clue to this understanding when he suggests that organizations have three levels: the technical, the managerial, and the institutional. It is chiefly at the institutional level that policy-making or legitimation, to use Parsons' term, goes on. The entire community, the board of education, and the chief administrator of the school system seem to us to be very directly involved with policy formation.

We shall first describe the process by which policy evolves,[1] then report an actual case in which a board of education sustains a policy decision, and finally suggest a few implications for the school administrator growing out of such an analysis.

---

[1] Some of the ideas expressed in this chapter first appeared in Roald F. Campbell, "Process of Policy Making Within Structures of Educational Government as Viewed by the Educator." In W. P. McLure and Van Miller, eds., *Government of Public Education for Adequate Policy Making* (Urbana, Ill.: Bureau of Educational Research, University of Illinois, 1960), pp. 59–76.

HOW POLICY EVOLVES

Basic Forces

Schools, like other institutions in our culture, are affected by basic social, economic, political, and technological developments. The amount of schooling of the adults of a community, for instance, is significantly related to the aspirations which that community holds for schools. Economic resources determine, in part, the level of program which a school may establish. For example, the relationship of the cold war to the establishment of the National Science Foundation is clear. Policies for education begin with the basic movements in society.

At the moment, these forces include international tensions, economic interdependence of all people, population mobility, widespread communication, technological advancement generally, the growth of knowledge, and the push for self-determination on the part of people everywhere. Moon shots and other events serve to dramatize the effervescence of the present day.

These basic social forces are not local in character; they are national and often world-wide in scope. Yet they impinge upon every local school community in the land. Every school budget is affected by the fact that defense needs require an $80 billion expenditure per year. Employment conditions in industrialized communities are not localized in their results. The movement of hundreds of blacks each month from the farms of the South to the city slums of the North is not merely a local problem.

Let us look at a specific case. A number of forces converged which encouraged the Congress to enact the Elementary and Secondary Education Act of 1965. These included widespread attention by public figures and the media to the presence of poverty in American society, growing recognition that urban problems were of special significance to the nation, and the social and political pressures generated by the civil rights movement.[2] These forces were superimposed upon more longstanding pressures to provide aid to nonpublic schools, to support educational research and to aid states. As

[2] See Philip Meranto, *The Politics of Federal Aid to Education in 1965* (Syracuse, N.Y.: Syracuse University Press, 1967).

noted in Chapter 3, the resulting legislation contained five titles which touched upon all these points but which was particularly noteworthy in focusing aid upon the educationally disadvantaged and in making benefits available to non-public schools. Nearly a billion dollars was appropriated to implement this legislation in its first year. All states, most school districts, and many colleges and universities benefited by its provisions.

To be sure, local implementation of the Act was subject to nominal approval by local boards of education and school officers. But there was considerable similarity among the ways in which various districts expended funds under the provisions of Title I. Federal guidelines and expectations shaped by national publicity influenced local decisions. In this instance and many more that could be cited, basic social forces, nation-wide and sometimes world-wide in scope, finally resulted in educational policy in many school districts.

ANTECEDENT MOVEMENTS

Movements designed to change educational policy are born in response to basic social forces. These movements may be nonofficial, such as the National Merit Scholarship Program, the Conant studies of high schools and teacher education, and the civil rights movement; or they may be official, such as the White House Conference on Education, the President's Committee on Education Beyond the High School, and President Johnson's task force study on education and the National Assessment Program.

It should be noted that these movements tend to be nation-wide in character. Funds for National Merit Scholarships included an initial grant of $18 million from the Ford Foundation and subsequent sums from over a hundred other donors. The President's Committee on Education Beyond the High School had a membership of thirty-eight, among whom were college presidents of both public and private institutions and a number of well-known industrialists. The report was aimed at the demand and need of education beyond the high school in the nation as a whole.

Significant in this connection is the way the press, television, and other media reinforce the national impact of such influences, as noted above. Sponsors of the nonofficial movements, particularly, are often skilled, or have ready access to those who are skilled, in mass media. These movements are good copy, hence releases by their sponsors are used widely by the newspapers of the nation.

The role of the philanthropic foundations in supporting the antecedent movements that often culminate in policy should be noted. For instance, foundations underwrote the National Manpower Council, the National Merit Scholarship Program, the Rockefeller report, the Conant studies, the National Assessment Program, and New York City experiments in decentralization. The relationship between some of the major foundations and the Executive Office of the President has tended to be a close one. All of these activities seem to be antecedents to educational policy.

We have noted that the forces which provoke educational policy are national and world-wide in scope, that the antecedents to policy may be official and nonofficial. These movements are often financed by the foundations. Moreover, the activities of the principals in these movements are given extensive reinforcement through the press, TV, and platform. Let us now examine another step in the evolution of educational policy.

POLITICAL ACTION

The antecedents and the resulting proposals provoke political activity in and out of government. One aspect of this activity is the debate that goes on among educators and among lay citizens, and between the two groups. Among educators these proposals are often met by opposition and defensiveness. For instance, the National Association of Secondary School Principals once advocated the banning of *Life* Magazine from high school libraries, in response to the series, "Crisis in Education," which appeared in that periodical. The series included a report of the Conant study on high schools and advocated programs for the gifted, ideas now actively espoused by the principals' organization. In another instance, the American Association of School Administrators proposed a position which they later modified in opposition to the National Assessment Program.

There may be good reasons for resistance on the part of school people. Sometimes these movements have ignored the educational fraternity, and non-educator enthusiasm may not have been tempered with the realities which school workers know reside in the situation.

Despite initial reluctance, however, educators usually respond by making studies of the problems related to the antecedent movements. Special provision for the education of the disadvantaged is a case in point. The urgency of the social needs to make better use of our manpower or to produce more scientists clearly prods school people toward making such an examination. The individual development of students has, by comparison, been a weak but perhaps a growing stimulation. In any case, studies of the disadvantaged have mushroomed. Some of these studies are being made by competent investigators, others by opportunists who do not wish to miss the bandwagon.

These studies by educators may come at the local, state, or national level. They may have official or semiofficial status, or they may be done by voluntary organizations such as state and national education associations. More and more, however, it appears that resources to conduct such studies are available at the national level. Again it should be noted that the foundations supply each year about $1200 million for various purposes, a large part for the study of education.[3]

The studies and reports engaged in by the educators often result in the endorsement of the original movement or some modification of it. Many educators, for instance, were not too comfortable with Mr. Conant's announcement that he proposed to study the schools of this country. His approach to the problem, however, proved to be reassuring; and his recommendations, although at first resisted in some quarters, have now become almost canons to many educators.

The antecedent movements to policy also stimulate lay citizens to action. Debate is aroused by such questions as, do our schools teach the 3 R's? Do our schools care about poor students? Do our bright kids just loaf? Discussion of this sort appears to have been particularly lively over the last decade. Analysis of the views of citizens on education reveals some of them to be basic and probing, some opportunistic and irresponsible. Perhaps we are coming into a period characterized by a little more sound inquiry into educational problems in addition to heightened public interest.

Newspapers, magazines, books, TV, and other media aid and abet this debate. The record of this debate has become so voluminous that anthologies are required even to sample it.[4]

As one might expect, debate and discussion, in the minds of some people, tend to crystallize positions. These people individually and through their organizations demand that local boards of education, state legislatures, and the Congress take action to rectify what they term weaknesses in our educational system. For instance, many

[3] Marianna O. Lewis, ed., *The Foundation Directory*. 3rd ed. (New York: Russell Sage Foundation, 1967).

[4] See C. W. Scott, S. M. Hill, and H. W. Burns, *The Great Debate: Our Schools in Crisis* (Englewood Cliffs, N.J.: Prentice-Hall, 1959).

school boards, particularly in Northern cities, have been pushed to eliminate de facto segregation, and many state legislatures have been confronted with pressures to abolish education courses required for the certification of teachers.

Again the local-state-national interrelationships of these debates, their wide publicity, and the subsequent demands on official bodies should be noted. The local post of the American Legion, for instance, may base its whole campaign for more Americanism in the schools upon the report of one of its national committees published in the Legion magazine. Or the argument to strip state boards of education of fiscal powers may emanate from the studies of the National Council of State Governments. Most local organizations are part of state and national networks. To assume that most problems are purely local in nature is sheer nonsense.

The activities of educators and lay citizens with respect to proposed educational policy may be reflected in the platforms of the political parties at state and national levels. Activities of citizens may also lead to studies and hearings on the part of government. A board of education may commission outside experts to study the extent of segregation in the schools. A state legislature may refer to a legislative reference bureau problems dealing with the foundation program or the tax structure of the state. At the national level the Hoover reports on the reorganization of government, as authorized by the Congress, are well known. The device of holding hearings is used broadly by local, state, and national policy-making groups.

Devices for study and investigation are a recognized part of the governmental process. It should be noted, however, that these are ordinarily employed *after* issues have been raised, debated, investigated, and perhaps polarized by lay citizens and educators. Seldom does government initiate. Ordinarily, governmental studies merely formalize what vigorous proponents have already said. Nor are politicians always adverse to settling for a study of an issue in place of action upon it.

FORMAL ENACTMENT

This process—change in basic social conditions, the organization of nation-wide antecedent movements, and political activity in and out of government—often culminates in policy. Usually policy requires some kind of legal formulation, an action that may be taken by local, state, or national governments. At any of these levels, particularly at state and national levels, the policy may be formalized by legislative, administrative, or judicial bodies.

At the local level, policy most frequently is formalized by the board of education and in some cases the city council. Many boards of education, however, give their superintendents leeway in formulating administrative regulations which also serve as guides to action and thus constitute policy statements.

Policy formalization for education at the state level is perhaps more complex. In the American scheme of things the state legislature is clearly the chief policy-making agency in education. Each state has a formidable body of school law which sets the formal limits within which all agencies can act. Literally hundreds of bills affecting education are introduced at each legislative session in most states, and these bills reflect the temper of the times and the antecedent movements to which we have referred. When "Americanism" rides high, we get bills, and some laws, requiring teachers to take oaths of allegiance. When education for the gifted is in fashion, we get bills, and some laws, establishing merit scholarship programs. But policy for education also emanates from state boards of education, special state commissions, state superintendents, state auditing agencies, state building boards, and the state courts.

Even though education is generally thought to be a state function, policy for education is also formed at the national level. The Congress cannot evade such questions as the need for scientists and mathematicians, the lack of research, the shortage of schoolhouses, and state differentials in the capacity to provide financial support for education. Deliberation on some of these questions led to the establishment of the National Science Foundation in 1950,[5] and to the passage of the National Defense Education Act in 1958,[6] both major policy enactments. Subsequent concern for the amelioration of poverty led to passage of the Elementary and Secondary Education Act.[7]

As noted in Chapter 3, educational policy also stems from the executive branch of the national government. The U.S. Office of Education is charged with the administration of the Elementary and Secondary Education Act. The administrative regulations formulated by the administrators who implement this measure far exceed in wordage the Act itself, and in many instances these regulations are policy interpretations. Much of this wordage is the product of the

[5] Public Law 81:507.
[6] Public Law 85:864.
[7] Public Law 89:10.

attorneys who in their endeavors to interpret policy actually become policy makers. In the Bureau of the Budget another set of policy makers is at work. What may have seemed to be a simple enactment on the part of the Congress becomes a veritable maze in the hands of administrators, attorneys, and budget controllers, all part of the executive branch of government.

By now it seems abundantly clear that the federal courts also make policy for education. Actually, the U.S. Supreme Court alone has made over fifty major decisions, of which the Brown case is but one, on educational issues.[8] These decisions cover such questions as the legality of private schools, public provision of textbooks to parochial pupils, public transportation of parochial pupils, released time for religious education, teachers and subversive organizations, and black-white integration.

A FLOW CHART

In summary, may we note that educational policy has its genesis in basic social change; its generation in nation-wide antecedent movements; its promotion by educators and lay citizens in and out of government; and its formalization in legal expression by local, state, or national government. This process is depicted in Figure 10.1.

I	II	III	IV
Basic Forces	*Antecedent Movements*	*Political Action*	*Formal Enactment*
Social, economic, political, and technological forces, usually national and worldwide in scope	Usually national in scope such as the Rockefeller Bros. studies, Conant Studies, National Assessment, etc.	By organizations usually interrelated at local, state, and national levels such as U.S. Chamber of Commerce, AFL-CIO, and NEA	May be at local, state, and national levels; and through legislative, judicial, and executive agencies

Figure 10.1 The policy-making process

Because basic social changes are usually nation-wide in scope, and the antecedent movements also often nation-wide efforts, inevitably

---

8 Clark Spurlock, *Education and the Supreme Court* (Urbana, Ill.: University of Illinois Press, 1955).

these forces tend to shift the major policy foci from local to state and to federal levels. Only the Congress can provide for education in terms of national survival. Usually, states talk of minimum foundation programs. Despite our tradition of localism, local boards of education find themselves ever more working within and restricted by the frameworks of state and national policy for education.

The flow chart in Figure 10.1 enlarges our concept of the policy-making process. We can no longer be concerned chiefly with the formal, legal expression of policy. Somehow we must give more attention to political action, to antecedent movements, and to basic social forces. In this task we have natural allies; the economist, the political scientist, and the sociologist have been at work on these matters for some time. With their help, our conception of this process can be further clarified.

Let us turn next to an actual case that illustrates the many forces playing upon a local board of education as it attempts to establish or reestablish policy.

A CASE: BOOK-BURNING IN DALEVIEW*

Daleview is a long-established suburban community of moderate size and rather favored circumstances, and is in a county that has been "Republican since McKinley." The present population of the high school district of about 30,000 includes many who live in newly developed sections, but the growth of the district, while rapid in recent years, has not been wholesale and uncontrolled. The district has a tradition of strong, well-educated boards of education, benefiting from the high professional level of many of the residents.

Dr. Charles Shields, the district superintendent, has held his position for seventeen years, and has a great respect for his community. The community returns the respect—or so we infer if supporting some twenty bond issues or tax rate increases during Dr. Shields' term means anything. Mr. Carl Priestly, the president of the board of education, is typical of the type of leadership to which Daleview has become accustomed. He was a Phi Beta Kappa and an athlete in his college days, and is now a senior partner in a prominent law firm in Metropolis. He is popular in his community for his vigor and forthright manner.

* The initial report of this case was written by Robert A. Bunnell.

Development of the Problem

Recently the social studies department of the Daleview High School developed, and received board approval for, a four-semester sequence of courses in American History to be taken by selected juniors and seniors. One of the three electives that could be taken as the fourth semester of this sequence was to be called "Contemporary American Civilization." This course went into operation in the spring semester following approval of the program.

As it developed, the talented young teacher of the course, Mrs. Shirley Harnet, distributed to the twenty-three seniors in her class a course outline containing the following statement:

> The basic text for the course will be Max Lerner's *America as a Civilization.* We will follow primarily his table of contents as our outline.

It was this use of the term *text* that was later to result in serious misunderstanding. The school code in this state required that a text must be adopted by the board of education and reported to state and county authorities. In fact, Lerner's book was one of thirty-three on the reading list of the course, and had never been adopted as a text in the legal sense, but was to be used as a reference in the course. In the debate that developed, the resolution of this question of fact was never fully reported—nor understood, it would seem—by the groups attacking the book.

With no advance notice of discontent in the community, the president of the board of education received a lengthy letter of protest from the Daleview post of the American Legion, dated February 10 of that year. The letter stated in part:

> It has come to our attention that the book entitled *America as a Civilization,* by Max Lerner, is currently being used as a textbook in one of the advanced history courses in the Daleview High School.
>
> We, of Daleview Post #52, The American Legion, feel that the selection of this particular book, written by Mr. Lerner, was indeed an unfortunate one. We respectfully wish to state our reasons for this belief and request that this matter be brought to the attention of the school board at your next meeting. . . . Please realize that we bring this matter to your attention without rancor and that we are seeking only to take a firm stand in regard to a matter which is of great concern to us. . . .

Our objections to this book may be briefly summarized under three main headings: the writer's background, the book itself, and the effect of this book on the students.

Under the first heading were listed seven Communist front organizations with the "evidence" that Lerner had been a member of importance in all of them. The next section objected to the book itself by noting that:

Again . . . we disagree with Lerner as he develops the false notion that we live in a "democracy" rather than a "republic." The motives he ascribes to those who would call our government by its proper name, "republic," rather than his "constitutional democracy," we believe grossly misrepresent their position and should not be stated as historical fact but as his personal opinion. As a result, we feel quite certain that no student having studied this text, will ever gain the clear conception and fundamental truth that the United States of America, governmentally, is not a "democracy," but a "republic."

 . . . . That he holds the Legion and VFW in contempt is obvious from his writings in his chapter entitled "The Joiners." It is indeed unfortunate, however, that the only contribution this scholar makes to the young people regarding the Legion and VFW is one of slander and vilification.

The final objection raised an issue of morals in addition to the problem of subversion:

We hope also, that the student will not be unduly influenced by the writer when he asserts that "sexual revolt in America has asserted three freedoms: the freedom to break the formal codes; the freedom to diverge from the majority sexual patterns *into deviant behavior* [emphasis supplied by the letter writers]; the freedom to lead a fully expressive sexual life in the pursuit of happiness. It is a . . . revolt for a healthy, expressive life" (p. 687). Should the suggestions made in this chapter be taken seriously by the student . . . and coupled with the problem of teen-age drinking . . . we suggest that only further impairment of teen-age morals can logically result.

We urge that another book be substituted as speedily as possible as a text in this course which will satisfy the standards of objectivity and integrity deserved by our students.

Following the receipt of the letter from the Legion, the teacher and department head involved prepared memoranda on the subject. Mrs. Harnet wrote that continued use of the book should be made because:

I. The class is made up of students of high academic ability. . . .

II. . . . Lerner's book acts as a stimulating and comprehensive outline. . . .

III. . . . We also have a full stock of books on all phases of American history (as a means of providing a contrast to Lerner).

IV. The role of the instructor is to remain objective and stimulating.

V. Many words can be said about academic freedom, but let it suffice to say that accepting pressure for censorship from any non-representative community group destroys the idea of public education.

The memorandum prepared by the department head dealt with the same problems and strongly recommended retention of the book:

There is no "basic" text for the course. The decision to use the book was based primarily on the fact that the department believes it to contain the best compendium synthesis of material upon the subject available. Hence, the structure of the course has been patterned on Lerner's table of contents.

In our opinion Lerner's book is not even controversial.

The author, it might be interesting to note, was mildly berated by *Time* —a publication hardly of the left-wing stripe—as having no point of view whatsoever. We heartily disagree, then, that Lerner is advocating anything—except understanding.
The fact remains, however, that Lerner's past record is absolutely irrelevant *unless* it can be demonstrated that this record is reflected *in the book.*

We recognize that the Legion is earnestly striving—as we all are—to keep America Free. It would seem that one way *not* to accomplish this aim would be to join the throng on *Unter den Linden* watching SS Troops burning books. . . .

The department strongly urges the Board of Education to permit continued use of the book.

The Legion letter was considered at the regular board meeting of February 27. At that time, the above memoranda were presented, though the fact was not noted in the board minutes, and the board proceeded to act as follows:

Mr. Priestly read excerpts from a letter from the American Legion, Daleview post, received by all Board members requesting removal of the book *America as a Civilization,* by Max Lerner, from use as supplementary text in the social studies department. Following discussion Dr. Karton moved that the board thank the American Legion for its thoughtfulness in calling this matter to the attention of the board, but decline to withdraw it from use as reference book in the class. Mrs. Bussee seconded the motion. On the roll call, voting "aye" were President Priestly, Mrs. Long, Mrs. Bussee, Messrs. Oak and Karton; "nay" Mr. Dyer. The President declared the motion carried.

The board then went on to its regular business and adjourned. Another phase of the problem was stirred by a letter published in the *Daleview Record*.

> The *Daleview Record* has given extensive coverage to the Daleview High School Senior Prom situation. [A decision by the board to discontinue proms on the grounds that parents had provided pre-dance cocktail parties; which decision was later reversed.] May I review the following in our defense.
>
> [Here the letter writer quotes Lerner's analysis of freedom in sex already quoted above in the Legion letter.]
>
> It seems to me that the very officials who are decrying the lack of parental responsibility are providing textbooks guaranteed to undermine the morals of our students in areas far beyond one yearly senior prom.

Mr. Vallencall, the department head, became increasingly concerned over this turn in the emphasis in the controversy, especially as the comment in the community became directed at the personality of the teacher, Mrs. Harnet. The board, in pursuing the resolution of the problem, had suggested that Mr. Vallencall not become involved as one who answered such criticisms as noted above, but rather that he serve the function of providing the board with appropriate information necessary to facilitate the board's continuing to work toward a solution. Consequently, Mr. Vallencall prepared a memorandum, which said in part:

> I feel there is a compelling need to clarify one particular theme that has turned up repeatedly in the anti-Lerner crusade.
>
> 1. Lerner is not advocating sexual revolt. . . .
> 2. It is an attempt to classify and categorize without any personal recommendation. . . .
>
> Mrs. Harnet concurs that this distortion of Lerner seems so vicious that it would be helpful to have our reactions on this point a matter of record.

On March 4, Mrs. Harnet received a letter from the author of the disputed book in reply to one that she had written to him.

I would very much appreciate your writing to me and sending a copy of the [Legion] letter to Mr. Priestly. . . .

. . . I would like to state, for the record, that I never was a Communist, and no sane person has ever dared make such an accusation.

I, too, am amazed at these outbursts, and can only attribute them to the tensions of the nuclear age, and of the recent Presidential campaign.

Mr. Lerner also wrote to the publisher of the *American Legion Magazine* in which he asked that ". . . some perspective be given to the Daleview Legion."

The continuing controversy over the book in the local, and finally in the Metropolis, papers and the national wire services, prompted Superintendent Shields and President Priestly to call in a good friend and head of a well-known public relations firm to assist them in the preparation of an open letter to the Legion. It was hoped, in the superintendent's words, that such a letter would "put out the fire." Pertinent portions of the carefully constructed three-page letter follow:

In view of your interest and that of the community at large, I am glad to make clear the position of the Board on this matter . . . The book, *America as a Civilization,* is a major reference work used in that course. There are a number of other source books recommended to the class, including *Democracy in America* by de Tocqueville, *The Public Philosophy* by Walter Lippmann, and *The Conscience of a Conservative* by Barry Goldwater.

The course was described in the school catalogue as part of the enriched social studies program. The catalogue states, "The program is designed to challenge the superior student to develop the technique of critical thinking regarding recurring issues in history; . . . to relate issues and events to present day situations."

The need for such courses was recently expressed by Dr. Conant in his report on *The American High School Today,* in which he urged that "Free discussions of controversial issues should be encouraged. This approach is one significant way in which our schools can distinguish themselves from those in totalitarian nations."

The book by Max Lerner, a Yale graduate and former faculty member at Harvard and Williams, is not designed as a text book and is not so used at Daleview. More than 1000 pages in length, it has extensive references to source material and cites the research of many earlier scholars in the field.

It might interest you to know that yesterday I talked on the telephone to James F. O'Neill, publisher of the *American Legion Magazine,* who said, "In my opinion Max Lerner is not pro-communist and is not subversive." Mr. O'Neill has agreed to send me a letter stating his views on this subject.

The letter then went on to quote liberally from reviews of the questioned book which appeared in national magazines such as *Time* and *Newsweek,* and in the *New York Times.* At the suggestion of the head of the department, Mr. Vallencall, the letter also dealt with the side issue of Lerner's treatment of sex:

> Reactions to a few observations in the book on sexual morality in the United States will naturally vary. Since the author comments as a reporter, not as an advocate, we are confident that, with proper guidance, students taking this course have the maturity to evaluate it as objective social commentary, not as personal doctrine.

The letter also offered support to Mrs. Harnet when it stated:

> Our students . . . will continually come into contact with a wide range of reading materials and varying points of view on all the controversial issues of our times. We believe that students are much more likely to react intelligently, critically, and objectively if they are introduced to such subjects under the direction of a skillful teacher.

The closing paragraph then made a plea for objectivity:

> This [objectivity] we believe is a basic part of the American ideal of liberty. Many years ago Jefferson said, "Here we are not afraid to follow truth wherever it may lead, nor to tolerate error so long as reason is left to combat it." More than one hundred years later Justice Holmes said, "The best test of truth is the power of the thought to get itself accepted in the competition of the market." And only a few years ago President Eisenhower reiterated this philosophy when he told a graduating class at Dartmouth, "Don't think you are going to conceal faults by concealing evidence that they ever existed. Don't be afraid to go into your library and read every book. . . . How will we defeat Communism unless we know what it is?"

On March 10, a resolution over the signatures of all members of the social studies department was transmitted to the board requesting,

> . . . the Administration and Board to issue a statement specifically in the defense of Mrs. Harnet. The current controversy has degenerated into personal attack upon the character of a member of the teaching profession. . . . Such a situation warrants a strong statement from the Administration and Board supporting Mrs. Harnet and the department.

In the ensuing weeks no such specific statement was forthcoming, probably due to the board policy of not adding fuel to the fire by making statements that opponents would feel obliged to counter.

March 13 may be noted as the climax and conclusion, for all practical purposes, of the crisis. The minutes of the board meeting tersely summarized the story:

> In view of the large number of visitors, the meeting was immediately recessed to convene at 7:45 P.M. in the speech lab of the high school.
>
> In addition to all members of the Board, the Director of Curriculum and the Business Manager were present. Absent: Secretary of the Board, Superintendent Shields.
>
> The President welcomed the visitors to the meeting. Mr. Priestly stated that the Board at its last regular meeting had voted not to remove the book (*America as a Civilization*) from class use, and read in full the letter dated March 7.
>
> The President next stated that visitors would be allowed to address the Board to present their views on the subject. The President first recognized Mr. H. R. Nash, Americanism Chairman of the Daleview Legion; Mr. Nash read his letter of February 10 and read another statement from the Legion to the Board.
>
> There followed general discussion with fifteen people participating.
>
> At 9:00 P.M., the President terminated the discussion and recessed the Board to reconvene in the board room to conduct the regular business of the Board.

The additional statement by the Legion, five pages in length, reiterated in some detail the earlier letter and went on to say:

> Our position has been badly distorted by some who perhaps have not been fully informed on the subject.

The statement went on to request that the department head's statement and the teacher's statement, as well as Priestly's letter and all the Legion letters, be given wide publicity. The statement continued:

> In conclusion, we respectfully suggest that there surely must be better tools than books of this type to stimulate the young mind.
>
> Once again we suggest the publication of the statements and letters previously referred to.
>
> We remain firm in our objections to the use of this book as a text and urge that you review your decision.
>
> The decision quite naturally and properly rests with you.

One aspect of the meeting which the minutes noted only briefly was the absence of the superintendent. The explanation was that a previously scheduled speaking engagement, out of town, happened to fall on that day. In line with the policy of minimizing these events, it was felt that the cancellation of such an engagement would be an error, in that it could be picked up by the press as evidence that the administration was "running scared." With the superintendent *not* present, the board's leadership in the fight was clearly noted, and the importance of the whole matter appeared diminished. The director of curriculum was present, and did in fact participate in gathering materials and dealing with some questions in the general discussion.

During the time that had elapsed since the first salvo of the Legion letter, Metropolis newspapers had from time to time published letters related to the controversy. On the day of the well-attended board meeting an interesting contrast in the views of two of the papers was noted. One carried an editorial that supported the stand the board had taken on February 27. The title of the editorial was "The Unburned Book":

> . . . True, the overview is undeniably Lerner's view. The book is not the same selection of facts that a de Tocqueville, a Lippmann or Goldwater would put into his overview. We presume that is why Goldwater's, Lippmann's, and de Tocqueville's books are included in the same course.
>
> It seems to us that this combination of viewpoints, far from tending to undermine the mind or morals, is about what a group of intellectually promising eighteen-year-olds ought to be digesting.

Meanwhile, another paper carried a by-lined story headlined: "Daleview Mothers Carry School Book Fight to Teachers." This article described a town where all the mothers would be going out that night on a "mother's march." The story went on:

> The battle lines are drawn. . . .
>
> The school is on the defense. . . .
>
> Divided also is the class of advanced students applying [sic] for enrollment in the course.
>
> The protesting mothers will march to the school tonight armed with copies of the prospectus which lists Lerner as the basic text.
>
> Meanwhile, State Senator, Mrs. Abby Winter, was contacted by the mothers. The Senator said, "Books like Lerner's contribute to juvenile delinquency."

And on that note, the news story ended.

Both papers carried stories the following day, including pictures taken at the open meeting. The *Metropolis News* headlined its story,

"Daleview Debates a Textbook"; the *Metropolis Citizen* headed its story, "That Book to Stay in Daleview School." Both papers carried statements of persons at the meeting, with the former reporting affirmative comment, "Our daughter is now doing some thinking," while the latter reported negative comment, "I'm wondering if the social studies department is going too far left." The two papers agreed when they reported that the board had pretty well made up its mind. Mr. Priestly was quoted as saying, "We already have had a full discussion of the subject. The issue is closed." And, except for a few parting shots from the other side, that was probably true.

While all this was going on in Daleview, interested persons favoring both sides were watching the events from outside the community. When the decision of the board was announced in the Metropolis papers and carried by the wire services, the superintendent and board began to receive calls and mail. Superintendent Shields has two lasting impressions of these communications:

> I was amazed at the vigor of the letters from *both* sides. You know, some thought the Legion was a little rough, but some of those liberals wrote some pretty strong letters. Both sides—the ones that wrote anyway—were real strong in their positions.
>
> Another thing that, well, didn't surprise me, but I found it gratifying, was that about 9 out of 10 calls and letters were complimentary. "Hooray for Daleview" and that sort of thing. They wrote from all over the country.

Some of the more surprising letters in the superintendent's file on this case came from persons of considerable prominence in Metropolis. Others were from teachers and students who praised the action in the name of academic freedom. Many local citizens also contributed their support in the form of congratulatory letters. Two interesting exceptions were to be found. In one letter, it was suggested that the board and social studies faculty were "dupes" of the Communists and were to be pitied and encouraged to read competent authorities to help them out of their misunderstanding. The valedictorian of a previous year's class at Daleview High, then a student in an Eastern college, was shocked at the board's failure to adhere to patriotic ideals. She felt that only at the college level could a person encounter strange ideas, and be able to evaluate them in terms of a good and sound American philosophy of life. Additional organized opposition in the form of letters came also from the Legion posts and VFW groups in surrounding communities.

Impact on School Policy

Two changes were effected in the policies of Daleview High School as a result of the controversy over this book. First, the administration and board of education, in co-operation with the heads of departments, worked out a detailed plan for the approval of books used in the school. A category called "On approval for possible adoption" was created to include books that might not be desired on a five-year basis as the law requires of the legally approved "textbook." All supplementary paperback books were to be ordered through the school bookstore, which makes monthly reports to the board of titles in use. No censorship was implied in this system, but rather the board preferred to know exactly what was being used to avoid being suddenly embarrassed by another "revelation" from the community.

The other change came in the staffing of the course. In the following semester, the course was to be continued, but due to the resignation of Mrs. Harnet, whose husband moved from the community, the course was to be taught by the head of the department. This step may be viewed as a concession to the community in that, although the adequacy of the teacher was never doubted by the school, the school was willing to adopt the view of the community that the course should be taught by a mature individual, "familiar with the attitudes and background of the community."

Whether the community will again engage in this kind of reaction to the school is a moot point. The critical groups remain, the need to teach the controversial issues persists, and possibility of disagreement is undoubtedly present.

SOME IMPLICATIONS

We shall first note some of the ways in which the case just presented illustrates the flow chart on policy-making presented earlier in this chapter. Then we shall suggest some of the more general implications for the administrator growing out of such a concept of policy formation.

REFLECTIONS ON DALEVIEW

The basic social-political force operating in Daleview at the time of the attempted book-burning was undoubtedly concerned with the growth of international Communism. The values of Communism and of the Western world are in many ways diametrically opposed. This conflict is reflected almost daily in tension spots over the world, in protracted but often useless attempts at negotiation, and in the use by both sides of many of the same words but with widely disparate meanings. The American Legion of Daleview was reacting to a world-wide movement.

A second political force also seemed to be operating in Daleview at the time of the Lerner affair; a hard fought and closely contested national election had just been concluded. The state in which Daleview is located was a key state in that election, and the results were so close as to be uncertain for several days. Finally, the opposition candidate, as far as Daleview was concerned, was found to have carried the state. This prompted accusations of fraud at the polls in nearby Metropolis. These circumstances led members of the Legion post and other citizens to view with considerable bitterness an author who seemed to have political views somewhat different from their own. Both national and world-wide movements were affecting the local serenity of Daleview.

The antecedent movements were also present in the case. The national emphasis on a more rigorous educational program had undoubtedly influenced Daleview school people to create an "honors group" in high school social studies and to bring to that group the writings of mature students of the social scene. Conant's studies of the secondary schools were known and were alluded to in the letter the board of education released to the public.

The local-state-national interrelatedness of those movements was illustrated in several ways. The whole controversy was covered in the local press, in the papers of Metropolis, and in the wire services that served the entire nation. The local post of the American Legion was not permitted autonomy; the national office of the Legion was brought into the picture. When the board of education took definitive action on the case, letters poured in from "all over the country." The issue in Daleview had more than local interest and import.

Political action was also illustrated in the Lerner affair. The local post of the American Legion, acting as a bona fide interest group, objected to the school program and attempted to have the program changed. The educators in the schools were requested by the board of education to stay out of the fight but to prepare memoranda for the use of the board as it weighed the problem. Mr. Lippmann and Mr. Goldwater, both political figures of considerable stature, were invoked in the controversy. The board, after exchange of letters with the Legion and considerable newspaper publicity, held an open meeting where some fifteen citizens expressed their views. All of this is political action in the best tradition of democratic societies. As with the other steps in policy-making, local political action has its overtones in the national arena.

Finally, we note that the Daleview Board of Education did formally enact some policy decisions. Most important, the disputed book was retained on the reading list. But two safeguards were provided: the status of the book was clarified, and the board was to be kept informed about supplemental books as well as textbooks used in the school. Possibly, the circumstance that permitted reassignment of the course to a more mature teacher who was "familiar with the attitudes and background of the community" was also in the nature of a policy decision.

In a sense this case had a happy ending. The freedom of students to read divergent views on controversial questions was sanctioned, even if under a somewhat greater prescription of conditions. But what might have happened in a community where the Legion had less restraint, where the board of education was less able, where the chairman of the board was less influential, where the professionals were less competent? Any one or more of these conditions could have altered the outcome.

Daleview dealt with policy-making at the local level, but the forces of the larger world were evident at every step of the process. The implications to which we now turn would seem to apply to policy-making at local, state, and national levels.

UNDERSTAND POLITICS

First, we think it is important that administrators understand the realities of politics. Contrary to what many have written (and perhaps more have wished), public education is squarely within the political realm. James has stated the matter succinctly in a research report on school finance:

All but negligible portions of their revenues are allocated through the voting mechanism, either at the state or at the local level. Three conditions are therefore essential to public school support. The first is that the expectations for service from the institution be sufficiently pervasive within a voting unit to receive majority support. The second is a system of voting that allows the voters to express preferences on the alternatives for allocating available resources between the public and the private sectors of the economy, among competing institutional components of the public sector, and among alternative services within the educational institution. The third condition is, of course, availability of resources.[9]

If the resources of our society are to be allocated among various institutions, including those in education, and if this allocation is dependent upon the voting preferences of people, and if these preferences are dependent on the expectations or values people hold, schools are inevitably in the business of creating expectations and of influencing voters. This is political action.

Nor is this political action limited to the local school district. Such action goes on at the state level, as school people attempt to influence the state legislature and other state policy-making bodies. Bailey has described this process as attempts were made to secure state foundation programs in the eight Northeast states.[10] Recent sessions of Congress have furnished abundant proof that education is involved in political action at the national level.

The people and the organizations that attempt to influence educational policy are numerous and persistent. A board of education may find that an election to consider an operating levy or a bond issue is greatly influenced by spokesmen who represent the local chamber of commerce, the farm bureau, or the labor union; or, as a board of education attempts to operate schools within the decisions made at the polls, it may find that the views of the local teachers' organization and of the local chapter of the John Birch Society have to be taken into account. But these influences come from more than local sources. Teacher selection is limited by state certification requirements. A school supply firm insists that it has an indispensable teaching machine. The physical science program emanating from work done at the Massachusetts Institute of Technology under the

[9] H. Thomas James, "School Revenue Systems in Five States." Co-operative Research Project No. 803, School of Education, Stanford University, 1961, pp. 2–3.

[10] Stephen K. Bailey, *et al., Schoolmen and Politics* (Syracuse, N.Y.: Syracuse University Press, 1962).

auspices of the National Science Foundation becomes a most persuasive innovation. The momentum of the National Merit Scholarship program with over a half-million high school students taking the examinations in a single year, and other forms of external testing, cannot be ignored.

At the state level Blanke found that in the judgment of chief state school officers, agriculture, business, labor, and professional educators were most effective in gaining access to state legislatures on educational issues.[11] Of these, in terms of techniques employed to gain access to the legislature, agriculture provided useful information often prepared by the land-grant colleges, organized effectively at the local level, and marshalled partisan political power. Educational groups supplied useful information and organized effectively at the local level, but were loath to employ partisan political power. Business seemed to be most effective in supplying information, and labor in utilizing partisan political power.

Clearly a part of the reality of politics is a recognition of the many influences that play upon boards of education, state legislatures, and other policy-making bodies. Moreover, an understanding of the nature of these influences and the methods employed by the groups that exert influence is also a part of the reality of which we speak.

In the public realm a review of the concept of federalism under which our government was organized may also be helpful to the administrator. As Grodzins has pointed out, federalism from the beginning has been a device for dividing the decisions and functions of government.[12] There has never been a time when it was possible to make neat divisions of federal, state, and local functions. Our system of government is really not a "layer cake"; it is more aptly described as a "marble cake."

No function of government is strictly local. Even a city police department, if it is to do its job, is dependent upon state crime laboratories, the Federal Bureau of Investigation, and other nonlocal agencies. In similar fashion most local school districts are greatly affected by actions of state legislatures, state boards of education, and other state agencies. The influence of the Congress and the federal

[11] Virgil E. Blanke, "Educational Policy Formulation at the State Level as Viewed by Chief State School Officers." (Unpublished doctoral dissertation, Department of Education, University of Chicago, 1961).

[12] Morton Grodzins, "The Federal System." In Report of the President's Commission on National Goals, *Goals for Americans* (New York: Prentice-Hall, 1960), pp. 265–282.

courts has already been noted. Our point is simply that federalism is also a reality in our local scheme of things.

While government, be it local, state, or national, often becomes the arena within which decisions about education are made, one must look at the private realm to see those groups which bring pressure on government. This is illustrated by a conversation one of us had with a secretary of a state chamber of commerce. The secretary had just attended a meeting of secretaries of chambers of commerce from midwestern states, called by the U.S. Chamber of Commerce. When asked if the U.S. Chamber had definitive positions on political issues that it had urged on the meeting, the answer was in the affirmative. "Did these positions receive support from the state secretaries?" the secretary was asked.

"Yes, they did," was the answer.

"And what do you expect to do about these matters in your state?" was the next question.

"I expect to hold meetings with every local chamber of commerce and work like everything to get them to endorse the positions we took at the meeting," he replied.

We think this little interchange illustrates not only what goes on in business organizations but also the process employed in agriculture, labor, education, and many other groups. In brief, we are suggesting that in the private realm there are numerous organizations with interlocking relationships at local, state, and national levels. Such arrangements permit pressure to be mobilized and applied where needed.[13] This phenomenon also appears to be a part of the reality of politics.

Both federalism in the public realm, and interlocking chains of influence in the private, reduce the amount of discretion left to a local board of education and alter the nature of that discretion. Burke, who examined this question for each of the fifty states, concluded that the trend in recent decades has been toward increased state control.[14] The trend seemed particularly marked in the areas of personnel and teacher certification, for instance, and in finance.

This brief discussion of the need of the school administrator to understand the reality of politics suggests that in his program of preparation major attention should be given to the concepts and

[13] For extension of this point, see Roald F. Campbell, *et al., The Organization and Control of American Schools* (Columbus, Ohio: Charles E. Merrill Books, 1970), Chap. 17.

[14] Arvid J. Burke, "Fifty State School Systems," 2nd ed. (Albany, N.Y.: New York State Teachers Association, 1961), Mimeographed.

research of the social sciences where political behavior has been systematically analyzed. There is also the need to extend these concepts from the campus to the real world, for the administrator is a man of action, not merely one of contemplation.

CLARIFY VALUES

But it is not enough that we see the political process in the clear light of reality. We must also ask what values we hold for that process. The ones we shall enumerate have their origin in our basic political documents. Some of our political leaders use these values as "liberal rhetoric" and resist any attempt to spell them out in terms of political action. We take the position, however, that they can and must be made operational if the policy-making process is to operate effectively. Some such value orientation as that discussed briefly below seems necessary.

We think that the individual is primary, the state secondary. This means that all people are important, and that all people are to have opportunity for individual development. It means that associations, organizations, and even governments are formed to help individuals achieve their utmost development, and that when these organizations no longer perform that function, they should be altered or destroyed.

While individual development to us is the ultimate goal, individuals live in a complex society, and in such a society there must be co-operation for the common good. This fact suggests that no individual has freedom to harm or restrain other individuals. The best society is one that protects the right of the most people to pursue their own purposes without subverting the purposes of others. Freedom then is relative, but it is also widespread.

We think that men, when adequately informed, make rational decisions. This statement presumes a belief that all men have some capacity to think and that the method of inquiry is an appropriate one. It assumes, moreover, that there are ways of providing relevant information so that the rational process may go forward. It does not deny the individual differences found in people nor the affective influences on decision-making, but it does place the emphasis on rational problem-solving.

Since capacity is widespread among men and opportunity is to be provided generally, it follows, we believe, that a mobile society is a better one. This belief suggests that any elite, except one of competence, is a dangerous one. Barriers to prevent upward mobility of the competent, or downward mobility of the incompetent, are to be removed. It follows that leaders in a society should be those who know more or who can apply knowledge more effectively.

While we accept the position that policy decisions by their very nature are public decisions, we also think that such decisions should take into account the specialized knowledge of the professional. Only by this kind of interaction can the alternative decisions be freely explored or the consequences of a particular decision ascertained. Such a procedure requires an enlightened lay leadership for education and competence on the part of those who speak as professionals.

The desirability that school administrators clarify their own values suggests a second body of knowledge which should be utilized in the preparation of administrators. We refer to the humanities. Surely those who would discern and influence educational policy should know and appreciate the values that have come to epitomize what we call Western civilization.

ACCEPT THE POLITICAL ROLE

As a final implication, we suggest that school administrators accept the fact that they are political functionaries. We do not imply that this is the only role of the administrator, but we do insist that when a status official is in the business of seeking the best agreements he can get from people within an institution and those without the institution who have some control over it, he is engaged in a political role. Unless the administrator can accept the political role, he will have few satisfactions and much discouragement.

For anybody who serves in a political role in our country, it is well to recognize that we live in a pluralistic society. While we may have a core of national values, with respect to many questions Americans have divergent views. Often these views are represented in a single school district. And it is with such divergent views that the school administrator must work.

The pluralism of our society, as well as the availability of resources and other factors, points to the necessity for each administrator to assess his situation as carefully as possible. While situations may have many things in common, each probably has a few unique characteristics. These common and unique characteristics may be found in the demographic, the physical, the financial, the cultural, or the attitudinal realm. As a wise politician the administrator comes to understand the circumstances in each realm.

But understanding is only a means to an end. The administrator is concerned with getting the best agreements possible in a particular situation at a particular time. People may approach these agreements from different philosophical bases and from varying motivations. The administrator is not basically concerned with philosophy, nor with motivation; he is concerned with operational agreements. He may, for instance, get people with much and with little schooling to agree that both academic and vocational programs are essential in the high school.

For each such agreement the administrator may be able to establish an "area of tolerance." Within such an area, people of divergent views will probably be willing to accept the programs and the direction given by the professionals. If the professionals exceed the "area of tolerance," dominant lay groups who can influence school policy will take steps to change school programs. Recent insistence on the part of some lay groups that schools provide for more integration is a case in point.

We should note, however, that the school may actually have exceeded the "area of tolerance," or it may have merely been perceived as doing so. Ethically, the administrator cannot ignore the actual situation; practically, he cannot ignore the perception of the situation. In the first instance, the professional staff must somehow come to understand what the "area of tolerance" is and be willing to work within it. In the second instance, the communication between school and community must be sufficiently complete and appropriate so that misperceptions and suspicions are kept at a minimum.

All of this may suggest that we seek a generation of administrators who are milquetoasts. Such is not the case. Just as we would have administrators determine what the area of tolerance is, we would also insist that the real challenge to administration is the enlargement or the extension of the area of tolerance. We advocate that administrators live dangerously. But to insist upon a program regardless of its acceptance in a particular situation at a particular time would probably mean the firing of the administrator. There are times when even this outcome may be good for a school organization. The dramatic events leading up to the firing might do much to crystallize difficulties in the organization or the community, and might lead to forthright steps designed to correct such difficulties.

More frequently, however, we think administrators must get their satisfactions from accurate assessment of a situation, from helping people see what can be done in that situation now, and from leading professionals and laymen to improve that which now exists. Such a plan may require the administrator to compromise at the level of program; it does not require him to compromise his goals.

SUGGESTED ACTIVITIES

1. Ascertain what revenues were received from the federal government by your school district during the past year. Determine what controls, if any, accompanied this money.
2. What school bill was debated vigorously in the last meeting of your state legislature? Why?
3. Determine how many teachers on the faculty of a city or county school district attended graduate school during the past summer on fellowships provided by some agency of the national government.
4. Check on the high schools of your county for the number of students who took the National Merit Scholarship qualifying test, the number of semi-finalists, and the number of merit scholars.
5. Find out how many high schools in your county are using curricular materials developed in the national curriculum programs in mathematics, physical science, biological science, chemistry, English, and social studies.
6. What do the findings for questions 3, 4, and 5 suggest?

SELECTED READINGS

BAILEY, STEPHEN K. *et al. Schoolmen and Politics.* (Syracuse: Syracuse University Press, 1962).

CAMPBELL, ROALD F., CUNNINGHAM, LUVERN L., McPHEE, RODERICK A. and NYSTRAND, RAPHAEL O., *The Organization and Control of American Schools,* 2nd ed. (Columbus, Ohio: Charles E. Merrill Books, 1970).

EDWARDS, NEWTON. *The Courts and the Public Schools.* 2nd ed. (Chicago: The University of Chicago Press, 1955).

IANNACCONE, LAWRENCE, *Politics in Education.* (New York: Center for Applied Research in Education, 1967).

KIMBROUGH, RALPH B. *Political Power and Educational Decision-Making.* (Chicago: Rand McNally, 1964).

MASTERS, NICHOLAS A., SALISBURY, ROBERT H., and ELIOT, THOMAS H. *State Politics and the Public Schools.* (New York: Alfred A. Knopf, 1964).

National Society for the Study of Education Yearbook, *Metropolitanism and Education.* (Chicago: University of Chicago Press, 1968).

National Society for the Study of Education Yearbook, *Social Forces Influencing American Education*. (Chicago: University of Chicago Press, 1961).

Report of the President's Commission on National Goals, *Goals for Americans*. (Englewood Cliffs, N.J.: Prentice-Hall, 1960). (Particularly Chap. 3 by John W. Gardner and Chap. 12 by Morton Grodzins.)

11

Personal Motivations
For
Administrator Behavior

Administrators, like all human beings, act in an environment in which the conditions are never completely known. Psychologists tell us that even the physical conditions which surround us have an effect upon behavior. The comfort of working conditions, the color of the room, the adequacy of the lighting, and the relative humidity of the atmosphere all have their effect upon what people do. When the environment contains people who react differently to these and other existing conditions, and to each other, the problem of explaining behavior becomes exceedingly difficult. Indeed, when we consider the fact that one's reaction to one's surroundings is a function of conditions within the person as well as those outside him, the intricacy of the science of human behavior is obvious.

FACTORS AFFECTING BEHAVIOR

In this chapter we shall not attempt to assume the role of psychologists or psychiatrists in explaining or dealing with the problems of human behavior. Nevertheless, since the administrator's stock in trade is human relationships, his behavior should have a sound psychological base. The most generalized principle provided him as a guide to understanding the basis for his actions is that *behavior is dependent upon the interaction of the conditions within the person and those which surround him.* Allport describes a field theory of personality in much the same way that the physical scientist speaks of the "field" in the atomic theory of matter. As he says, "Roughly speaking, the field theory of personality regards the total environ-

337

mental setting as well as the inner structure of the person as decisive in the shaping of conduct."[1]

Allport's field theory is similar to what many psychologists refer to as an "open system" in which one's own fund of understandings forms the basis for his understanding of the world around him. In turn, what he perceives in the outside world affects his inner self. A transaction between his inner and outer worlds is constantly changing both of them.[2]

Thus, psychologists provide us with a clue for thinking about human behavior. To understand it we must know something about the nature of the "field" in which behavior is exhibited. Yet the characteristics of the field are not directly observable. They must be inferred from the observations of people who, themselves, are a part of this field. To illustrate this in educational administration, let us take the case of two administrators who at different times held the same administrative position. For one of them, the position presented the challenge through which he successfully developed his leadership potential. The other found the position uninteresting and exceedingly limited in the opportunity it gave him to do those things that he felt compelled to do as an administrator.

Apparently *the man in the situation* made the difference. Conditions in the situation elicited different responses in each of the two men. In turn, the two men had different effects upon the situation. Forces, reactions, circumstances, and relationships among things and people were altered by the exchange of the two administrators. Observing these two administrators, one would find it difficult to attribute differences in their behavior merely to the observable conditions in the school district in question. Part of the cause must be attributed to what Allport has referred to as "the inner structure" of the persons involved.

Careful observers of human behavior find it difficult to attribute a specific behavior to a particular cause. Rather, they agree that the behavior of individuals is due to a combination of causes difficult to unscramble. There is, therefore, a reluctance among these observers to establish a cause and effect relationship between specific behaviors and the elements of the situation merely on the basis of observational

---

[1] Gordon W. Allport, *Personality: A Psychological Interpretation* (New York: Holt, Rinehart & Winston, 1937), p. 364.

[2] For a brief review of pertinent literature, see Daniel E. Griffiths, Lawrence Iannaccone, and James Ramey, *Perception: Its Relation to Administration* (New York: University Council for Educational Administration, 1961), p. 11.

evidence. At the present stage in the development of the science of human behavior, it is probably more meaningful to speak not of causes of behavior but of factors that may affect behavior. We shall deal primarily with those factors which may be altered by educational processes—namely, one's assumptions, beliefs, values, concepts, motivations, perceptions, and skills.

The major purpose of this chapter is to help the prospective administrator begin his assessment of the internal conditions that prompt him to act as he does. Our chief concern will be with those personal factors that may be changed by the individual as he comes to develop an understanding of the ways in which these factors may affect how he behaves. One ever-present danger of such self-examination is that introspection may block desirable action and result in indecision. The reader should keep this caveat in mind as he examines his own behavior in light of the factors that we discuss in the remainder of this chapter.

The four factors that we will consider include: (1) the administrator's perceptions of others; (2) his perception of himself; (3) his values and beliefs; and (4) his concepts of success. In our discussion of these factors we will illustrate how they may affect the administrator's behavior.

PERCEPTION OF OTHERS

How an administrator works with people is partially dependent upon the assumptions which he makes about them. Two such key assumptions center around what people *will* do and what they *can* do. These assumptions about people's motives and abilities form a set that influences how the administrator assesses individuals and how he behaves toward them.

An administrator can, for example, be predisposed to attribute negative motives to his subordinates. He may view them as working only to maintain a decent standard of living for themselves and their family, as wishing to avoid responsibility, as having little or no ambition, as wanting security above all else, as being indifferent, and as having a "take-it-easy; don't burn yourself out" attitude.[3] On the other hand, the administrator may be inclined to attribute positive motives to subordinates. He may believe that work is their central life

---

[3] Douglas McGregor, *The Human Side of Enterprise* (New York: McGraw-Hill, 1960).

interest, that they are self-directed and industrious, that they derive a sense of accomplishment from doing a job well, and that they are challenge-seeking rather than challenge-avoiding.

Similarly, an administrator can ascribe either positive or negative abilities to his subordinates. He may assume that they are creative, that they know what to do when discretion must be exercised, that they have the capacity to induce and deduce, and that they are capable of doing a variety of things. On the other hand, the administrator may be pessimistic about his subordinates' abilities and operate on the assumption that they are unimaginative, unable to work jointly with others on a common task, possess limited intellectual resources and competencies, lack ingenuity, and are incapable of consistently exercising good judgment.

The nature of the abilities and motives which the administrator attributes to the people with whom he works can influence his actions and reactions in a variety of ways. His assumptions can affect how he defines his role as a supervisor, how he deals with people who break organizational rules, and how he approaches the task of introducing organizational change. Let us now look at the manner in which the administrator's assumptions may guide his behavior in each of these areas.

SUPERVISION

A major responsibility of administrators is the supervision of subordinates' performance. How the administrator elects to carry out this function is determined in part by his assessment of his subordinates' motives and abilities.

If he assigns negative motives and abilities to them, he is apt to regard close supervision as an organizational imperative. A subordinate who is viewed as being an unwilling contributor to the achievement of the organization's goals and as having little concern for the quality of his performance is one who certainly bears watching. The administrator who suspects his subordinates' motives and abilities will no doubt feel the need to hold frequent inspections to assure himself that their behavior conforms to the organization's expectations. He will frequently check to see that people are reporting to work on time, that they are not leaving the building before the prescribed time of departure, that they are at their work stations, that they are adhering to the course of study, and that they are exercising good judgment in using it. In short, the suspicious administrator is driven by the constant need to verify that rules and regulations are being followed and that performance meets acceptable standards.

If, on the other hand, the administrator believes that his subordinates are highly motivated and are capable of superior role performance, then his approach to his supervisory responsibilities may be quite different. The administrator who trusts his subordinates will monitor their work efforts less frequently.[4] In consequence, his chief concern as a supervisor may shift from an identification of individual departures from organizationally prescribed role expectations to a search for the barriers that hamper the performance of his subordinates. The administrator not only locates such obstacles; he also removes them. Furthermore, he is confident that his subordinates are capable of and interested in identifying the resources which will facilitate their performance; and, he actively seeks to secure these resources for them.

RULE-ENFORCEMENT

The motives and abilities which an administrator attributes to organizational participants also influence how he attempts to explain their behavior. In seeking to find a sufficient reason for people's actions, the administrator may look for an explanation based on either some *inner* qualities of the individuals involved or some *external* environmental factors acting upon them at the time. The capabilities and the intentions which the administrator ascribes to people affect whether he is likely to establish an internal or an external locus of causation for their behavior. Where the administrator locates the cause for individuals' actions determines how he evaluates them and subsequently behaves toward them.[5]

Let us consider an example of how these attribution processes may influence the way in which an administrator handles behavior that violates certain rules of organization. A high school principal reported having received the following note from one of his English teachers:

Mr. Jones, Bernie Miller has been a persistent problem in my class. During study periods he wastes time and makes it difficult for his

---

[4] Lloyd H. Strickland, "Surveillance and Trust," *Journal of Personality* **XXVI**, 2 (June, 1958), 200–215.

[5] F. Heider, *The Psychology of Interpersonal Relations* (New York: Wiley, 1958).

neighbors to do their homework. He seldom has his assignments ready to hand in and shows no interest in school. I've kept him after school and punished him in other ways, but NOTHING SEEMS TO WORK! My class would be better off without him so why don't you transfer him or assign him to a study hall?

In this episode the principal, Mr. Jones, has several possible ways of coping with this situation; the options he considers are determined in part by the assumptions which he makes about students' motives and abilities. If the administrator believes that most high school students are in attendance against their will and will do only what is demanded of them, then he is apt to think about the various sanctions that he might use or threaten to use in getting the boy to do his homework. The principal might insist that the student remain in school each day until he completes his homework. The principal might threaten to call in the boy's parents if he continues to ignore his teacher's assignments. Or, the principal might threaten the student with dismissal or suspension from the basketball squad.

If, on the other hand, the principal is inclined to attribute a full measure of interest in school to students, then he is likely to look elsewhere for the cause of the student's failure to hand in his homework. In this particular case Mr. Jones doubted that motivation was the problem and sought to locate other possible causes for the boy's behavior. The principal's first step was to ask the English teacher, Mrs. Pollock, if there were other students in the class who were not handing in their homework. Mrs. Pollock identified nine other students—five boys and four girls—who frequently did not complete their assignments; however, these students, unlike Bernie Miller, behaved themselves in class.

With this additional information, Mr. Jones set out to discover what distinguished these ten students from the seventeen other pupils who seemed to do their work consistently in Mrs. Pollock's class. The search was a brief one. The ten non-homework students were at least three full years below grade level in reading while the text from which the homework assignments were made was written at grade level. Mr. Jones made these findings available to the teacher; she requested and received materials that were within the reading comprehension of the students and which appealed to a broader range of interests than the single text.

The problem had nothing to do with motives; rather it stemmed from a combination of internal (low reading ability of students) and external (available reading materials) factors. The student was not punished, nor was the organization's homework requirement set aside. However, the subsequent assignment of homework took into account the varied abilities and interests of students in the class.

MANAGEMENT OF CHANGE

A third area in which the administrator's basic assumptions about people's motives and abilities are partial determinants of his behavior is that of organizational change. How he approaches the problem of effecting change in organizational goals, structure, practices, and procedures is influenced by his conceptions of his subordinates. The administrator may assume that people have a preference for predictability; that people when confronted with a choice between stability and change will opt for stability; that people by their very nature will resist any tinkering with the status quo; that people develop vested interests in organizational arrangements which accentuate their fundamental orientation to resist changes; and that people are security-conscious, always favoring the old and established ways of doing things to the new, untried, and unproven ways.

Or, the administrator may assume that human beings are novelty-seeking; that they are eager to experiment because such occasions offer opportunities to develop competence and to demonstrate mastery of the environment; and that they derive satisfaction from such activities as exploring, investigating, and manipulating an unknown environment.[6] These two conceptions of how man orients himself to change, coupled with assumptions about the individual's abilities, can heavily influence the manner in which the administrator approaches change as shown in the example that follows.

In recounting a recent experience he had with his math department, a high school principal in his first year on the job told about the way he had handled a decision concerning whether the school should adopt new programmed texts in algebra and geometry. Shortly after the opening of school the principal received a memo from his superintendent about these programmed texts. The superintendent stated that he was impressed by the idea of individualized materials which enabled students to proceed at their own pace and that he hoped the high school math staff would use these materials, at least

---

[6] Robert W. White, "Motivation Reconsidered: The Concept of Competence," *Psychological Review,* **66,** 5 (1959), pp. 297–333.

on a trial basis with several classes. As the principal re-read the note from his superior, he recalled a sarcastic comment made by his predecessor, "Those old-guard math teachers are really in a rut. They are the arch enemies of institutional change."

Faced with a superior who was obviously interested in new curriculum ideas and practices, and a staff who had been labeled as being opposed to innovation, the principal pondered several possibilities. He could accept the previous principal's view of the teachers in the math department. If he did this, he recognized that his strategy would be aimed at minimizing staff resistance to an administrator-initiated change. To cut down the opposition and perhaps even avoid intentional efforts to sabotage the new practice, the principal considered that he would need to give the staff full information about the necessity for the change. At the same time, he thought that he might share control in putting the change into effect by having the math department decide how many algebra and geometry classes would use the new programmed materials. Through such tactics the principal did not expect to eliminate the resistance; however, he did anticipate that the staff would be less likely to torpedo his efforts.

Another possibility which the principal considered was that these teachers would be willing to try a promising idea and would welcome the chance to experiment with a challenging practice. The principal seriously entertained this more positive view of his staff's motives and eventually decided to have his staff scrutinize the texts and decide whether they should be used.

The staff ordered the programmed materials, wrote the publisher for the names of schools in the area who were using the new texts, requested and received permission to visit these schools, and set out to locate penetrating analyses of this approach to math instruction. After five months of intensive study, the math department unanimously recommended the use of the texts only as supplementary materials for students who were experiencing difficulties in mastering specific math concepts.

Accompanying the recommendation was a thoughtful, detailed commentary on the shortcomings of the approach and on the conditions under which the new materials showed some promise of being useful and effective. The report which the staff prepared was sufficiently convincing that the superintendent realized how even a limited, full-scale trial in but a few math classes could have led to serious problems. To his surprise, the report reflected the staff's willingness to innovate and showed its ability to gather evidence and use it wisely.

PERCEPTION OF SELF

How an administrator perceives himself influences his thoughts and actions in several important ways. First, the administrator uses himself as a norm for judging others; what he looks for in people is influenced by his own traits. The more he understands himself and the kind of person he is, the fewer errors he is likely to commit when making inferences about other people. Second, the administrator makes certain assumptions about what controls his behavior. Some administrators tend to see their behavior in the organization as being largely self-determined; others believe that events external to themselves and beyond their control govern their behavior. The administrator's perceptions of the primary locus of causation for his own behavior shapes his organizational conduct. Third, administrators make certain assumptions about their ability to act as a causal agent for the behavior of others. Some administrators expect that certain anticipated consequences will follow from their actions while other administrators lack this sense of efficacy. What the administrator chooses to undertake is partially determined by how efficacious he views himself in generating the outcomes he seeks.

AWARENESS OF SELF

People use themselves as the standard by which they perceive or judge others; administrators are no exception. One way in which the administrator's traits influence what he looks for in someone else is that they help to furnish the categories he uses in perceiving others.[7] His characteristics, needs, and values both expand and limit his vision as they sensitize him to certain aspects of other people and blind him to other aspects. For example, an administrator who is a non-authoritarian person is more likely to view other individuals in terms of their psychological and personal characteristics and be less concerned about their orientation to power than is an authoritarian administrator. An administrator who is warm and friendly is apt to look for these qualities when he forms impressions of others. An adminis-

---

[7] Sheldon S. Zalkind and Timothy W. Costello, "Perception: Implications for Administration," *Administrative Science Quarterly*, **VII** (September, 1962), pp. 218–235.

trator who is blunt and straightforward may tend to use these characteristics in describing other people.

Whether the administrator rejects or accepts his own characteristics also determines in part how he perceives and evaluates others. What the individual *does not accept* about himself he is set to recognize in other individuals. For instance, the administrator may be assertive and inclined to impose his will on those who work with him. At the same time, he may be extremely sensitive to this characteristic in others—even to the point of seeing an autocratic intention behind people's actions when there is none. Since the administrator regards the trait as being undesirable in himself, he negatively evaluates those people in whom he sees a similar trait.

An administrator who is *accepting* of a particular characteristic in himself is also set to look for this same quality in others. How he responds depends upon whether he views his trait as a deficiency or as a virtue. If the administrator has a deficiency (not meeting deadlines for periodic reports or being late for appointments) which does not disturb him, then he may make undue allowances in others who have near-identical deficiencies. On the other hand, if the administrator prizes the quality in himself, then he is likely to be attracted to others who have the trait and to be repelled by those who lack it. For example, the administrator who is obeisant to his superiors and assigns substantial significance to this characteristic will judge his own subordinates in terms of their obeisance to him; submissive subordinates will be accepted and non-submissive subordinates will be rejected.

However, the administrator's own personal characteristics are not the only inner factors which may color his perceptions of other people. The current emotions which the administrator is experiencing also can shape what he sees in others.[8] An administrator who becomes insecure when an organizational change is announced will look for signs of insecurity in those with whom he works. As he interprets the behavior of others as revealing "unmistakable" signs of insecurity, his own feelings of security will be correspondingly diminished. Similarly, an administrator who is anxious about how others are perceiving him during an important meeting may discern meanings in people's actions which were never intended.

The administrator who has insight into his own personality is less

[8] S. Feshback and S. D. Singer, "The Effects of Fear Arousal upon Social Perception," *Journal of Abnormal and Social Psychology,* LV (1957), pp. 283–288.

likely to have his perceptions of others distorted by his own personal characteristics.[9] Admittedly his perceptual processes, like those of other individuals, are intricate and complex. However, as the administrator comes to know the categories he uses in perceiving others, the amount of weight he attaches to these categories, and how the categories and their significance to him are related to his own characteristics, he can have somewhat greater confidence in his judgments. In the meantime, the administrator is advised to guard against making snap judgments and to seek reliable evidence as a firm basis for his evaluations of others.

PERCEIVED CONTROL OF SELF

Some persons believe that they are, in a sense, masters of their fate. They approach life as though they can do what they will to do. Such individuals are inclined to view their actions as products of their own choosing; they initiate rather than follow. Other persons consider that their behavior is determined by external forces beyond their control. These people link what they do to outer factors rather than to inner ones. This type of person tends to see few options for himself and to act only when he has a clear, unambiguous mandate to do so. Where the administrator locates the control of his own behavior will partially determine how he enacts his organizational role.

In the mid-1960's, a number of big city school systems sought to decentralize their operations. The trend toward decentralization was prompted by several conditions. There was a growing recognition by chief school officers that a six- or seven-layered bureaucratic cake was inefficient. So many decisions were being referred to the top that long delays resulted; patient and impatient citizens alike charged officials with being evasive and unresponsive. Simultaneously, school administrators were becoming convinced that the right to make final decisions should be vested closer to the scene of action where knowledge of local problems and circumstances was greatest. By increasing the amount of discretion which could be exercised by administrators at lower levels, the men at the top hoped to cut down their own occasions for decision; to reduce the time lag between the occurrence of a problem and its attempted resolution; and to effect more intelligent, informed choices throughout the organization. What

[9] Zalkind and Costello, *op. cit.*

frequently happened was more of a change in rhetoric than a change in actual practices, however.[10]

A sizable number of lower level administrators failed to exercise the newly granted discretionary powers. Administrators did not adopt the new view of themselves and continued to behave as though they lacked the ability to control their own actions. In the face of unclear boundaries around their choices, administrators would not make decisions independently; they continued to seek approval to make decisions or to pass the problems to higher levels for a resolution. Some of these administrators undoubtedly were unsettled by the responsibility which accompanied the redistribution of decision-making authority. Others, however, because of their innate or organizationally acquired predispositions to ascribe an external locus of control for their own behavior, could not act as though they were self-governing. They did not test the limits of their powers because they perceived they had none.

Perceived Control of Others

A pervasive but frequently unstated assumption in the myriad discussions of leadership is that a leader views himself as being a causal agent of other people's actions.[11] By implication the administrator who does not believe that the behavior of others is contingent upon his own actions is not apt to engage in leadership acts. Unfortunately, we lack much systematic research into the conditions under which an administrator is likely to connect the behavior of others with his own deliberate management of the environment. Also, we do not know a great deal about how an administrator behaves when he does and when he does not regard himself as being a significant factor in what others do, think, and feel. Although our knowledge in this area is limited, what we have learned is enlightening.

At least two conditions can affect whether an administrator perceives himself as being a causal agent for another's actions. If the administrator ascribes the quality of immutability to other people's behavior, then he is apt to persuade himself that no one can have an

---

[10] See Thomas R. Williams, "An Exemplary Design for the Administrative Organization of an Urban Public School System" (Unpublished doctoral dissertation, University of Michigan, 1968).

[11] Edwin M. Bridges, "Administrative Man: Origin or Pawn in Decision Making?" *Educational Administration Quarterly.* **6,** 1 (Winter, 1970), 7–25.

impact on the person and he acts accordingly. For example, in a recent study,[12] elementary principals expressed the belief that the expressive (personal-social) characteristics of beginning teachers were not amenable to change. At the same time, the principals seemingly were convinced that the instrumental (task performance) characteristics of teachers could be modified. Since the principals ascribed stable and enduring properties to the expressive characteristics, they were significantly less inclined to invite a teacher with somewhat weak expressive qualities for a job interview than a teacher with weak instrumental characteristics.

How an administrator perceives his own skills, resources, and characteristics can also color his inferences about his potential for acting as a causal agent for others. By way of illustration, former President Lyndon B. Johnson decided not to seek re-election to his country's highest executive office; he gave as a major reason his conviction that he could not unify the nation. Johnson evidently believed that unification was possible; however, he felt that he was not the man who could help the country achieve a unified perspective. He cited several of his own qualities (being from the South at that period in American history and lacking the personal characteristics which appeal to fairly large segments of the American public) as representing significant obstacles to his being able to develop the sense of national unity which the country sorely needed. If Johnson had perceived himself differently, he might have sought re-election and, perhaps, even won it.

Important as perceptions are in determining behavior, they are subject to error. Administrators can misjudge their own available resources for affecting the actions of others and can err in their judgments of the immutability of certain human characteristics. We suspect that administrators are more likely to underestimate than to overestimate their potential for influence. As a consequence, we believe that the prospective administrator can profitably examine the assumptions which he brings to the causal agent facet of his organizational role. If he is to function as a leader, he must necessarily view other people's actions as contingent upon his own behavior. Some of the conditions which may affect his perceptions about his capacity to influence others are discussed in Chapter 7.

---

[12] Edwin M. Bridges, "Preferences of Principals for Instrumental and Expressive Characteristics of Teachers," *School Review,* **76,** 3 (September, 1968), pp. 324–338.

VALUES AND BELIEFS

Values and beliefs also partially determine a person's behavior as they constitute important premises which guide and direct action. These two types of decisional premises[13] differ in several respects. A belief is an expectation held by an individual that a given cause leads to one or more results. The results may be either positive or negative, wanted or unwanted; what is significant is that the person connects the results with a particular cause. For example, an administrator may have a belief about how certain teacher characteristics affect what students learn or fail to learn. Specifically, the administrator may have formed the expectation that students will learn more when taught by warm, friendly, and understanding teachers. With this belief, the administrator is apt to rate teachers with these characteristics much higher than teachers who are businesslike, cold, and aloof. Not infrequently, the connective link between the expected cause and result is unclear to the individual with the belief. He does not know, nor has he thought about, how the cause produces the result. Nevertheless, he acts as though the belief were a valid one.

A value, on the other hand, is an expectation by the individual about what ought to be. Unlike a belief, a value is concerned with what should be the case rather than with what is the case. An individual acting consistently with his values does what he does because he feels that it is legitimate, good, or right. If a person believes that by acting in a particular way he can effect a given result, he may be unable to take the action because it is inconsistent with his values. By way of illustration, an administrator was being urged by his subordinates to take action with which he was not in basic agreement. He was convinced that he could successfully avoid giving into their demands and escape a charge of dereliction by using the technique of "negative timing."[14] Use of this power tactic would involve his initiating action on the demand but delaying final action until it was either too late or the plan "died on the vine." The administrator, however, elected to take a riskier action because the

[13] Manley Howe Jones, *Executive Decision Making* (Homewood, Ill.: Richard D. Irwin, 1962), pp. 56–96.

[14] Norman H. Martin and John Howard Sims, "Power Tactics," *Harvard Business Review* (November–December 1956), pp. 25–29.

negative timing technique ran counter to his moral code. Let us now look at three areas in which the administrator's values and beliefs can make a difference in his behavior.

ROLE OF AUTHORITY

Most organizations are hierarchically structured with superordinates having authority over their subordinates. Although superordinates possess organizational authority or the right to command subordinates, the superordinate still faces the task of influencing subordinates to act in ways consistent with his directives.[15] What distinguishes a leader from an administrator, as we noted in Chapter 7, is that the leader is successful in his attempts to influence others. Therefore, for the administrator to function as a leader he must be able to convert his organizational authority into compliance by his subordinates. How the administrator chooses to exercise authority over his subordinates is affected by his beliefs and values about the nature of authority and the way in which an authority relationship is established.

Some administrators believe that their subordinates will do simply as they are told. When faced with the necessity to guide and direct the choices of subordinates, these administrators use straightforward and uncomplicated tactics to effect an authority relationship. They may say on an individual basis to a subordinate, "I wonder if you would have time to . . . ," "Would you please . . . ," or "From now on we will need to. . . ." Or, they may issue a memorandum to the work group stating, "In the past we have. . . . Henceforth, we will. . . ."

Other administrators believe that their subordinates will obey instructions out of a sense of duty to the organization or because they fear sanctions for non-compliance. An administrator with these beliefs is likely to sandwich an order between an emphasis on the subordinates' organizational obligations and some sort of veiled threat. The announcement might read something like the following: "In the best interests of the organization and everyone involved, the staff will be expected to . . . beginning next week. Regrettably some individuals were penalized in the past for ignoring instructions; I'm sure such action won't be necessary this time."

Still other administrators believe that subordinates will follow commands which are accompanied by proof[16]—proof of the wisdom

---

[15] Jones, *op. cit.*, pp. 125–126.
[16] *Ibid.*, pp. 173–182.

of the administrator's proposal for action. To elicit support for his recommended course of action, the administrator may take one or more of the following steps:

1. He elaborates on the problem which gave rise to the need for such action.
2. He specifies in detail the various other alternatives which were considered.
3. He shows how the orders he has issued will eliminate the problem completely or will check the unwanted consequences in the problem situation.
4. He comments about the possible effects of the administrator's instructions on the individual as well as the organization.

The administrator fully expects such steps to result in willing compliance.

Values also figure in how an administrator responds to the authority inherent in his organizational role. An administrator may feel that his orders should never be questioned by subordinates. He views arguments which are raised against his proposals as challenges to his authority and as assaults on the authority structure of the organization. His reactions are swift. He reprimands his subordinates. He lets them know how inappropriate their actions are. He even threatens them with dismissal if the behavior is repeated.

Another administrator may feel that it is quite proper for subordinates to raise questions about the instructions he gives. He regards such behavior as their legitimate right. Consequently, when subordinates oppose his attempts to exercise authority over them, the administrator seeks reasons for their opposition. He listens attentively to what they say. He probes for unwanted consequences which they may see but to which he may be blinded. He searches for what and how they feel about the matter. Even if the administrator chooses not to reverse his earlier decision, he does not censor his subordinates for their actions unless they subsequently refuse to follow his directions.

Role of the School

The concepts that people have of education's role in our society differ greatly. For some, the major function of education should be to bring everyone to a given standard of performance in reading, writing, and arithmetic. Those people who place heavy emphasis on the 3 R's maintain that no one who possesses the necessary intellectual prerequisites should fail to reach a certain minimum level of performance in the basic subjects. Other people insist that the essential function of public education should be to enable each person to attain his full potential. The individuals holding this view of education stress above everything else that the schools should help a person achieve optimum expression and realization of his talents and interests. Neither of these views necessarily excludes the other; however, an emphasis on one as opposed to the other will result in different patterns of behavior. Consequently, the way an administrator defines what the role of the school should be makes a difference in the kind of leadership which he gives in developing the school program.

The administrator with an educational philosophy which attaches considerable significance to a universal standard of performance in the basic skill subjects is likely to behave in certain ways. He scrutinizes the results of standardized achievement tests. He looks for individual as well as group departures from the criterion of mastery which has been set. He stimulates teachers and other members of the professional staff to define precisely the nature of the substandard performance, to identify its causes, and to institute both corrective and preventive measures. He searches for and eliminates institutional obstacles and barriers to students' productivity. He holds tenaciously to the view that environment, rather than heredity, is a principal determinant of the student's in-school performance. In short, this type of administrator believes that the school can effect certain minimal results in the basic subjects for almost everyone and, furthermore, that it should. Activities which are less relevant to his notion of the school's central mission are regarded as frills and potential time-burners.

An administrator who assigns an individual self-actualizing function to the schools is apt to reflect a different emphasis in the leadership he gives to the school's program. He looks for evidence that teachers and other professional staff members are conscientiously searching for the special genius, talent, or strengths which each student has. He urges school personnel to structure numerous opportunities for students to explore a variety of interests, to determine whether they have the competencies required for successful performance in a number of fields, and to assess whether there is a fit between themselves and the modes of thought peculiar to a given field of study. He works for the removal of institutional requirements that prevent students from exploring their interests and talents in a range of future work roles.

Being concerned with creating an institution which is responsive to the needs and goals of students, the administrator also develops mechanisms for receiving and acting upon student-initiated ideas. He strives to nurture these ideas, and he does this in a variety of ways. He arranges for students to receive help in sharpening and clarifying their thoughts. He acts quickly and responsibly upon their requests. He seizes upon opportunities in the extra-curriculum, as well as in the curriculum, for students to discover, to test, and to develop their abilities and their interests. The administrator consistently behaves in ways that mirror his beliefs and values concerning the feasibility and desirability of the schools' fulfilling a self-actualizing role.

ROLE OF THE EDUCATIONAL ADMINISTRATOR

School districts vary in the expectations which they hold for the occupants of administrative roles. One district might expect its administrators to give priority to the definition and determination of ultimate, intermediate, and proximate goals. Another district might feel that its administrators should spend the bulk of their time on matters relating to instruction. Still another district might expect its administrators to determine what educational services should be offered to the students and residents of the community, and to secure the resources which are needed to provide these services. No doubt, such organizationally prescribed duties and priorities influence an administrator's leadership style; however, the administrator's own personal values and beliefs concerning the role of the educational executive also shape the behavior he exhibits in the organization.

Some administrators feel that administrative roles should be geared to achieve specific organizational results. Although these administrators may share a similar set of values about what the role of the educational administrator should be, they may have dissimilar beliefs about how the desired results are achieved. One administrator may believe that satisfactory results are obtained by constantly letting people in the organization know what the actual results are and how they deviate from established standards. He, therefore, sets up procedures for gathering information about system performance, monitors what is happening, and sees that people are acting intelligently upon the information at their disposal. Another administrator may believe that he contributes to a realization of the intended outcomes by checking upon people to see that their behavior matches the expectations for their role. He sees that courses of study are being followed, that available instructional materials and resources are being used, and that recommended procedures are in effect.

A quite different role for the educational administrator is one that stresses his obligation to foster high staff morale. An administrator who feels that he should create a high level of *esprit de corps* within the organization may have any one of several beliefs about how morale is built and maintained. He may believe that people are most satisfied when they have a clear notion of what the organization's goals are and what procedures they are to follow in achieving these goals. The administrator seeks to build morale by delineating the relationship between himself and members of the work group, and by establishing well-defined patterns of organization, channels of communication, and methods of procedure.[17]

On the other hand, an administrator who values a role definition which stresses the morale of subordinates might believe that they develop *esprit de corps* when the administrator shows them consideration.[18] He does personal favors for his staff members and looks out for their welfare. He makes staff members feel at ease when talking with them. He spends time listening to his subordinates' problems and difficulties; he both empathizes and sympathizes.

There are countless other ways in which the educational administrator can define the role he should play in the organization, just as there are numerous beliefs about how the role can be effectively fulfilled. Our examples have merely served to illustrate the impact that personal values and beliefs can have on administrative behavior. Most administrators never bother to reflect on the values and beliefs which guide their behavior. However, a few examine them and agonize over the issues which an intensive examination inevitably raises. When not done in excess, this soul-searching activity can inform administrative action and can provide a significant basis for altering how the individual behaves in his role as an educational administrator.

CONCEPT OF SUCCESS

In understanding the emotional status of a person, his goals, and his social relations the importance of success and its stablemate, failure, has been universally recognized.[19] The expectation of success and

[17] Andrew W. Halpin, *Theory and Research in Administration* (New York: The Macmillan Co., 1966), pp. 81–130.

[18] *Ibid.*

[19] Kurt Lewin, "The Psychology of Success and Failure." In Harold J. Leavitt and Louis R. Pondy, eds., *Readings in Managerial Psychology* (Chicago: University of Chicago Press, 1964), pp. 25–31.

the fear of failure orient an individual's behavior and outlook. People usually thrive on success—the sense of accomplishment and well-being which derives from the knowledge that a goal has been achieved. At the same time, they are inclined to wither when they experience failure—the sense of inadequacy which stems from the knowledge that a goal has not been attained. Consequently, how an administrator defines what constitutes success and failure and how he reacts to these two conditions should play a significant role in how he behaves. However, before examining these issues, let us look briefly at the more general phenomenon of success and failure.

Objective achievement does not necessarily correlate with the feeling of success or failure. "The same achievement can result once in the feeling of great success, another time in the feeling of complete failure."[20] Furthermore, the same achievement can be a success for one person and a failure for the other. For example, a high jumper may leap 6'4". He may experience success for this feat at the beginning of the track season and experience failure if the performance is repeated near the end of the season. On the other hand, another high jumper may deem himself successful if he can jump consistently at his height. What determines whether an achievement is regarded as a success or as a failure depends upon the relationship between the achievement and the person's level of aspiration.

An individual's aspiration level is not fixed. Generally, the level is set quite low when an activity is done for the first time.[21] How the person performs in this situation affects his subsequent level of aspiration. If he succeeds, he is likely to raise his expectations. Similarly, if he fails, he is apt to reduce his level of aspiration. Although these responses to success and failure are typical ones, they by no means exhaust the various ways in which people react to either the congruence or the incongruence between their level of aspiration and their actual performance.

THE NEED FOR KNOWLEDGE OF RESULTS

People differ in their capacity to work without knowledge of results.[22] Some individuals can exercise discretion for long periods of time and be unaffected by a lack of information about the conse-

[20] *Ibid.*, p. 26.

[21] *Ibid.*

[22] Elliott Jaques, *Measurement of Responsibility* (Cambridge, Mass.: Harvard University Press, 1956).

quences of their actions. They are content to act with little or no knowledge of how well they are doing, and experience minimal discomfort when they have no idea of the quality of their performance. These people can function effectively for a lengthy time span without any evidence of success or failure. Other people function best when they have full knowledge of the wisdom of their actions. They bog down if they have no feedback about the consequences of what they have been doing. These people become unsettled unless there is some immediate knowledge of results. They are unable to sustain effective performance without fairly regular evidence that they are succeeding or failing.

Just as people vary in their capacities to work without knowledge of results, work roles vary in their potential for yielding information about success and failure. For instance, a researcher may decide to inquire into the antecedents and consequences of executive succession and wait three to five years before he learns whether he succeeded or failed in his undertaking. A personnel director may know inside a week or two whether he made a wise choice in the secretary he hired. A TV repairman who specializes in trouble-shooting may be called in to repair a perennially troublesome TV and locate the difficulty within an hour.

The myriad activities associated with the same work role also may differ in the opportunities which they afford for knowledge of results. For example, an administrator may know in less than an hour how well he has handled an irate parent. He may wait three to four months before he learns about the outcome of his negotiations with his teaching staff. He may even go a year or two without any really clear picture of how his Board of Education feels about the leadership he has been giving the school district.

When we combine the differences in the feedback potential of various roles and activities, with the differences among people in their desire for feedback, we can begin to get some idea of how these differences can influence what an administrator chooses to do in his organizational role. The administrator who wants to know in a relatively short period of time the results of his actions may occupy himself with routine activities which provide immediate tangible results. He may spend a great deal of time on clerical matters and attack personnel problems with gusto. He burdens himself with day-to-day matters that generate a quick payoff and neglects the intermediate and general planning activities which may give continuity to his actions over time. He does not labor over long-range goals which can offer no clear-cut evidence of attainment, nor does he set goals which entail long periods of uncertainty before success or failure can be assessed. The organization may suffer because this type of administrator is unwilling to introduce changes that involve a lengthy time span during which it is difficult to ascertain the extent of success or failure.

DEFINITION OF SUCCESS AND FAILURE

What results people regard as significant and the yardsticks they use to measure success and failure are as diverse as the line and staff roles pictured on an organizational chart. Some persons may judge the extent of their success by the speed with which they move up the district's administrative ladder and the rung they finally reach. This type of individual engages in GASing (Getting the Attention of his Superiors)[23] behavior and is extremely responsive to the criteria which he perceives that his superiors use in evaluating performance. These criteria guide the choices he makes about how to allocate his time and efforts. The GASer is likely to make heavy investments in what he deems to be high payoff activities and to slight responsibilities which his superiors regard as being less important.

Other persons may view their success in terms of their progress through the profession; these people, unlike the GASers, are career-bound rather than place-bound.[24] To facilitate his mobility to more and more prestigious roles within the profession, the career-bound individual may behave in one of several ways. For example, a career-bound superintendent may strive to earn a reputation for doing some task very well; therefore, he specializes in such areas as public relations, buildings, curriculum, or finance. He concentrates his energies and efforts on his specialties and is both prepared and eager to move to a more prestigious superintendency which needs the unique strengths and competencies which he has.

Another career-bound superintendent may take pride in moving all phases of the educational program. This type usually stays in the same position for five or ten years before moving to a more highly regarded school district. He is concerned with upgrading the quality of all aspects of the district's operations and with maintaining a similar standard of quality for each and every aspect.

A third possible yardstick of success which an administrator might

[23] Daniel E. Griffiths, et al., "Teacher Mobility in New York City," *Educational Administration Quarterly*, **I**, 1 (Winter, 1965), pp. 15–31.

[24] Richard O. Carlson, *Executive Succession and Organizational Change* (Chicago: Midwest Administration Center, The University of Chicago, 1962).

use is the opinions of subordinates. An administrator who records his success in these terms looks carefully at the satisfaction exhibited by his subordinates. He wants people to feel good about the organization as a place to work, and he attaches great importance to the feelings of success which they experience in doing their work. He, unlike the GASer, is willing to act as their advocate and does not hesitate to confront his superiors if he believes that the welfare of his subordinates is at stake. He is sensitive to the personal goals of his subordinates and is anxious to please them. Because of the priority he assigns to their feelings, he may even set aside the interests of the organization when these come into conflict with individual goals and concerns.

There are other administrators who measure their success by how smoothly the organization runs. These "efficiency experts" pride themselves on having a predictable, well-organized, and synchronized organizational environment. They carefully attend to details and derive immense satisfaction from bureaucratizing the organization's operations. They develop rules, systematize procedures, and elaborate policies. They experience a profound sense of accomplishment when people conform to regulations, when people know what is expected of them, and when things happen as planned and scheduled. Success for these administrators is the attainment of order and predictability in organizational life.

RESPONSE TO SUCCESS AND FAILURE

When administrators receive knowledge of the results they have achieved or failed to achieve, there are a number of possible responses they can make. With the knowledge that aspiration has exceeded performance, one administrator might rid himself of the feeling of failure by rejecting his responsibility for the outcome. He might try to do this by attributing the disappointing result to bad luck or to someone having a grudge against him. If he arrives at the latter conclusion and firmly believes that he has been denied success as represented by his being bypassed for promotion, he may adapt by developing an "I don't care" attitude. He reduces his commitment to the organization and is content to do no more than is necessary to retain his present position in the organization.

Acceptance of personal responsibility for the failure is another possible response. An individual who blames himself for his failure may lower his self-confidence and self-esteem. If he comes to doubt his ability to achieve the results he desires, he may re-set his goals and become satisfied with a much lower level of performance. A fairly extreme reaction might be for the person to withdraw completely from situations where he risks experiencing success or failure.

Diminished self-confidence is not the necessary outcome of assuming personal responsibility for one's own failures, however. An individual might fail but continue to hold a positive view of himself. Consequently, he is able to react by studying the situation carefully in an effort to identify how his behavior contributed to the unsatisfactory outcome. He uses occasions of failure to develop self-awareness; the insight which he achieves may even add to the confidence that he shows when he approaches his next task.

People's responses to success are also varied. One person might be inclined to set an unrealistic and unattainable goal for himself subsequently. His sense of accomplishment may prompt him to overestimate his capacities. His aspiration level soars in consequence and destines him to failure. Another individual might attribute his success to good fortune and, as a result, act conservatively in the goals he sets because the law of averages will be against him in the future. Still another person might be spurred to analyze what led to his success in the expectation that he might be able to repeat the performance or to reach a slightly higher goal if he thoroughly understands the ingredients of his present success.

SUMMARY

In essence, we have said that there are many factors, both within and without the person, which affect behavior. Our primary concern has been with the inner factors which may be altered by the individual as he becomes aware of the personal bases for his actions. We intended for this chapter to stimulate the reader to think about himself and to consider how his perceptions of others, his perception of self, his values and beliefs, and his concept of success guide and shape his behavior. The conscientious student of administration will continue his personal assessment while on the job, and will strive to develop the self-awareness necessary to perform effectively in his administrative role.

SUGGESTED ACTIVITIES

1. Interview several administrators and try to determine how they judge their success, whom they regard as the people who are in the best position to judge their success, and the reasons for these perceptions.

2. Read one of the cases in the series prepared by the University Council for Educational Administration[25] and analyze the administrator's behavior in terms of some of the ideas contained in this chapter.

3. Go with an administrator (principal, supervisor, or superintendent), and observe his behavior in all of the activities in which he is engaged in fulfilling his professional responsibilities for the day. Try to analyze his behavior in terms of the assumptions, values, and beliefs that seem to underlie his behavior.

4. Observe an administrator in a staff meeting, a meeting of the board of education, or a meeting of his administrative advisory council. From what he does, interpret his view of the role of authority and the role of the educational administrator. Give reasons for your interpretation.

5. Think of an instance in which you have disagreed with the action of the administrator of your school. Describe the situation briefly, tell what the administrator did, tell what you would have done, and try to indicate the nature of the inner factors which you believe lie behind the two different kinds of behavior.

SELECTED READINGS

ALLPORT, GORDON W. *Pattern and Growth in Personality.* (New York: Holt, Rinehart & Winston, 1961).

ARGYRIS, CHRIS. *Personality and Organization.* (New York: Harper & Row, 1957).

BLAKE, ROBERT R., and MOUTON, JANE S. *The Managerial Grid.* (Houston, Texas: Gulf Publishing Co., 1964).

CARTWRIGHT, DORWIN, ed., *Field Theory in Social Science.* (New York: Harper & Row, 1951).

HEIDER, FRITZ. *The Psychology of Interpersonal Relations.* (New York: Wiley, 1958).

JONES, EDWARD E., and DAVIS, KEITH E. "From Acts to Dispositions" in Leonard Berkowitz, ed., *Advances in Experimental Social Psychology.* (New York: Academic Press, 1965), pp. 220–266.

McGREGOR, DOUGLAS. *The Human Side of Enterprise.* (New York: McGraw Hill, 1960).

OHMANN, O. A. "Skyhooks," *Harvard Business Review,* 48, 1 (January-February, 1970), pp. 4–22.

---

[25] Available through the University Council for Educational Administration, 22 Woodruff Ave., Columbus, Ohio, 43210.

12

Choosing
Educational Administration
As A Career

In this chapter we shall focus on the decision to become an educational administrator and on some of the issues which are relevant to this career choice. While the ideas we set forth may seem more useful to one who has just begun to consider administration as a possible career, the person who has already given serious thought to what his life work will be, can also benefit from our discussion. The discussion is intended to assist anyone who is deciding whether to commit himself to a career in educational administration, to remain in his current post, or to seek another type of educational position.

Although a person may wish to ponder such decisions indefinitely in order to reduce the risk of making an unwise choice, postponement of commitment can create problems for one who eventually decides to become an educational administrator. In the first place, delay can hinder a person's advancement within the profession. For most administrators the route to a top-level administrative post proceeds through several positions of lesser responsibility. The older a person is before he starts in an administrative position, the fewer opportunities he will receive to realize his full potential.

Secondly, administrative positions currently require more formal education of their incumbents than was once the case. It is not at all unusual today to find vacancy notices for superintendencies and for high school principalships which state that preference will be given to the holders of a doctor's degree. Acquiring formal education takes time. Many universities discourage students from undertaking a doctoral program after they reach the age of forty. Additionally, few men and women who have reached that age can afford the educational costs and the loss of income which are entailed in full-time graduate study. While exceptions could be pointed out, the decision to start a doctoral program in educational administration is probably best made before a person reaches the age of thirty.

A third problem generated by procrastination in the career decision-making process is the delay it causes in making and following a plan to implement the decision. Ordinarily, there are many steps required between making a decision and reaching the point dictated by that choice. These steps need to be planned carefully if the ultimate goal is to be reached. Whether or not a person decides to enter administration, he does have a future ahead of him. The longer a person takes in deciding what he wants this future to be, the less future remains for him to realize his aims.

As a person attempts to make a decision about his future in educational administration, he should not restrict the scope of his choices to one position—for example, the city superintendency. Unfortunately, many writers use the terms *educational administration* and *superintendency* as if the latter were all-inclusive of the former. Such a concept produces an unnecessarily limited view of administration and forces unrealistic choices upon anyone who thinks that he wants to be an administrator but is certain he does not want to be a superintendent.

To illustrate the wide variety of opportunities in the profession of educational administration, we will describe in the next section a number of different types of positions and will highlight their functions. Although our overview will tend to emphasize administrative positions in public school systems, we will pay some attention to opportunities in higher education and other educational agencies. Following our discussion of the available positions, we will examine what research has to say about the requisite competencies and traits for some of these administrative posts, particularly the superintendency and the school principalship. The chapter will close with a portrayal of the intrinsic and extrinsic rewards and the stresses and the strains of executive headship.

POSITIONS AVAILABLE

Within this country there are literally thousands of administrative positions. The largest employer is the public school system. More people are employed in the school principalship than in any other administrative role. There are approximately 80,500 principals:

55,500 are elementary school principals[1] while the remaining 25,000 are secondary school principals.[2] In addition there are about 50,000–60,000 positions in the schools in which the title "supervisor" is used.[3] As one would expect, there is much less room at the top, with the number of local district superintendents at 14,391.[4] Assisting the chief executive in the running of the school system are countless central office administrators functioning between the superintendent and the building principal. Administrative opportunities also exist outside of local public school systems; there are positions in state educational agencies, the United States Office of Education, and institutions of higher education. Regrettably, there are no reliable estimates on the number of these positions.

As we begin to describe the administrative positions mentioned in the preceding paragraph, it seems important to indicate that the positions and functions as we picture them are under careful study and review by both educational practitioners and theorists.[5] The prospective administrator finds himself at a point in time where one of his crucial tasks will be the restructuring of the organization and adminstration of education. His viewpoints, then, should not be "frozen" by a description of what exists.

Principalships

Description. The principal is the chief administrative officer of an attendance unit in a school system. Such an attendance unit may be an elementary school, a junior high school, a senior high school, or some combination of these, according to the organization of the school district. In some cases, the administrative head of a junior college is referred to as a principal, but this usage is not common. The common pattern in describing the principalship is to speak of elementary school or secondary school principalships. The junior

---

[1] Estimate supplied by Frank W. Hubbard, Consultant (Washington, D.C.: Department of Elementary School Principals), February, 1970.

[2] Estimated from statistics in *NEA Research Bulletin,* **48,** 2 (May, 1970), 35–41.

[3] Estimate is based on an analysis of various statistical reports and may not be completely accurate because of problems of definition and reporting.

[4] Estimate supplied by Forrest E. Conner, Executive Secretary, American Association of School Administrators, January, 1970.

[5] For example, see Donald A. Erickson, "Forces for Change in the Principalship," *Elementary School Journal,* **LXV** (November, 1964), 57–64.

high school is usually considered to be a secondary school, although somewhat inaccurately. In some states, a junior high school principal may hold either a secondary or an elementary school principal's certificate; in others, the required certificate depends upon whether the junior high school is a departmentalized school (secondary school) or consists primarily of self-contained classrooms (elementary school); and in still others, a junior high school principal's certificate is issued.

In the larger school systems, the meaning of the term "principal" is quite clear. But in smaller school systems, usage often leads to confusion between principalships and superintendencies. It is often true that the administrator in a small school faces the difficult task of attempting to perform three roles—those of teacher, principal, and superintendent. The great difficulties of such a task are often not fully appreciated. For the purposes of this discussion, a principal is considered to be the executive officer of an attendance unit, but not the executive officer of an administrative unit. He does not, for example, have responsibilities as the professional executive officer of a board of education. In several states, the term "supervising principal" is used to describe what is essentially a superintendent. For our purpose, we would not consider this position a principalship.

Functions. Most educators would agree that the principal's basic responsibility should be directing the educational program of the school he heads. To fulfill this responsibility the principal should engage in a variety of activities. He should work with teachers in the appraisal and improvement of the educational program. He should work with the superintendent of schools to secure staff, material, and facilities for this program. He should work with his community to determine its specific educational needs and the extent to which the school is meeting those needs.

How principals actually spend their time on the job does not match perfectly with the prescribed role priorities, however. For example, elementary school principals typically spend 13 percent of their work week on routine clerical tasks processing records and reports. These same principals devote 30 percent of their time to the supervision and co-ordination of instruction and another 30 percent to administration—*i.e.,* making management decisions, formulating rules, maintaining communication with other schools and the central office, and co-ordinating activities of pupils and teachers. Less than 7 percent of the elementary school principals' work week involves activities with parents, laymen, and civic groups. Only about half of the principals report involvement in the selection of instructional materials; one-third have nothing to say in the selection of teachers.[6] Principals of junior and senior high schools describe the distribution of time among these various activities in much the same terms.[7] The one major difference is that secondary school principals report spending considerable time on disciplinary matters.

Principals at all three levels devote a great deal of time to their jobs. The typical principal works from fifty to fifty-four hours per week at school and in school-related activities. At the senior high school level, 29 percent of the principals report that they work more than sixty hours per week. The percentage drops to 15 percent for junior high school principals and to 2 percent for elementary school heads. Less than 5 percent of all principals work less than forty hours weekly.[8]

SUPERVISORY POSITIONS

Description. The supervisor in a local school district is usually attached to the central staff of a school system rather than assigned to a single building. Supervisors are also found as staff members in intermediate units serving a number of smaller districts, and, in many states, certain supervisors of specialized types of instruction are members of a state department of education rather than staff members in intermediate or local administrative units. Supervisors are usually classified in one of several ways. It is common to speak of elementary school or secondary school supervisors. Within these classifications are found general supervisors and special supervisors; the latter deal with special subject matter areas, while the former deal with more general questions of methods and materials. It is thus likely that a larger school system will have one or more general

---

[6] Department of Elementary School Principals, *The Elementary School Principalship in 1968* (Washington, D.C.: Department of Elementary School Principals, National Education Association, 1968).

[7] See Donald A. Rock and John K. Hemphill, *Report of the Junior High-School Principalship* (Washington, D.C.: The National Association of Secondary School Principals, 1966) and John K. Hemphill, James M. Richards, and Richard E. Peterson, *Report of the Senior High-School Principalship* (Washington, D.C.: The National Association of Secondary-School Principals, 1965).

[8] Estimate based on data from the three national studies of the principalship. See Department of Elementary School Principals, *School Principalship, 1968;* Rock and Hemphill, *Junior High-School Principalships;* and Hemphill, *et al., Senior High-School Principalship.*

elementary supervisors and general secondary supervisors, as well as several special supervisors.

Functions. The supervisor plays a special role in the program for the improvement of instruction. Lucio and McNeil state that supervision is concerned with the determination of ends to be attained, the design of procedures for effecting the ends, and the assessment of results.[9] In meeting this function, supervisors perform a number of activities. Included among these are individual classroom visits and teachers' conferences; evaluating and selecting books and other instructional materials which can subsequently be recommended to individual teachers or to groups of teachers for use; helping individual teachers or groups of teachers develop resource or teaching units; organizing and working with groups in curriculum development or improvement programs; organizing and directing conferences or workshops for teachers; assisting individual teachers or groups of teachers in the administration of tests and the interpretation and use of test data; preparing or assisting in the preparation of manuals and bulletins to aid teachers in instruction; assisting in the development and use of programs for the general evaluation of a school program or phases of the program; conducting demonstration teaching classes; performing as a consultant for local faculties as they study instructional problems; or assisting in the development of plans for reporting pupil progress to parents.[10] Even though this list is by no means exhaustive, it indicates the scope of the activities that may fall within the duties of the supervisor.

While we would not attempt to discuss in detail here the function of the supervisor, it is important to mention that ability in getting along with people is a vital asset. Often the supervisor must inspire teachers who are self-satisfied to strive for improvement. At times the supervisor must overcome a teacher's opinion that he is a "central office inspector." Not only must the supervisor be knowledgeable in the field of general instruction and perhaps also in special subject matter areas such as art or music, but he must have the ability to work with people so that this knowledge can be put to use in the improvement of instruction. Skills in group processes, individual

[9] William H. Lucio and John D. McNeil, *Supervision: A Synthesis of Thought and Action* (New York: McGraw Hill, 1969), p. 46.

[10] For a comprehensive list of supervisory activities, see Lucio and McNeil, *Supervision.*

conferences, and general human relations are important parts of a supervisor's equipment.

CENTRAL OFFICE POSITIONS

Description. In speaking of central office positions, we are referring to those positions in a school system which are concerned more with some phase of the overall operation of the system than with the operation of a single attendance unit within the system. While it is somewhat difficult to generalize on the exact titles or descriptions of these positions as found throughout the country, certain positions are common. Some of the more common positions include administrative assistant to the superintendent, assistant superintendent for instruction, assistant superintendent for business, assistant superintendent for staff personnel, assistant superintendent for pupil personnel services, director of buildings and grounds, and director of planning.[11] Obviously, only the largest system would have all of these positions on a full-time basis. In many cases, for example, an assistant superintendent for instruction would fulfill the functions covered by such additional positions as director of elementary education, director of secondary education, and director of curriculum. It should also be noted that there is usually a hierarchy in central office positions. A number of directors responsible for various phases of the instructional program would be under the immediate direction of the assistant superintendent for instruction.

Functions. The central office administrative staff is necessitated by at least two major facts. In the first place, even a small school system is a complex operation. One man cannot be everywhere and do everything involved in the overall administration of such a system. For this reason, he must have the help such a staff provides. Secondly, studies of administration have long shown that the top administrator in an organization cannot deal effectively on a direct and continuous basis with every other member of the organization. We have mentioned earlier the concept of span of control[12] and

---

[11] See C. Arnold Anderson and Mary Jean Bowman, "Theoretical Considerations in Educational Planning." In Don Adams, *Educational Planning* (Syracuse, N.Y.: Syracuse University Press, 1964).

[12] For an extensive review of the theoretical and empirical work concerned with "span of control," see Robert J. House and John B. Miner, "Merging Management and Behavioral Theory: The Interaction Between Span of Control and Group Size," *Administrative Science Quarterly*, 14, 3 (September, 1969), 451–465.

indicated that many people feel that the chief administrator should have a limited number of people reporting directly to him. The implementation of this concept requires a central staff through which the great number of people in an organization can report indirectly to the chief administrator.

One major function of central office staff members is the direction of various parts of the school organization. In order, however, that the school system as a whole operate as an integrated unit, this same staff must assist in the equally important task of co-ordinating these various parts of the organization. Often the major administrative assistants in a larger school system form a kind of cabinet which works with the superintendent on problems of co-ordination as well as on other aspects of administration. In somewhat smaller school systems, this same function is performed by the building principals.

Members of the central office staff also function as advisers to the superintendent on matters relating to their special fields of competency. Because the staff members are dealing only with segments of the total school system, they have opportunities to keep abreast of trends, techniques, skills, needs, and content in their respective areas which are not possible for the superintendent. Effective superintendents must become effective generalists and rely upon central staff members for specialized advice.

SCHOOL DISTRICT SUPERINTENDENT

Description. Probably little needs to be said to define the position of school district superintendent. We find in practice, however, that there are differences in terminology even in listing this position. We define a school district superintendent as the chief administrative officer of an administrative unit that operates public schools. He is directly responsible to a local board of education, although there are some few states where he is elected rather than appointed by the board of education. He is the executive officer of the local board of education.

While the common term for such a person is "superintendent of schools," certain variations are found, particularly in rural school districts. In some cases, and in terms of our definition presented above, people with the following titles are actually superintendents: supervising principal, local executive, general superintendent, local superintendent, and superintendent of instruction. So long as the title describes a person who meets the criteria implied by our earlier definition, we consider the position to be that of a school district superintendent, now commonly known as the superintendent of schools.

Functions. The major functions of the district school superintendent are to help define and clarify the purpose and direction of the school system, to establish and maintain an organization to work at these purposes, and to secure and allocate resources needed by the organization to achieve these purposes. While the traditional view is that the superintendent is a mere implementor of school board policies, in the real world the superintendent and board of education function more nearly as partners in the establishment of policy. Most boards seek advice from their superintendent on policy questions.[13]

Although the superintendent plays an important role in the definition and clarification of direction, he occupies an even more central role in the establishment and maintenance of the organization. The superintendent has a great deal of discretion in how school personnel are deployed to get the job done. In maintaining the staff the superintendent stimulates, challenges, rewards, and creates the conviction that the organization has a worthy purpose that is fully capable of being achieved.

To support the school system as it strives to attain its purposes, the superintendent is expected to assume a major role in securing and allocating resources. His efforts to secure funds frequently lead to active involvement at local, state, and federal levels of government. Perennially faced with a shortage of money the superintendent has the heavy burden of allocating the available financial resources to promote the greatest educational benefit for pupils. With increasing frequency the superintendent is called upon to answer questions such as: Should an additional $50 per child be spent in reducing class size, in acquiring more instructional equipment, in providing a mathematics supervisor for each building, or in raising teachers' salaries?

STATE EDUCATIONAL AGENCIES

Description. The state, as we mentioned earlier, is the governmental unit in our country that is responsible for the development and general control of systems of public schools. While states do not

---

[13] This section on functions of the superintendent is based on Roald F. Campbell, "The Changing Role of the Superintendent," *Contemporary Education,* **XXXIX,** 6 (May, 1968), 249–254.

usually operate schools, there are a number of administrative positions associated with state educational agencies. State departments of education, as these state agencies are most commonly known, are under the direct administrative control of a professional educator. This officer usually has the title of state superintendent of public instruction and is responsible to a governing board. Under the superintendent are a number of divisions, each of which is headed by a director. Some typical divisions in state departments of education are certification, vocational education, federal programs, research, and school plant. These major divisions are further subdivided into branches, with lower level administrators being responsible for the activities of each branch.

Functions. The broad functions of state departments may be classified under five principal headings: operational, regulatory, service, developmental, and public support and co-operation.[14] Operational functions refer to those activities in which the state department directly administers schools and services. An example is the operation of special schools for the blind, the deaf, and the otherwise handicapped. The administration of such services is largely a twentieth-century addition to the duties of state departments.

According to state and federal statutes, state departments must regulate many aspects of the programs, plants, and administrative procedures of local districts. These regulatory activities involve systematic monitoring of local school districts to determine their conformance to certain minimum standards and imposing penalties and sanctions whenever these standards are not being met.

Service activities of the department, on the other hand, entail the dissemination of expertise to the local schools. The majority of service activities are geared toward the improvement of instruction. Some specific examples of service activities are preparation of curriculum materials, consultation on new instructional approaches and technology, and advice on legal aspects of school system operation.

Developmental functions center around long-range planning and staff improvement. Planning necessitates making an assessment of the long-range needs of local schools, while staff improvement relates

---

[14] This section on functions of state agencies is drawn from Roald F. Campbell, Gerald E. Sroufe, and Donald H. Layton, *Strengthening State Departments of Education* (Chicago: The Midwest Administration Center, University of Chicago, 1967).

both to the recruitment of talent and the extension of the capabilities of existing personnel.

A final set of state department functions is concerned with securing the support and co-operation of the general public and of subsections within the public. Support is needed to maintain the numerous current activities and to launch new projects. Support activities include communication through the mass media, political activities with the legislature and governor, relations with the federal government, and intrastate co-operation and articulation.

UNITED STATES OFFICE OF EDUCATION

While considering governmental service and educational administration, it is important to devote some attention to educational administration at the federal government level. The United States Office of Education is one of several agencies in the Department of Health, Education and Welfare. It is under the leadership of the United States Commissioner of Education, who serves directly under the Secretary of Health, Education and Welfare. The United States Office of Education is organized in divisions, each one under the direction of an assistant commissioner. The divisions are organized in branches, each of which is headed by a director. Within some branches there are also bureau chiefs. The Commissioner is an appointive officer, while the remaining personnel in the Office are wholly or partially under Civil Service.

The primary function of the Office of Education is to marshal resources on a national scale for the improvement of public education in the nation. In addition, the Office provides valuable consultative service as well as conducting many statistical studies to provide insight into national educational trends. The Office has few regulatory functions, in keeping with the established doctrine that public education is a state matter.

There are, however, a variety of operational responsibilities within the functions of the Office. Beginning with the passage of the National Defense Education Act, the participation of the federal government in education has grown rapidly and extensively, culminating in the passage of the Elementary-Secondary Education Act of 1965 (PL 89-10), which represents the greatest single commitment ever made by the federal government for the support of education. This legislation, coupled with the massive Higher Education Facilities Assistance Act passed in 1964 and the Higher Education Act of

1965, has placed great responsibilities and major operational functions within the U.S. Office of Education. The staff of the Office, both in Washington, D.C., and in regional centers throughout the country, is expanding at such a rate that opportunities for service at this level are almost unlimited for qualified people.

ADMINISTRATION IN HIGHER EDUCATION

There are many educational administration positions in higher education. It should be noted, however, that administrators in higher education are not drawn only from the ranks of those we have been calling educational administrators. It is unlikely, for example, that the dean of a college of commerce would be selected from the field of educational administration, even though his position would be an administrative position in an educational undertaking. Those to whom this text has been primarily addressed might more logically aspire in higher education to one of the following positions: chairman, department of education; director, school of education; dean, college of education; registrar, college or university; and president, college or university.

In addition, there are many administrative positions in junior colleges which are well within the province of educational administration. Some junior colleges are organized under the control of local boards of education and offer positions somewhat similar to those of a superintendent or of a principal. Other junior colleges are organized more in terms of college or university structure under the direction of a board of trustees. In this case, junior college administrative positions may be similar to college deanships or presidencies.

PROFESSORSHIPS

One final kind of position is available to the person interested in educational administration. This position involves the preparation of educational administrators through service as a professor in an institution conducting such a program of preparation. Although this position is not in itself an administrative position, it is a position for which administrators might aim.

The professor of educational administration has unique opportunities to engage in the three activities commonly considered a part of university teaching: instruction, research, and service. He is, first of all, a teacher who is concerned with developing the prospective administrator's skills, attitudes, and values. He is, secondly, a researcher who is concerned with the advancement of knowledge about the organization and administration of schools. Finally, he provides service to the field. Because of continuing opportunities in research and study which are not ordinarily available to the practicing administrator, the professor can be of assistance to practicing administrators in helping them develop new approaches to the solution of administrative problems.

REQUISITE COMPETENCIES AND TRAITS

As our preceding discussion of available administrative positions suggests, there are numerous opportunities for those who are interested in a career in educational administration. Unfortunately, however, not everyone who aspires to be an administrator is selected to be one; nor is everyone who is chosen to hold an administrative post destined to become a successful administrator. Confronted with these harsh realities, the administrative aspirant undoubtedly wants to know what research has to say about the competencies and traits which are related to appointment as an educational administrator and to success in the job once he is appointed.

For purposes of our discussion, we will distinguish between personal and prestige traits. Personal traits are those individual attributes, qualities, or characteristics which are innate and not subject to environmental influence—for example, sex and age. Prestige traits, on the other hand, are those qualities or characteristics which an individual acquires through affiliation with an institution or a formal organization. Experience as a teacher, degree held, and field of graduate work are examples of prestige traits.

Competencies, unlike traits, refer to skills and abilities that can be developed. The emphasis is on what an individual can do and accomplish rather than on what personal and prestige traits he possesses. One specialist in administration maintains that effective administration depends upon three basic competencies or skills: technical, human, and conceptual.[15] Technical skill involves specialized knowledge and facility in the use of specific tools and techniques. Human skill is primarily concerned with building co-operative effort within the human organization the administrator leads. Conceptual skill relates to recognizing the interrelationships of the various situa-

---

[15] Robert L. Katz, "Skills of an Effective Administrator," *Harvard Business Review*, 33, 1 (January–February 1955), 33–42.

tional factors and to taking that action which achieves the maximum good for the total organization.

WHO GETS APPOINTED?

Personal traits. There is little doubt that educational administration is a profession dominated by males. Although principals and superintendents are drawn almost exclusively from the teaching ranks and there are more females than males in the teaching force, the percentage of administrators who are female is relatively small (see Table 12.1). Only in the elementary principalship is there any sizable

TABLE 12.1   Sex of Administrator by Type of Position Including Nature of Sample and Year Reported

POSITION	MALE	FEMALE	NATURE OF SAMPLE	YEAR
Elementary Principal	77.6%	22.4%	National	1968[a]
Junior High Principal	96.0%	4.0%	National	1966[b]
Senior High Principal	98.0%	2.0%	National	1965[c]
Superintendent	100.0%	—	National	1960[d]
	98.0%	2.0%	Statewide (California)	1966[e]

[a] Department of Elementary School Principals, *School Principalship*, 1968.

[b] Rock and Hemphill, *Junior High-School Principalship*.

[c] Hemphill, Richards, and Peterson, *Senior High-School Principalship*.

[d] American Association of School Administrators, *Professional Administrators for America's Schools* (Washington, D.C.: The Association, a department of the National Education Association, 1960).

[e] William C. Schutz, *Procedures for Identifying Persons with Potential for Public School Administrative Positions* (Berkeley, Calif.: University of California, Cooperative Research Project No. 1076, 1966).

proportion of women; even here the percentage is steadily declining. In 1928, 55 percent of the elementary principals were women; forty years later, the figure was only 22 percent (see Figure 12.1). Regrettably, the data do not allow us to answer this important

Men	45%	59%	62%	78%
Women	55%	41%	38%	22%
	1928	1948	1958	1968

Source: Department of Elementary School Principals, *School Principalship*, 1968.

Figure 12.1   Sex of elementary principals for the period 1928–1968 question: Do the percentages reflect less of an interest in administration by women than men? Or, do the percentages reflect a preference of employing officials for male administrators?

Age is another personal trait which has relevance to appointment as an educational administrator. Individuals are most likely to be appointed to their first principalship between the ages of 30 and 34. Few people become principals before age 25. For example, only 11 percent of the senior high school principals are under 25 years of age at the time of their first appointment.[16] After a person reaches the age of 45, the probability of selection for a principal's post declines. Less than 8 percent of the senior high school principals are older than 45[17] when they are appointed to their first principalship, while the figure is approximately 16 percent for elementary principals.[18] There are some sex differences, however. Men are far more likely than women to be appointed before age 35 (67 percent v. 39 percent).[19] After age 35, a woman has a greater likelihood of being appointed than a man does.

PRESTIGE TRAITS

Graduate work leading to an advanced degree is an imperative for those who aspire to appointment as educational administrators. More than 90 percent of the principals and superintendents in this country have at least a master's degree. Moreover, the trend is toward higher and higher levels of formal education. For example, in 1928 only 16 percent of the elementary principals had a master's; twenty years later the percentage had climbed to 67 percent; by 1958 the figure was 82 percent; and today it is 90 percent.[20] The doctorate is more apt to be held by superintendents (21 percent)[21] than by principals (approximately 3 percent). As the size of the district increases, there is a correspondingly higher probability that the superintendent will need a doctor's degree. In cities with more than 30,000 population the figure is 41 percent.[22]

[16] Hemphill, Richards, and Peterson, *Senior High-School Principalship.*
[17] *Ibid.*
[18] Department of Elementary School Principals, *School Principalship, 1968.*
[19] *Ibid.*
[20] *Ibid.*
[21] American Association of School Administrators, *Professional Administrators.*
[22] *Ibid.*

The field in which the graduate work is taken is most likely to be educational administration and supervision. From 76 to 79 percent of all principals and superintendents have selected educational administration as their major field of concentration. Few administrators, less than 4 percent to be exact, have majored at the graduate level in one of the traditional academic subjects (English, mathematics, science, or social studies).

In addition to possessing an advanced degree with work concentrated in educational administration and supervision, the administrator is likely to have taught either at the elementary or secondary levels. The average junior high and senior high school principal has taught from seven to nine years,[23] while the average elementary principal has six years of classroom teaching experience.[24] Ninety-nine percent of the junior high school principals have taught for at least one year[25]; the percentage for senior high school principals is quite similar (98 percent).[26] The typical woman elementary school principal has three times as much experience in the classroom as does her male counterpart.

The experience picture is somewhat different for the superintendency, though not markedly so. Nearly 90 percent of the superintendents have teaching experience. The setting for this experience is far more likely to have been at the secondary rather than at the elementary level; only 22 percent of the superintendents report experience in elementary teaching. Most superintendents (83 percent) have also served as building principals.[27]

Competencies. Researchers have virtually ignored descriptive data dealing with the relationship between specific administrative competencies and appointment to different types of administrative positions. If some minimal level of performance in any given category of competencies is demanded for appointment to an administrative position, the research literature that we have examined provides no clue as to what the minimal levels might be. The fact that the literature is silent on this issue does not mean, however, that school

[23] Rock and Hemphill, *Junior High-School Principalship;* Hemphill, Richards, and Peterson, *Senior High-School Principalship.*

[24] Department of Elementary School Principals, *School Principalship, 1968.*

[25] Rock and Hemphill, *Junior High-School Principalship.*

[26] Hemphill, Richards, and Peterson, *Senior High-School Principalship.*

[27] American Association of School Administrators, *Professional Administrators.*

districts take no steps to ascertain the kinds and levels of competencies which potential candidates possess.

Some districts may require some minimal level of performance on a test of professional knowledge (the *School Administration and Supervision* section of the National Teacher Examinations). Other districts may arrange for candidates to exhibit certain competencies by reacting to case studies and by indicating how they would handle different kinds of administrative problems posed by an interviewing committee. Still other districts may seek to assess administrative competencies by introducing candidates to a mythical school district through the use of films, filmstrips, printed materials, and recordings. After this introduction, the candidates receive items which are typically found in an administrator's in-basket. The responses of the candidates are judged to determine how well the problems have been handled.

WHO SUCCEEDS?

How to judge success in administration is a persistent problem for both researchers and employing officials. Interest in the problem stems from a desire to help individuals make wise career choices and a wish to increase the number of sound personnel decisions which are made by institutions. Three unresolved issues have made the judging of success problematic:

1. The criteria to be used.
2. The kind of evidence to be gathered to establish the extent to which the criteria have been met.
3. The priority to be assigned to each criterion.

For the most part, success in administration has been determined by using effectiveness ratings provided by the administrator's superiors or subordinates. Seldom are the criteria and the importance which is attached to those criteria made explicit. With these caveats in mind, let us now turn to the results of the studies which have been undertaken to differentiate between successful and unsuccessful administrators.

Personal traits. In our earlier discussion of *appointment* to administrative roles, we noted that sex has utility as a predictive factor; significantly more men than women occupy administrative posts. When sex is related to success in an administrative role, however, it has little value in differentiating between successful and unsuccessfi administrators. Studies of the principalship by Hemphill, *et al.*[2] Lipham[29]; and Schutz[30] show that males and females do not diffe in how they are rated by either superiors or subordinates. In a majc study of the elementary principalship, Gross and Herriott reporte that sex was unrelated to Executive Professional Leadership—*i.e* efforts by the principal to upgrade the performance of his staff.[31]

The evidence regarding age of the principal is less clear. Hemphill, *et al.*, and Lipham found little relationship between age and successful performance of the principal's duties. Gross and Herriott, on the other hand, concluded that older principals provide less Executive Professional Leadership than younger ones do. Gross and Herriott also observed a trend which suggests that the younger a principal is at the time of his first appointment to the principalship, the stronger his subsequent professional leadership is likely to be.

Prestige traits. Most studies show no relationship between amount of educational training and subsequent success as an administrator. Four different measures of educational preparation apparently are unrelated to judged effectiveness: (1) number of years spent in college,[32] (2) number of years devoted to graduate study,[33] (3) number of hours taken in undergraduate education,[34] and (4) number of hours in graduate education courses.[35] A fifth measure, the total number of courses in educational administration, is related to the exercise of Executive Professional Leadership; moreover, the relationship is negative. Principals with less extensive formal preparation in the field of educational administration exhibit greater professional leadership.[36] Unfortunately, none of these studies concen-

---

[28] John K. Hemphill, Daniel E. Griffiths, and Norman Frederiksen, *Administrative Performance and Personality* (New York: Teachers College, Columbia University, 1962).

[29] James M. Lipham, "Personal Variables of Effective Administrators," *Administrator's Notebook,* **IX,** 1 (September, 1960).

[30] Schutz, *Procedures for Identifying Persons with Potential.*

[31] Neal Gross and Robert E. Herriott, *Staff Leadership in Public Schools* (New York: Wiley, 1965).

[32] Hemphill, Griffiths, and Frederiksen, *Administrative Performance and Personality.*

[33] Lipham, "Personal Variables of Effective Administrators."

[34] Gross and Herriott, *Staff Leadership in Public Schools.*

[35] *Ibid.*

[36] *Ibid.*

trated on the nature of the training received or considered qualitative differences among training programs.

Teaching experience, much like training, bears no relationship to success as an administrator when simple forms of statistical analysis are used, and no effort is made to control for the effects of other variables. Hemphill, *et al.;* Lipham; and Gross and Herriott found that the amount of teaching experience a principal has is unrelated to his success in the principalship. Using a much more complicated type of statistical analysis, which is designed to detect a relationship masked by the influence of other important variables, Schutz uncovered a negative relationship between teaching experience and success as a principal. In fact, total experience as a classroom teacher was more negatively related to administrative effectiveness than any other variable studied.

Competencies. Measures of technical and professional knowledge generally show little or no relationship to success on the job; when a relationship is reported; it is a very weak one. Schutz found that mastery of the content of educational administration—namely, school law, finance, personnel, and school facilities—was unrelated to administrative success either as a principal or superintendent. On the other hand, the study by Hemphill, *et al.,* of elementary principals uncovered a moderate, positive relationship between professional knowledge and ratings by superiors.

SITUATIONAL CORRELATES

Research in the field of educational administration, as well as in the fields of business and public administration, points rather clearly to success as being in large part a function of situational circumstances.[37] An individual who is successful as an administrator in one type of situation may be a dismal failure in another. Research which has examined the correlates of success by taking into account the possible interaction between characteristics of the individual and the institutional setting has yielded somewhat more informative results than research which has focused solely on the individual. Schutz, for example, using various measures of school district type, was able to increase the predictive power of personal traits and competencies when

[37] R. M. Stogdill, "Personal Factors Associated with Leadership: A Survey of the Literature," *Journal of Psychology,* 25 (January, 1948), p. 64.

type of district was introduced into his analyses.[38] Furthermore, the traits and competencies associated with success differed among district types. Unfortunately, studies of success that consider individual and institutional factors simultaneously are rare.

REWARDS

Rational decision-making involves a consideration of the costs and benefits that may follow from taking a particular course of action. If the decision to become an educational administrator is to be a rational one, then the individual must balance the costs against the benefits before he makes his final choice. Costs in the form of stresses and strains are the subject of the next section of this chapter. Our current concern is with the benefits—the extrinsic and intrinsic rewards associated with headship. For purposes of our discussion, we will treat extrinsic rewards solely in terms of tangible financial earnings; intrinsic rewards, on the other hand, will be viewed in terms of the gratifications derived from performing administrative tasks and from having chosen educational administration as a career.[39]

Extrinsic Rewards[40]

Current salary situation. Not surprisingly, the extrinsic rewards for superintendents and principals exceed the rewards received by classroom teachers. The latest nationwide figures (see Table 12.2) show that superintendents earn approximately 93 percent more on the average than teachers. The discrepancy is somewhat lower when the salaries of principals are compared with those of teachers; the difference (52 percent) between elementary principals and teachers is the smallest.

There are, however, marked differences within each type of ad-

---

[38] Schutz, *Procedures for Identifying Persons with Potential.*

[39] The definition of intrinsic rewards is drawn from Neal Gross and David A. Napior, *The Job and Career Satisfaction of Men School Principals* (Cambridge, Mass.: Harvard University, Graduate School of Education, Cooperative Research Project No. 2536, 1967).

[40] This section on extrinsic rewards relies heavily on data reported in Research Division, National Education Association, *24th Biennial Salary Survey of Public-School Professional Personnel, 1969* (Washington, D.C.: National Education Association, 1969).

TABLE 12.2   Mean Salaries Paid in 1968–1969, by Type of Position

TYPE OF POSITION	MEAN SALARY (WEIGHTED AVERAGE)
Superintendent	$15,131
Senior High Principal	12,348
Junior High Principal	13,032
Elementary Principal	11,957
Teacher	7,841

Source: Calculated from *24th Biennial Salary Survey of Public-School Professional Personnel, 1969* (Washington, D.C.: National Education Association, 1969).

ministrative position, and these differences are most pronounced when size of the school district is taken into account. Generally, the larger the number of students enrolled in the school district, the larger is the salary paid on the average to administrators; this pattern holds irrespective of the type of position held (see Table 12.3).

TABLE 12.3   Mean Salaries, 1968–1969, by Enrollment Grouping and Type of Position

Enrollment Grouping

TYPE OF POSITION	25,000 OR MORE	3,000–24,999	300–2,999	UNDER 300
Superintendent	$28,798	$20,112	$14,538	$10,424
Senior High Principal	15,515	13,116	11,539	9,335
Junior High Principal	14,485	13,825	11,021	10,249
Elementary Principal	14,072	12,261	10,561	8,242

Source: Calculated from *24th Biennial Salary Survey of Public-School Professional Personnel, 1969* (Washington, D.C.: National Education Association, 1969).

The salary situation over time. With the upsurge and spread of collective bargaining by teachers, we expected that the discrepancy between administrator and teacher salaries, though currently sizable, would show a narrowing over the past eight years. Our expectation was not confirmed, however. Using 1962–1963 as the base year and the nationwide average salaries for teachers and administrators, we found that from 1962–1963 to 1968–1969, teachers' salaries increased by 36.4 percent while the increases for administrators ranged from 42 to 50 percent. Elementary school principals showed the greatest increase while junior high school principals showed the smallest.

When the percentage increases are examined by two-year periods, the information is even more revealing. Since 1962–1963, the percentage of the salary increases for each succeeding two-year period generally has climbed for both administrators and teachers (see Table 12.4). However, administrators clearly are receiving higher

TABLE 12.4 Percent of Salary Increase in Mean Salary over Preceding Two-Year Period, by Type of Position and Year

Two-Year Period

TYPE OF POSITION	1964–1965	1966–1967	1968–1969
Superintendent	10.2%	15.6%	16.6%
Senior High Principal	11.6	11.2	17.5
Junior High Principal	11.7	9.5	16.0
Elementary Principal	11.7	11.8	20.0
Teacher	8.3	11.0	13.6

Source: Calculated from *24th Biennial Salary Survey of Public-School Professional Personnel, 1969* (Washington, D.C.: National Education Association, 1969).

rates of salary increases than are teachers. The figures are based on nationwide averages for each type of position. Superintendents, for example, earned 10.2 percent more in 1964–1965 than in 1962–1963. Teachers, on the other hand, received 8.3 percent more in 1964–1965 than in 1962–1963. In 1968–1969, superintendents received 16.6 percent more on the average than they did in 1966–1967, while teachers earned 13.6 percent more on the average in 1968–1969 than they earned in 1966–1967.

The pattern of percentage increases in salaries since 1962–1963 does not change drastically when district size is taken into account. Only in school districts with an enrollment of less than three hundred pupils is the trend reversed. Teachers in these smaller districts are earning on the average 54.1 percent more in 1968–1969 than they did in 1962–1963. Comparable figures during the same period for administrators in these districts range from a low of 36.1 percent for elementary principals to a high of 53.3 percent for senior high school principals. Interestingly, 1968–1969 was the first time in which principals of the smallest districts earned more on the average than teachers employed in the largest school districts.

INTRINSIC REWARDS

Systematic inquiry into the intrinsic rewards experienced by educational administrators is quite limited. Studies which compare the intrinsic rewards of administrators with teachers are even more rare. Investigations that focus on intrinsic rewards for administrators at different time periods and which might show definite trends are nonexistent. However, the data which are available on intrinsic rewards suggest that they are adequate for the majority of people who occupy either a principalship or a superintendency.

One way in which researchers have examined the issue of intrinsic rewards is by asking administrators some variation of the following question: Would you make the same choice if you had it to do all over again? In one national study, 54.4 percent of the superintendents responded that they certainly would choose educational administration again, while only 6.1 percent indicated that they probably would not or certainly would not.[41] Similarly, 52.9 percent of the elementary school principals reported they certainly would become elementary school principals if they were starting over, while 6.8 percent said that they probably would not or certainly would not.[42] Junior high and senior high school principals, on the other hand, were somewhat more likely to indicate that they would not choose educational administration as a career if they had their life to live over; the exact figures were 12 percent for the former and 17 percent for the latter.[43] Even so, 64 percent of the principals at the junior high school level and 60 percent at the senior-high school level reported that they would make the same choice; the remaining principals were uncertain.

A second technique used by researchers to examine the intrinsic rewards of administrators is to assess how much satisfaction and enjoyment administrators derive from performing a variety of their activities. Gross and Napior, for example, looked at the degree of enjoyment male elementary, junior high, and senior high school

[41] American Association of School Administrators, *Professional Administrators.*

[42] Department of Elementary School Principals, *School Principalship*, 1968.

[43] Rock and Hemphill, *Junior High-School Principalship;* Hemphill, Richards, and Peterson, *Senior High-School Principalship.*

principals experience in twenty separate work activities.[44] In approximately 75 percent of these activities, more than half of the respondents indicated that they experienced either a great deal of or very much enjoyment. There were five work activities in which 80 percent or more of the principals expressed that they enjoyed the activity a great deal or very much; these activities included the following:

1. Working with exceptionally able teachers.
2. Supervising the instructional program.
3. Working with guidance personnel.
4. Talking with parents about a problem concerning their child.
5. Talking with a group of parents about a school problem.

There was no work activity in which a majority of the principals reported very little or no enjoyment.

The degree of gratification experienced by educational administrators apparently is less a function of the characteristics of the individual than of the situation. Gross and Napior found that only four of the myriad individual attributes which they examined were related to job satisfaction. Principals who were disposed to accept authority and who were positively oriented to authority figures were more satisfied than principals with more negative orientations toward authority. Individuals who underplayed rather than emphasized the hierarchical aspects of the teacher-principal relationship were somewhat more satisfied with their work. Blacks were more satisfied than whites, Jews were more satisfied than Catholics who, in turn, enjoyed their work more than Protestants.

According to Gross and Napior, situational characteristics which are related to principal job satisfaction tend to center around the relationships a principal has with his superiors and his subordinates. Particularly crucial in the relationship between the principal and his superior is the amount of autonomy a principal is granted by his superior; the importance a superior attributes to the principal's work; the degree of role ambiguity present; the adequacy of communications from the superordinate; the availability of constructive suggestions, professional encouragement, and socioemotional support from the superior; the effectiveness of the decision-making machinery at

[44] Gross and Napior, *The Job and Career Satisfaction of Men School Principals.*

higher levels; and the skill with which the superior handles his own routine managerial tasks. With respect to the relationships a principal has with his staff, four factors seem to affect his level of work satisfaction: (1) the amount of personal loyalty and support the staff gives him, (2) the interest it has in innovation and change, (3) the commitment of staff members to their work responsibilities, and (4) the quality of the staff's performance.

A number of properties of the school setting in the Gross and Napior study did not differentiate between highly satisfied and less well-satisfied principals, however. These properties included size of the school, socioeconomic composition of the student body, and grade levels encompassed within the school—namely, elementary, junior high, and senior high.

Unfortunately, little or no attention has been devoted to the intrinsic rewards of the superintendency. We lack information such as the following: the amount of gratification associated with the performance of various work activities, how the degree of work gratification compares with principals and teachers, what personal characteristics are related to work satisfactions, and what situational characteristics affect the superintendent's enjoyment of his work. Perhaps, future researchers will inquire into such issues and others that relate to the intrinsic rewards of managerial roles in education.

STRESSES AND STRAINS

Occupational Stress and Its Physiological Correlates

The significance of occupational stress has been demonstrated by medical researchers in recent years. Work-connected emotional stress has been linked to a range of physical disorders including coronary disease, high blood pressure, and high cholesterol levels which presumably foreshadow strokes and heart attacks. The deleterious effects of occupational stress have been evident when researchers have controlled for previously identified causes such as heredity, dietary fat, tobacco smoking, obesity, and physical activity. Studies which have shown that occupational stress leads to unwanted and undesirable physical consequences for the human organism have essentially been of two types. One type has been concerned with the relationship between the incidence of physical disorders and the stress levels of various occupational groupings.[45] A second type has concentrated on physical changes as a function of cyclic variations in job stress within the same occupation.[46] The findings of both types have been generally consistent; increases in occupational stress are accompanied by a higher incidence of physical ailments and undesirable changes in bodily functions.

OCCUPATIONAL STRESS AMONG BUSINESS EXECUTIVES

When we consider executives or managers as one occupational category, we find an interesting pattern with respect to stress and physiological correlates. In board rooms, hallways, executive suites, and popular novels, there is an emphasis on the strains of executive responsibility. The theme usually runs like this. Promotion which entails an increase in executive load is almost certain to result in psychic and physical disturbances. The verbal imagery is striking. The picture of the executive is one of a man doubled-over clutching his ulcer-ridden stomach with the left hand and reaching frantically for a bottle of tranquilizers with the other hand. Tension, anxiety, high blood pressure, stomach troubles, and chest pain frequent the conversations about administrative man.

Although the folklore abounds, serious systematic study of executive stress is scant. What evidence we do have is not altogether consistent with the personal tales, testimonials, and accounts of what it is like to be an executive. In fact, executives appear to be in better physical condition than non-executives.[47] Moreover, level of responsibility within the administrative group is unrelated to differences in physical health; top executives do not have higher incidences of arteriosclerotic disease and heart disease than middle management and minor executives.[48]

[45] H. I. Russek, "Emotional Stress and Coronary Heart Disease in American Physicians, Dentists, and Lawyers," *American Journal of Medical Science,* **243,** 1962, 716–725.

[46] M. Friedman, R. H. Rosenman, and V. Carroll, "Changes in the Serum Cholesterol and Blood Clotting Time of Men Subject to Cyclic Variation of Occupational Stress," *Circulation,* **17,** 1958, 852–861.

[47] See Richard E. Lee and Ralph F. Schneider, "Hypertension and Arteriosclerosis in Executive and Non-executive Personnel," *The Journal of the American Medical Association,* **167,** 12 (July 19, 1958), 1447–1451. See also Robert L. Kahn, Donald M. Wolfe, Robert P. Quinn, and J. Diedrick Snoek, *Organizational Stress* (New York: Wiley, 1964).

[48] Lee and Schneider, *op. cit.*

OCCUPATIONAL STRESS AMONG SCHOOL EXECUTIVES

Role conflict as a source of stress. The empirical work dealing with stress among school executives has primarily been of one type. Researchers have focused on role conflict and have made the assumption that role conflict leads to stress and has adverse consequences for individuals who are exposed to such conflict.[49] Rarely has this assumption been tested, however.

In studying role conflict among school administrators, researchers have almost exclusively been concerned with examining the extent to which administrators are confronted with role conflict. Generally, the presence of conflict has been signaled by the existence of incompatible expectations for performance. By *incompatible expectations,* researchers mean that there are simultaneous demands for behaviors which are mutually exclusive, contradictory, or inconsistent.

The research in this area clearly shows that school administrators, particularly principals and superintendents, are highly vulnerable to role conflict. Incompatible expectations for the administrators' performance seem to arise in three ways. One source of role conflict is the conflict that arises between two roles held by the same person. For example, Gross, *et al.,*[50] found that 48 percent of the superintendents he studied confronted conflicting expectations in their roles as school administrators and as fathers. Superintendents were expected to spend a lot of time working in the evening on school-related matters and also to be with their families attending to their needs. Superintendents also reported conflict stemming from role obligations to personal friends and the school system. Friends sought special consideration and treatment for their children in such matters as assignment to or transfer from a particular school or to a particular teacher; consideration of this sort resulted in conflict when the superintendent was expected by the school board and teachers to follow a set of procedures which were at variance with the requests of friends.

A second source of role conflict is the conflict that develops when

---

[49] For a review of the role conflict studies, see Jacob W. Getzels, James M. Lipham, and Roald F. Campbell, *Educational Administration as a Social Process* (New York: Harper & Row, 1968).

[50] Neal C. Gross, Ward S. Mason, and Alexander W. McEachern, *Explorations in Role Analysis* (New York: Wiley, 1958).

two or more groups have incompatible expectations for the same role. Halpin, in his influential study of the school superintendency, found that school board members expect superintendents to be very strong in initiating structure while staff members prefer much less structure.[51] In other words, school staffs and boards of education differed significantly in their expectations for leadership behavior, which involved efforts to establish well-defined patterns of organization, channels of communication, and methods of procedure. Hencley[52] also discovered inconsistencies between teacher and school board expectations for the superintendent's behavior in three major administrative task areas: staff personnel, curriculum and program, and finance and business management.

Incompatible expectations held by two or more groups also have been observed for principals. On the basis of a comprehensive study of the school principalship, Moser[53] concluded that principals are subjected to conflicting expectations by teachers and superintendents. Teachers want their principals to keep things on an even keel, to cater to the individual needs of staff members, to advocate the staff's point of view with top management, and to seek suggestions from the staff when action is needed. The superintendents of these same principals, on the other hand, expected the principal to be forceful in his relationships with subordinates, to initiate action, to emphasize the achievement of organizational goals, and to show greater concern for the institution than for the individual.

A third source of conflict for school administrators rises from *contradictory expectations held by members of the same group for the occupant of the same role.* Moyer,[54] for example, in his study of teacher expectations for the leadership behavior of principals showed that teachers within the same building had opposing conceptions of how their principal should behave. One group of teachers believed

[51] Andrew W. Halpin, *Theory and Research in Administration* (New York: The Macmillan Co., 1966).

[52] Stephen P. Hencley, "A Typology of Conflict between Superintendents and Their Reference Groups" (Unpublished doctoral dissertation, Department of Education, University of Chicago, 1960).

[53] Robert P. Moser, "A Study of the Effects of Superintendent-Principal Interaction and Principal-Teacher Interaction in Selected Middle-Sized School Systems" (Unpublished doctoral dissertation, Department of Education, University of Chicago, 1957).

[54] Donald C. Moyer, "Teachers' Attitudes Toward Leadership as They Relate to Teacher Satisfaction" (Unpublished doctoral dissertation, Department of Education, University of Chicago, 1954).

that the principal should make the decisions and run the school according to his best judgment while another group expected the principal to rely heavily upon his teachers for help with school problems.

The vulnerability of school administrators to role conflict is also evident in studies concerned with the number of administrators experiencing role conflict in certain areas of decision-making. By way of illustration, Gross, *et al.,* found that a high percentage of superintendents had been exposed to role conflict in the four decision situations which he examined. More than 90 percent of the superintendents were faced with role conflict when making budget decisions; a similar percentage was exposed to conflicting expectations when deciding what level of salary increases to recommend for teachers; nearly three-fourths of the superintendents encountered role conflict in hiring and promoting personnel; and slightly more than one-half reported contradictory expectations for how they should spend their time outside their regular office hours.

This study by Gross is one of the few studies which has sought to test the assumption that exposure to role conflict results in adverse consequences for the individual. Superintendents faced with contradictory demands in making budget recommendations were much less satisfied with their jobs and worried more than superintendents who were not exposed to role conflict in this area. Superintendents who encountered role conflict with respect to time allocation also seemed to worry more than those who perceived no role conflict in this area. Many more studies of this type must be conducted, however, before we can conclude that role conflict does lead to occupational stress which in turn generates physical disorders and disturbances for the individual.

OTHER SOURCES OF OCCUPATIONAL STRESS

Role conflict is not the only factor which is presumed to be a contributor to occupational stress among school executives. Stress apparently is engendered by a number of conditions in the administrator's work environment which do not necessarily involve incompatible, contradictory, or inconsistent expectations for performance. Although these conditions have not been studied as systematically as role conflict has been, the available evidence is highly suggestive, nonetheless.

Four conditions which seemingly lead to stress among school executives are decisions in the face of uncertainty, decisions in the midst of crisis, obligations to make decisions that affect the fates of others, and occasional periods of role overload.

Spalding's[55] comprehensive and analytical treatment of the anxieties inherent in the superintendent's role focuses on uncertainty as a major determinant of executive stress and strain. One area of uncertainty is the impact of administrative action on organizational achievement and functioning. According to Spalding, the effects of an executive's decisions are not always immediately observable. Rather, the degree of success is evident only after a considerable length of time; and, in some instances, the results are never clearly evident. At the same time and in the absence of any knowledge of results, the superintendent must continue to take action which assumes that earlier decisions led to successful outcomes. The exercise of discretion under such circumstances, as Spalding notes, is not conducive to an easy state of mind.

Stress is also engendered by the need to make decisions under crisis conditions. With increasing frequency, school administrators are having to reach decisions in situations which involve a time deadline and threat of injury or harm to both the organization and administrator. Confrontation and crisis-induction are becoming standard tactics for militant community groups, teachers, and students.[56] These power-oriented techniques cause administrators pain and anguish as evidenced by the upsurge of premature retirements and requests for transfer.

A third source of felt difficulty for administrators is in the area of personnel decisions. In every organization, someone is assigned the responsibility for deciding whether individuals are to be re-appointed, promoted, demoted, or discharged. Ordinarily, principals and superintendents are expected to make these choices in educational organizations. Decisions of this type involve a lot of stress and anxiety for the decision maker,[57] as he recognizes that the decision has important, serious, and potentially negative consequences for the future life chances of the individual who is demoted or fired. Frequently, the individual's family is adversely affected by the administrator's judgment as well. More likely than not, such decisions stress and disturb administrators because few people like to view themselves as precipitating life crises for others.

[55] Willard B. Spalding, *The Superintendency of Schools—An Anxious Profession* (Cambridge, Mass.: Harvard University Press, 1954).

[56] Edwin M. Bridges, "Student Unrest and Crisis Decision Making," *Administrator's Notebook,* **XVIII**, 4 (December, 1969).

[57] Harry Levinson, "On Being a Middle-Aged Manager," *Harvard Business Review,* **47,** 4 (July–August 1969), 51–60.

Role overload[58] is a fourth potential source of stress and strain for the administrator and may take one of two forms. Role overload may represent a condition in which the individual is faced with a set of obligations which requires him to do more than he is able in the time available. When considered separately, each demand is within the capabilities of the administrator; however, time limitations and deadline pressures make it impossible for him to deal with the entire set of obligations. Role overload also may represent a condition in which the individual lacks either the personal or organizational resources to meet his role obligations. In either case, the role overload can have similar consequences—high levels of stress and physical or emotional disturbances.

SUMMARY

Throughout this chapter we have concentrated on factors which individuals may wish to ponder as they consider their choice about a career in educational administration. We have shown that a person interested in administration can serve education in a wide variety of ways; the field, as we noted, offers an exciting array of career possibilities. Furthermore, we have cited evidence which shows clearly, if not dramatically, that the extrinsic rewards are greater for administrators than for teachers. Our discussion of the intrinsic rewards and the stresses and strains inherent in executive roles has provided a glimpse into the affective side of administration, a side which has been somewhat neglected by previous theorists and researchers interested in administration as a field of inquiry. Our review of the research dealing with traits and competencies has furnished some clues as to who gets appointed and as to who succeeds in various types of administrative positions. Hopefully, the knowledge we have brought to bear on the topics in this chapter will enable the individual to arrive at a more rational career choice than otherwise would have been possible.

SUGGESTED ACTIVITIES

1. Interview a number of superintendents and principals to determine what it is about their work that either makes them feel uncomfort-

[58] Stephen M. Sales, "Organizational Role as a Risk Factor in Coronary Disease," *Administrative Science Quarterly,* 14, 3 (September, 1969), 325–337.

able or leads to a state of uneasiness. Compare the results of your interviews with the ideas presented in the section on stresses and strains.

2. Select a number of school districts in your area and seek to identify the competencies and personal and prestige traits which are associated with or which figure in appointment to administrative positions.

3. In several local school districts, make an effort to describe the procedures for assessing administrative competence. Note particularly the criteria which are used, the evidence used to establish the extent to which the criteria are being met, and the priority assigned to the various criteria.

4. Talk with a number of superintendents and attempt to find out what they regard as the sources of joy and pleasure in their work.

SELECTED READINGS

ERICKSON, DONALD A. "The School Administrator," *Review of Educational Research,* **XXXVII,** 4 (October, 1967), 417–431.

GOODE, WILLIAM J. "A Theory of Role Strain," *American Sociological Review,* **25,** 1960, 483–496.

LEVINSON, HARRY. *Emotional Health in the World of Work.* (New York: Harper & Row, 1964).

LEVINSON, HARRY. *The Exceptional Executive: A Psychological Conception.* (Cambridge, Mass.: Harvard University Press, 1968).

SPALDING, WILLARD B. *The Superintendency of Schools—An Anxious Profession.* (Cambridge, Mass.: Harvard University Press, 1954).

13

Qualifying
For
Educational Administration

In the preceding chapter we focused on the decision to become an educational administrator; our attention now shifts to the plans necessary to implement such a decision. A decision by itself is not enough; after a choice is made, the next task is to create a plan to meet the requirements implied by the decision. There are three major functions to be served by this career plan: One is to increase the probability of attaining the hoped-for objective, another is to maximize the opportunities which a person may have to qualify for a post in educational administration, and the third is to provide a means by which the prospective administrator can evaluate his career choice. Conceivably, as he attempts to follow his plan, a person will discover that his original choice was an unwise one. By having a plan, the person may be able to determine quite early if he has made an error in judgment. With this knowledge, he can adjust his career choice accordingly and minimize the costs involved in pursuing a goal which has a low probability of attainment.

CREATING A PLAN

A classic poem reminds us that "The best laid schemes o' mice and men" often go astray. As children, we all read—but probably did not wholly comprehend—the rhyme that told of the kingdom that was lost "for want of a nail." Must we then infer that man is foolish to plan when his plans are so easily laid low? History is replete with famous men who seem to have been cast by destiny rather than self-planning into heroic or villainous roles. Careful analysis, however, indicates that planning by men is far more successful than might be

394

assumed, and is far more prevalent among men than might be evident. History also does not reveal to us the names of potentially great men who did not make important contributions for the lack of a plan.

Without going into detailed documentation of the need for careful planning if decisions are to be carried into reality, we shall merely state that planning seems to us to be an essential step in qualifying for educational administration. It is necessary to examine the elements of a good plan and to provide some insights into planning for a specific field—educational administration.

ELEMENTS OF A GOOD PLAN

It seems to us that planning involves clarifying purposes; defining the problem; gathering, analyzing, and interpreting facts; and deciding courses of action. This is, of course, very similar to the whole process of decision-making as we defined it earlier. For our purpose here, however, it will be assumed that earlier decision-making procedures have led to a clear statement of purpose and that the problem is well defined. There will, obviously, be sub-purposes and sub-problems. It will be necessary to gather, analyze, and interpret facts and, certainly, to decide courses of action.

The plan should, then, be based on a clear understanding of the ultimate purpose and of the steps necessary to meet this purpose. Next comes a consideration of the qualifications required to make the steps. The basic elements of a good plan seem to be statements of purpose, of qualifications needed to meet purposes, and of the steps required to gain these qualifications. Thus, if one's ultimate purpose is to become a city superintendent, one's plan must include certification, university work for advanced degrees, and experience. It will undoubtedly also include a principalship as a step toward the ultimate purpose, and this step will require consideration of appropriate certification, degree work, and experience background necessary for the principalship.

Thus both short-term and long-term goals should be included in a good plan. The short-term goals should be stated in order that sequential progress toward the ultimate goal is understood and planned. The long-term goal must be stated to provide a frame of reference as one has opportunities to change positions, to go to school, or to do both. It is the long-range goal that can help a person decide if he should accept a new position or if he should stay where he is and complete, for example, the program for his master's degree.

INCLUSIVENESS OF THE PLAN

A plan such as we have been discussing cannot be too detailed, particularly as it is projected ten or even more years into the future. In addition, the plan should not be unduly specific. While, for example, it is understandable that a person might desire to be the superintendent of schools in his home town, it is not wise to restrict planning to such specific goals. The old home town can have only one superintendent at a time, and the person who clings tenaciously to this specific goal may wait in vain for an opportunity to realize it. The specifics of certification and advanced degrees are appropriate, but specifics as to geographical location of future position, exact places where nonteaching experience is to be gained, or exact salaries to be earned along the way are not.

In general, the plan should include types of positions desired, types of nonschool work or activity experiences deemed necessary, and a general picture of the economic well-being desired as the plan progresses. Just as an attractive woman may be a spinster because she waited in vain for a blond lawyer, six feet tall, earning $30,000 a year, and with a Cadillac convertible, to show up and propose, so the prospective administrator can wait in vain for a board of education in a given school district to offer him a given job at a given salary. It is far better that a plan be developed which is sufficiently inclusive of the general progress desired than that a plan be cluttered with specific and unrealistic details.

FLEXIBILITY VERSUS VACILLATION

The above discussion makes it clear that some flexibility is desirable in a plan for the future. Earlier, when the necessity of evaluation of the basic decision to pursue a specific ultimate goal was described, it was pointed out that changes in plan may be necessary and wise. How does one tell when one is being wisely flexible and when one is being foolishly vacillatory? Generally, the most simple and basic way is to test possible changes in position or in objectives against the framework of the ultimate goal and the reasons that led to the choice of that goal.

Does experience show that some of the basic reasoning which led to the choice of the ultimate goal was in error? If so, a change in goals may be wise. Does momentary fatigue or irritation seem to demand a change in the ultimate goal? If so, such a change may be extremely unwise. Does a new position fit the requirements of the next step toward the ultimate goal even though it was not a position that was envisioned earlier as a good one? If so, accepting it may be wise. Does a new position offer financial rewards but no real progress toward the ultimate goal? If so, it may prove to be unwise both professionally and financially.

A well-made, carefully considered plan, drawn up in realistically general terms, should be discarded only for major reasons related to the ultimate goal and the basis for accepting that goal. Too many "temporary" deviations from the plan for reasons that are attractive but unsound can lead to permanent failure to reach an ultimate goal. This is the reason that long-range goals are necessary and should play an important role in reaching short-term decisions.

THE PLAN IS CREATED

We have now considered the making of a decision and the creation of a plan to implement it. We need now to turn our attention to a specific plan to implement a specific decision—qualifying for educational administration. The remainder of this chapter will explore some of the specific considerations to be made as one attempts to create and follow a plan that will lead to a desired position as an educational administrator.

USING TEACHING EXPERIENCE

Many would-be administrators fail to realize and to profit from the opportunities for qualification as an administrator which are inherent in a teaching position. We have already described in some detail the role of the teacher in school administration. Undoubtedly, the fulfillment of this role will lead to increased qualification as an administrator. Certain features might well be pointed out here to relate teaching experience more specifically to qualification as an administrator. Before doing this, however, we must stress that we do not view the main function of teaching to be that of a stepping-stone to administration. The teacher who holds the attitude that teaching is only a necessary evil before entering a "real" job, will probably achieve only minor success both in teaching and in the "real" job—if, indeed, the so-called real job is ever attained. While we do want to point out that teaching experience can help qualify a person for administration, we would not want to imply that this is a major purpose of teaching.

LEADERSHIP OPPORTUNITIES

In qualifying for educational administration, the teacher should take advantage of the many first-hand opportunities which are available for gaining experience and skill in administering and leading groups. In the classroom, the processes of decision-making, programing, stimulating, co-ordinating, and appraising should be studied and techniques improved. Not only will this lead to future qualification as an administrator, but it will lead to increased competence as a teacher. In addition, the teacher should seek out opportunities for leadership in teacher organizations and in community groups. These activities will provide insight into the required skills and techniques of leadership and will provide valuable experience in their utilization.

Many teachers, for example, find themselves involved in scouting or Sunday school activities. These are organizations which provide leadership opportunities with both children and adults. When, as often happens in such activities, the teacher is sought out by other members of the community as a leader, the experience can be used both as a means of community service and as a means of developing skills in leadership.

A number of teachers gain leadership experience in local, state, and national organizations. Not only is the president of a local classroom teachers' association given practice as a leader, he also is provided with opportunities to observe educational administration from a closer vantage point than is usually afforded the teacher. In working on problems of teacher welfare, professional growth programs, or matters dealing with the evaluation of teaching, the association officer gains experience both in leadership and in the more specific areas of educational administration.

SEMI-ADMINISTRATIVE POSITIONS

It is difficult to draw a line and declare that certain positions are administrative while others are not. In Chapter 12, we described the positions we have defined as administrative. It will be noted that such positions as department heads, athletic directors, or activity fund treasurers were not listed. For purposes of clarity, it seems best to define these and similar positions as semi-administrative positions.

There may be a number of such positions, particularly in a large high school. A high school with an enrollment of three hundred students or more might well have full-time or part-time staff members with the following semi-administrative positions: co-ordinator of instruction, director of activities, director of guidance, director of health and physical education, director of athletics, heads of departments, attendance supervisor, director of testing and research, director of cafeteria, and registrar. Certainly, in the smaller school, not all of these positions would be found, and probably none of them as full-time positions. In the larger school, most of them would be found, and many of them would be full-time positions. The fact is that regardless of the size of the school, these positions represent functions that need to be performed, and some arrangement of time and assignment will be developed to facilitate this performance of function.

In the elementary school, there is less opportunity for a teacher to gain experience in semi-administrative positions. Elementary schools are usually smaller and generally understaffed in terms of administration. The opportunities for leadership, not only for the teacher but also for the administrator, are reduced due to the heavy load of routine and clerical duties which must be assumed by the professional staff. If the elementary school teacher is to gain valuable experience through holding semi-administrative positions, he must seek committee chairmanships of both school and school district committees, such as textbook selection committees or curriculum development groups. While the position as an adviser of a student activity may sometimes not clearly fill the role of a semi-administrative position, it is more often true than not that such a position does have administrative overtones.

The acceptance of and performance in a semi-administrative position in a school or school system can aid greatly in one's attempt to qualify for educational administration. The prospective administrator often gains through such a position the chance to try his wings under the guidance of an experienced administrator.

RELATIONSHIPS WITH ADMINISTRATORS AND BOARD

Many teachers enter university courses for the preparation of educational administrators without ever observing a board of education meeting or taking a firsthand look at the work which crosses the desk of a school principal. Curricula in teacher education rarely include any courses aimed at providing the prospective teacher with some insight into such matters as school budget-making, procedures of boards of education, or administrative organization of a school district. The continued pressure from many sources for increased general education, increased subject-matter preparation, and decreased professional education courses for the prospective teacher makes it unlikely that courses or units dealing with educational administration will be added in any quantity to programs for undergraduate teacher education.

Hence even a basic familiarity with such problems must be gained on the job and in graduate courses by the in-service teacher. Many teachers ignore on-the-job opportunities to learn about educational administration and thus ignore an opportunity to begin the process of qualifying for educational administration. We have, for example, observed committees dealing with teachers' salaries both neglect and refuse to become familiar with the school budget, even though the salary program they are attempting to develop may require as much as 70 to 80 percent of this budget for its implementation. We have heard teachers complain about "secrecy" or "lack of information" when even a cursory inquiry would have revealed to them that the information they desired was a matter of public record in the central office of the school district and in the offices of the county superintendent of schools and of the state department of education. We have known teachers who did not know how many members were on their local school board, how they were selected, when or where they met, or what even one major duty of this board was.

In some cases, to be sure, inadequate or ineffective administrators make it difficult for teachers to observe the processes and details of educational administration in their school districts. For the most part, however, it is apathy rather than antagonism which leads to the teachers' lack of knowledge about administration. Certainly, the prospective administrator cannot afford such apathy. He needs to attend some board meetings, to study some budgets and other records, and to inquire about administrative problems. While course work and reading may make a real contribution to the development of an administrator, there is little doubt but that the prospective administrator should also learn through observation of and participation in administering. Careful observation of administrators in action and of administrative skills, techniques, and details in the actual school setting is one way in which the teacher who is considering administration can begin to qualify for administration.

EXPANDING EXPERIENCES

Just as teaching experience when appropriately utilized can aid in qualifying for administration, so can other experiences gained while teaching aid in the development of a school administrator. We will not repeat in detail here the various kinds of experience which increase one's potential as an educational administrator. It does seem worthwhile to point out, however, that many teachers are particularly lax in studying some of the nuances of school-community relations that can be observed by the teacher. In addition to observation, there are many forms of participation available to the teacher which aid in increasing the qualifications of a prospective administrator.

Teachers can—and administrators must—study the community forces that impinge upon the school program. Teachers can pay some attention to the extent of community understanding of school problems and can analyze some of the reasons for the presence or absence of understanding. Teachers can attend P.T.A. meetings, not as reluctant back-benchers, but as interested participants in and observers of school-community relations in action. In these and many other ways the teacher who is interested in educational administration can increase his knowledge of and his competency in the area of school-community relations.

The prospective administrator can also gain experience in the area of understanding communities while teaching. What is a community? What makes this community tick? Upon what economic base does it rest? What roles do churches, service clubs, business organizations, labor groups, or farm groups play in the community?

Every teacher lives in a community. If, as we believe, one of the important qualifications of an educational administrator is the ability to recognize and understand community forces, the teacher and prospective administrator need to utilize every opportunity to gain experience in these difficult tasks. There is no better place for the teacher to start developing this competency than in his local community.

Some examples might serve to point up the possibilities in this area. The teacher in a school district can often gain significant understanding of the influence of a community on the educational program in that district. Is science neglected while a trade and industry program flourishes? What elements in the community might have a bearing on this situation? Is a large industry the dominant force in the community? Is science important to this industry? To what extent do board members come from the personnel of the industrial firm? Answers to these and other questions can provide a great measure of community understanding.

Or, as the teacher develops a course of study, he might well consider the ways in which community resources could be used in implementing the course of study. What possibilities for field trips exist? Are there any members of the community who might discuss certain phases of a subject with the class? To what extent will service clubs or business and labor organizations provide materials or underwrite costs of special activities? Answering questions like these will not only provide the teacher with increased understanding of his community, it can also play a major role in the improvement of the instructional program.

While the above comments emphasize experiences in the area of school-community relations, experiences in other administrative task areas are also available. The prospective administrator should be alert to such opportunities and take advantage of them as a valuable part of his preparation.

FORMAL PREPARATION

Many aspects of one's teaching experience can aid in helping one qualify for educational administration. The time must come, however, when the prospective administrator begins his formal preparation for administration, usually under the direction of an adviser from an institution accredited by the state to prepare educational administrators. The several aspects of this formal program will be considered in some detail here. It should be remembered, however, that each state has specific patterns of requirements for the administrator and that no text, article, or lecture can replace the state certification handbook as a prime source of information during the formal preparation period. By the same token, the catalog of the university or college chosen by the prospective administrator for his course work must also become a key reference book as he plans his work.

CERTIFICATION OF ADMINISTRATORS

In discussing the certification of administrators, we would stress at the outset our belief that certification requirements represent, at best, minimum requirements. Too often, an administrator-to-be gains the impression that, with certification, he is fully and perpetually prepared for any and all administrative positions. The generally low requirements for certification in most states should make it obvious that such is not the case. We believe that a master's degree is a minimum standard for administrative certification and that regular graduate work—either leading to a doctor's degree or taken as part of a post-master's nondegree program—are essential to the continuing qualification of an administrator. Certification alone is a completely inadequate criterion of the readiness of a person to assume an administrative position; a fact that has been recognized by professional associations, which have developed membership requirements more stringent than those required for certification in a number of states.

Because the certification of administrators, like that of teachers, is a responsibility and an authority held by each state, requirements for certification vary from state to state.[1] In the states that grant administrative certificates, varied types are issued. These include elementary principals' certificates, secondary principals' certificates, general principals' certificates, superintendents' certificates, and general administrative certificates. Without exception, one requirement for certification as an administrator is teaching experience, with three years of such experience being the usual requirement. In addition, many of the superintendents' or general administrative certificates require two or three years of administrative experience as a principal as a prerequisite. Almost all the states stipulate certain kinds of graduate courses for administrative certification. Generally, graduate credit is required in such areas as curriculum, supervision of instruction, and general administration, and in such specialized fields as school law or school finance. In addition to course work, many states require a master's degree for certification as an administrator.

It is also true that, regardless of certification requirements, many school boards are including the doctorate as a prerequisite for consideration as a superintendent in their districts and, as we have already mentioned, the American Association of School Administrators requires a two-year graduate program in an accredited institution as a prerequisite for membership in the Association. Furthermore, the six regional accrediting associations for secondary schools and colleges generally create standards for administrators in accredited

---

[1] For these state requirements, see Elizabeth H. Woellner and M. Aurilla Wood, *Requirements for Certification of Teachers, Counselors, Librarians, Administrators for Elementary Schools, Secondary Schools, Junior Colleges,* 33rd ed., 1968–1969 (Chicago: The University of Chicago Press, 1968). This publication is revised annually.

schools that are often higher than the minimum standards for state certification.[2] Therefore, as a prospective administrator considers the steps necessary to quality for educational administration, he must consider requirements for both certification and a graduate degree.

As the administrator-to-be plans to qualify for educational administration, the question of certification must loom large. Many excellent opportunities are lost because a teacher or a principal has not taken the time and effort to be certificated for a higher administrative position. Either the state department of education or a university approved by the state to certificate administrators can supply complete details concerning certification requirements. These sources of information should be contacted early in the planning phase as the prospective administrator prepares to qualify for administrative positions.

ADVANCED DEGREE REQUIREMENTS

The above discussion makes it clear that the prospective administrator must consider advanced degrees as he attempts to qualify for administration. In general, there are five advanced degrees which should be included in the consideration of a long-range plan: the Master of Arts, the Master of Education, the sixth-year degree or certificate, the Doctor of Education, and the Doctor of Philosophy. In discussing these degrees or certificates, it is necessary again that we remind the prospective administrator that this discussion can be only a general one and that there is no satisfactory substitute for personal contact with the degree-granting institutions as a source of specific information about the requirements for higher degrees.

The Master's Degree. The day will undoubtedly soon be here when in every state a school administrator will be required to hold a master's degree for his initial administrative position. Usually, either a Master of Arts or a Master of Education degree will be available and will be acceptable. It is difficult to say which degree should be sought. The Master of Arts degree has, in most cases, more requirements in course work outside of the specific area of professional

---

[2] The regional accrediting associations referred to are Middle States Association of Colleges and Secondary Schools, New England Association of Colleges and Secondary Schools, North Central Association of Colleges and Secondary Schools, Northwest Association of Secondary and Higher Schools, Southern Association of Colleges and Secondary Schools, and Western College Association.

education than does the Master of Education degree, and the former often requires a research project or thesis which may not be required for the latter degree. Many prospective administrators earn the Master of Arts degree with emphasis on their teaching field, a procedure that has much to recommend it.

Remembering that we have stressed earlier the necessity for a broad educational background and for familiarity with both educational and other social problems, techniques, and skills, the prospective administrator should study the specific requirements in the institution of his choice and make a decision in terms of the program and his own needs and plans.

The sixth-year program. Many universities have instituted a degree or certificate program that comes between the master's and doctor's degrees. The sixth-year program generally requires thirty semester hours of graduate work beyond the master's degree. Usually about one-half of this work is in the specialized area of educational administration, while the other half is in closely related supporting areas. Most of the programs require either a thesis or a report on a field project as one of the requirements for receiving the degree or certificate. In addition, one characteristic of most of these programs is a period of time the student spends in supervised field experiences. Often these programs require some period of residence as a full-time student.

In general, the student who definitely plans a doctoral program should not contemplate the sixth-year program. It is important, however, for all prospective administrators to realize that such programs do exist and, as their future plans are made, to include a consideration of these programs.

The doctoral program. There are no figures which indicate precisely the number of school administrators who possess doctors' degrees. There is evidence, however, that this number is continually increasing; and placement offices report that the possession of a doctor's degree is becoming more common as a prerequisite listed by boards of education for major administrative positions. Certainly, the prospective college professor of educational administration needs to consider the degree as a prerequisite to the attainment of his goal.

The question of whether the Ph.D. degree or the Ed.D. degree should be sought is becoming almost an academic question. At one time, the Ph.D. degree was in no way related to preparation for engaging in any highly specialized, technical occupation. This is no longer the case. In such fields as chemistry, mathematics, or engineering, where great numbers of doctoral degrees are earned, Ph.D. programs have become specialized and professional in much the same way that an Ed.D. program represents professional training in education. Actually, there are probably more differences among various programs for these degrees than there are between the two degrees. The choice of doctoral program, then, becomes much more a matter of personal preference and specific institutional programs than of the "worth" of the degrees.

Thus the major choice that faces the prospective administrator is whether or not he should include a doctoral program in his plan. Because the doctoral program is expensive in both time and money, the candidate must be willing to make a sacrifice to secure his degree, a sacrifice borne also by his wife and children. The acknowledgment often found in a dissertation in which the student expresses gratitude for the faith, support, patience, and understanding of his wife and family is much more than a mere formality. The candidate should know where he is going and how he hopes to get there if he is able to make the commitment to a doctoral program that is necessary for success.

In making this choice, the administrator must remember that many administrative positions will never require the doctor's degree as a prerequisite, that advanced graduate work can be taken without entering a doctoral program, and that the returns to him from such a program will probably be deferred ones. On the other hand, the administrator should recall that many major administrative positions do require a doctor's degree, that there is much personal satisfaction in completing a difficult intellectual task, and that the completion of a doctoral program gives a person greater flexibility in seeking advanced positions. Certainly, the majority of the educational administrators in our public schools will not complete such a program. It should be considered, however, as a part of the planning to qualify for educational administration. Intellectual ability, professional goals, research interest and ability, and personal motivations will play major roles in the decision.

Timing the degree programs. The decision as to when one begins to pursue an advanced degree is one based on both professional and personal factors. In general, however, a master's degree program is not started until after at least a year's teaching experience and, for most students, is completed in from one to three years, depending on whether the course work is all summer work or done during the regular academic years. If done during the summer, the student usually accumulates three or four years of teaching experience by the time the master's degree is earned and may, therefore, be ready to assume an administrative position. Care should be taken to insure that course work taken during the master's program will meet certification requirements so that the administrator-to-be is eligible to convert the "to-be" to "is."

The post-master's program should not be delayed too long after completing the master's program. We have mentioned earlier that a doctoral program is probably best begun before the doctoral candidate reaches the age of thirty. The doctoral program usually requires at least one year of full-time residence on campus. Course work plus the completion of a doctoral dissertation will usually lengthen the doctoral program to a total of from two to five years. Two full years on a doctoral program—"full" meaning that the student is not attempting concurrently to hold a position as a full-time administrator—is, for many people, a realistic estimate of the time necessary for completion.

SUPERVISED FIELD EXPERIENCE

In addition to meeting degree and certification requirements, the prospective administrator should be learning about administration and learning to administer. As we stress certificates and degrees, we must also stress that the only value of either is as they represent increased professional growth and knowledge. The mere possession of a degree or certificate does not guarantee excellence.

One aspect of the formal program for the preparation of educational administrators which has received particular attention in recent years is supervised field experience. In field experience programs, the prospective administrator has a chance to practice administration, usually under the joint sponsorship of university and school district personnel. In this way, theory and practice are related, and the qualifications of the prospective administrator can be considerably enhanced. Supervised field experience is usually gained in one or more of three ways: as a part of class activities, in a cadet program, or in an internship program.

Field experience. There are many ways in which formal class work can be supplemented by supervised field experience. Term projects, for example, can deal with real rather than imaginary problems.

Possibilities also exist during the term for field affiliations that are related to, and aid the attainment of, the objectives of a course. Students in courses that deal with school-community relations might, for example, have close relationships with local community agencies during a quarter or semester. In one such course with which we are familiar, students spent a great deal of time working on an individual basis with local Community Chest agencies on problems with educational implications. Similar possibilities exist in courses in all areas of educational administration.

Another possibility is the development of courses that revolve around field activities. Students might conduct a comprehensive educational survey in a school district and report their findings and recommendations to the board of education of the district. Or, students might survey an actual problem in that district, with the findings of the survey being examined in class sessions.

Field trips are also used in many courses. School plant and school business administration courses offer a wide variety of possibilities for field trips. While such trips offer observation rather than participation opportunities, they do create another chance for the student to see theory in action.

Another type of field experience is the social science field research project, in which the students work as members of a social science research team. The students may have a major responsibility in defining, developing, and carrying out a significant administrative task in connection with the research project, or they may act as assistants to the staff that is responsible for the project. Experiences such as these provide students with opportunities to see theory in practice and to put their own theories to test in the field.

Internship programs. The internship program is primarily a university-sponsored program to provide a type of on-the-job training. The internship stresses the assumption of responsibility. In practice, the internship program in educational administration involves placing a student or intern in an administrative position in a school district under the joint supervision of a local school administrator and university personnel. The intern assumes responsibility for the completion of one or more administrative tasks in the district. Although in most cases he is at least partially paid by the school district, the emphasis is upon his learning and growth rather than upon service to the employing district. Such service results from the program, but it is incidental to the main purposes of the internship program.

Several dangers exist in the internship program, and several problems are present. Hooker provides an excellent cautionary statement when he indicates that:

> If the internship experience is to provide graduate students with something more than the art of being wrong with greater confidence, considerable inquiry into the professional climate of the sponsoring school district is necessary. It should be borne firmly in mind that interns are not apprentices. They are not learning the tricks of the trade nor formulae for solving problems. Under supervision they make logical deductions from basic knowledge and inference from observations.[3]

It is sometimes difficult to develop a program in which the intern assumes real rather than artificial responsibility. There is sometimes a tendency to assign interns to positions where they are familiar with practices and problems instead of utilizing the program to fill gaps in the background of the student. While this practice usually results in greater service to the school district, it does not always serve the purposes of the intern well. The internship program is costly on all sides. The intern must devote a full year to the program, usually at a low salary. Supervision, both on the part of the university and the local district, runs high in time and money. The program usually includes a seminar on campus for interns, and travel requirements between campus and school district may become burdensome both for interns and for supervisors.

A variation of the internship program is the cadet program through which a school district attempts to select, train, and promote administrative candidates within the system. Such programs usually concentrate on the training of principals, although some school districts also use the cadet program to train central office personnel.

In general, cadet programs include some class sessions under the direction of school district personnel and assignment to various semi-administrative or administrative positions in the district under the supervision of an administrator in the system. While early cadet programs did not include university affiliations, sometimes these programs do include either regular university course work or a special cadet seminar as an integral part of the plan.

The internship program is obtaining more and more recognition as a fitting climax to a program of formal preparation. In spite of the difficulties mentioned above, and others, this program appears to

---

[3] Stephen B. Hencley, ed., *The Internship in Administrative Preparation* (Columbus, Ohio: The University Council for Educational Administration, 1963), p. 23.

offer an excellent opportunity for the welding of classroom theory and field practice in the university program. The prospective administrator would do well to consider the possibility of an internship as another step in his plan to qualify for educational administration.

PLANNING THE FORMAL PROGRAM

We have now shown that the formal program for the preparation of an educational administrator will include factors involving certification, advanced degree requirements, and supervised field experiences. In any plan for a formal program, one should also consider the experience which he is gaining in teaching and plan the program to supplement and reinforce this experience. Remember too that the formal program should not result in narrow specialization. The prospective administrator should make every effort to insure that his higher education will result in his becoming a well-rounded, intellectually developed individual. It is at this point that the strengths and weaknesses of individual universities which prepare administrators should be sought out and evaluated. The kinds of programs offered, the selection procedures utilized, the kinds and scope of fellowships offered, the degrees granted, and the general reputation of higher institutions are important factors to the prospective administrator. There are certain advantages to be gained from doing graduate work in more than one university and, if this seems advisable, problems concerning the transfer of credit should be considered in advance. But, above all, as plans for the formal program are developed, the prospective administrator should remember that there are no substitutes for the written certification requirements of the state and the printed catalog of the university as authoritative and accurate sources of information concerning program requirements. And finally, the prospective administrator must always remember that his ultimate concerns are competency and professional growth. Certificates and degrees are of value only as they reflect competency in educational administration.

SEEKING THE FIRST POSITION

Both formal training and experience finally culminate in the first administrative position for the prospective administrator. One qualification or set of qualifications which the administrator-to-be needs to consider, then, is the ability to seek and gain an administrative position.

There are several ways in which administrative positions are filled. Many principalships and assistant superintendencies and some superintendencies are filled by promotion from within a school system. When persons from outside the system are brought in, it is either by virtue of individual applications for the positions or through recommendations from commercial or university placement offices. Almost all college and university professorships are filled through placement office recommendations, while administrative positions in higher education are filled through promotion or placement office recommendation. Each of these avenues will be discussed briefly here, and then some attention will be given to selection procedures common to all of these approaches.

PROMOTION FROM WITHIN OR WITHOUT

Some large school districts fill all of their principalships by selection from the staff of the system. The assumption is made that the larger district has sufficient personnel to permit the discovery of prospective principals from within who are as well qualified as those who could be found by going outside the system.

The major danger in the process of promotion from within is "inbreeding." If all new administrators in a system are products of the same training program, new ideas and new approaches in educational administration may be scarce. This danger is not impossible to overcome, but the administrator who reaches his position by promotion from within a system should make sure that he has an open mind for ideas from outside.

One other point should be mentioned here. Sometimes those within a school system feel that it is not fair to offer administrative positions to "outsiders." The only fair policy that a board of education can follow in filling administrative positions is one which states that these positions should go to the most highly qualified applicants. The "insider" has no inherent right to such a position except as he possesses qualifications that suit him for the position better than other applicants. This implies that criteria have been developed to aid in the selection process and that these criteria are based on descriptions of the position which adequately define its duties and responsibilities.

There are two conflicting philosophies regarding the relative weight to be given an insider as opposed to an outsider. Some feel that if all other things are equal, the position should go to the insider. This feeling is based on considerations of morale of the staff, familiarity with the problems and processes of the district, and creation of an incentive for those in the system interested in administration. The other viewpoint is that if all other things are equal, the position should go to the outsider. This viewpoint is based on considerations of getting new blood and new ideas into the system, the avoidance of cliques or other human relations problems which may result from inside promotion, and the hope that more qualified people will apply for a position when this philosophy is dominant.

Each of these viewpoints has both strengths and weaknesses. The important point for the prospective administrator is that he know which of the two ideas is prevalent in his school district. Because each viewpoint can be supported on rational grounds, the prospective administrator should not feel that he is unfairly treated if the viewpoint opposite to his is the one that prevails. If he knows the situation, he can and should plan his actions accordingly.

PLACEMENT OFFICE SERVICES

A placement office is, of course, a rather dignified form of employment agency. Every university that prepares educational administrators offers placement services. These are usually free to the student, although small charges are sometimes made to cover a part of the clerical services necessary for the preparation of credentials. In addition, there are many commercial educational placement agencies. A number of these agencies are associated with the National Association of Teacher's Agencies (NATA), a voluntary organization of agencies which maintains certain minimum standards for member agencies. University placement offices also have a voluntary organization known as the National Institutional Teacher Placement Association (NITPA). Commercial agencies are probably more active in the placement of teachers than of administrators, but they do provide services in both areas. Commercial agencies have three general ways of charging for their services—a registration fee, a fee which is a percentage of the first year's income, or a combination of both. For the most part, we feel that university placement offices are more acceptable than commercial offices. The university placement personnel have a better knowledge of the candidates for positions, generally attempt to assess the position as well as the candidates in order to insure a good fit, and provide the same or better results than a commercial office, at much less cost to the candidate. It is our feeling that the profession—in this case represented by the training institutions—should provide its own placement services.

The candidate for an administrative position should take steps to see that the placement office with which he is working is aware of the types of position in which he is interested. His credentials in the placement office should be up to date and inclusive of all important data. As placement services will be utilized beyond the initial position, it is important that the administrator keep his credentials up to date while he is holding an administrative position. Many prospective and practicing administrators fail to gain new positions for which they are qualified because they have not maintained contact with a placement office. A candidate who feels that a placement agency is not serving him well may not have submitted complete records, may not have asked that recommendations for him be submitted to the agency, or may not have indicated to the agency his interest in a position. Good relations between candidate and placement office are another important part of the procedures as one attempts to qualify for and to obtain an administrative position.

INDIVIDUAL APPLICATION

The question of whether or not to apply for an administrative position on one's own in the absence of placement office or school system backing is a difficult one. The candidate, particularly for the first administrative position, must take some initiative. He must, in a real sense, be a job seeker. This fact is generally much less true as one considers administrative positions of major importance. In such cases, the job seeks the man to a much greater extent than in the case of an initial administrative position.

It is impossible to generalize about the so-called lone-wolf approach to seeking an administrative position. We do believe, however, that the approach of the position seeker to those with a position to fill is strengthened considerably if someone other than the candidate shares the candidate's confidence that he is qualified for the position. This "someone" may or may not be a placement officer, a school administrator, or a professor. In any event, the position seeker who attempts to go it alone with no recommendations of any kind will usually find the procedure a difficult one.

Thus it seems evident that the candidate for an initial administrative position should employ initiative wisely. He should be on the alert for positions in which he is interested and for which he is qualified. He should bend every effort to making his interest and his qualifications known. He should work with a placement office if possible, but he usually cannot afford to sit back and await placement. He should secure a list of people who know him and who will recommend him for a position. And—finally, but really at the head of the list—he should be sure that he is prepared for an administrative position, should one become available. The importance of being "at the right place with the right preparation at the right time" cannot be overlooked.

SELECTION PROCEDURES

Let us assume that, through a placement office or through recommendation from some other source, the prospective administrator has been invited to submit a formal application for an administrative position. What can he expect as he seeks this first position? It is difficult to specify the procedures that may be used by a given district as the candidates for an administrative position are screened for selection of the ultimate appointee. Several common procedures will be discussed here, although it is not likely that many districts will use all of these procedures.

Application forms. While detailed application forms are common for teaching positions, less use of them is made in seeking candidates for administrative positions. The basic reason for this is probably that when administrators are sought, reliance is put upon the interview, a possible field investigation, and the credentials of the candidates. However, care should be taken to complete any required application forms promptly, accurately, neatly, and completely. Even if not interested in the position, the candidate who is asked to apply should write a letter briefly indicating that he is not presently interested and expressing some appreciation for the invitation. This practice is more than mere courtesy, for the ignored invitation can sometimes loom large in the future.

Tests. Some school boards are using one or more tests as screening devices for the selection of administrators. Such tests include written and oral English tests, essay tests over the field or fields included in the position applied for, performance tests in which candidates are appraised in situations similar to those which might be encountered in the position, physical examinations, and objective examinations organized around such areas as general administration, curriculum, guidance, methodology, and supervision. Testing procedures are found more often in city school districts than in smaller districts, but the use of tests as a part of the selection procedure is becoming more common.

The candidate for a given administrative position should ascertain if tests are given as a part of the selection procedure for that position, if examples of questions or specific descriptions of the tests are made available to candidates, and if such tests are given individually or are given to a group at a given time and place. It is likely that the tendency for school districts to give some kind of test to candidates for administrative positions will increase in the future, and the candidate should be aware of this trend.

Interviews. After the screening process, most boards of education interview the final two or three candidates for a superintendency, or the superintendent and other central administrative personnel interview the final candidates for a principalship. Although in many cases these interviews are rather vague and general in nature, a number of districts have developed a check list of specific desired qualifications about which the interviewing team plans to gain information and make evaluations during the interview. The interview is generally used to provide the prospective employer with some indication of the appearance, poise, speaking ability, and knowledge of the candidate.

The candidate should realize that the interview is a time of mutual exploration. He is being looked at, but he is also looking at the position. Thus the interview should include some time when he can become the interviewer. He should make sure that he understands the duties and responsibilities of the position, the opportunity it offers to work toward mutually satisfying goals, and the conditions of employment. He should ask some questions about the school district and the community. Often one of the factors that an employer uses in evaluating a candidate after an interview is the nature of the questions asked. For example, the young man seeking his first principalship who asks only about tenure and retirement reveals much about himself through his questions. As he prepares for his interview, then, he should be concerned with both his answers and his questions.

Field rating. While it is not a usual procedure for the selection of a person for his first administrative position, some mention should be made of the field rating. When a list of applicants for a position is reduced to only a few, many boards of education or professional employing personnel visit the school districts in which the remaining candidates are presently employed to gain an on-the-spot evaluation. There they interview administrators, teachers, and lay citizens so that the employing officials can gain further insight into the qualifications of the candidates. There is little that a candidate can do to prepare for this procedure other than to insure that he is doing his best wherever he is. Many candidates for administrative positions have found that because they have considered their present position beneath them and have acted accordingly, they have never been able to rise to a position they consider appropriate to their ability.

THE ETHICS OF JOB-SEEKING

We have already said enough about the professional nature of educational administration to make it unnecessary to dwell at great length on the ethics of seeking an administrative position. Only a few points might be mentioned here and these but briefly. As a prospective administrator, the candidate for a position should proceed through the established channels in a district rather than trying, for example, to go directly to individual board members. The subordinate who attempts to gain an administrative position by assisting in the downfall of his administrator is unethical and is establishing a precedent that may be used by his own subordinates in the future.

A candidate for an administrative position should strive to gain that position in open, ethical competition with other qualified candidates. One cannot be proud of gaining a position by manipulation or secrecy so that the employing agency does not compare his qualifications with those of others. If he is not the best-qualified person for the position, he should not have it, and he should have additional incentive to increase his qualifications.

IN REVIEW

We have pointed out that in seeking his first administrative position, the prospective administrator should become familiar with the avenues that seem to lead to the position he desires. These may involve promotions within a system or promotions to another system. The candidate should associate himself with a university placement office and insure that his credentials are in order and up to date. He should be aware that his best chance for gaining an administrative position will usually be based on recommendations from a placement office, from administrative personnel in his district, or from both, rather than only on his individual application.

As he becomes an active candidate for a given position, the prospective administrator will find himself facing several kinds of selection procedures. These may include a review of his credentials and recommendations, the submission of a formal application, participation in a testing procedure, an interview, and a field rating. Throughout the entire process, the candidate needs to remember that he is seeking a position in a highly skilled profession and that it is important to him and to the profession that all of his acts be ethical.

CONTINUED PROFESSIONAL GROWTH

Every administrator who assumes an administrative position is only partially prepared for that position. He will probably never be able to say realistically that he is completely prepared for the position he holds, and there will always be other administrative positions for which he is even less well prepared. Thus the effort to qualify for a position should not end upon its assumption.

Continued On-Campus Preparation

Many major administrative positions, as we mentioned earlier in this chapter, now require that the incumbent possess a doctor's degree. The administrator will undoubtedly seek his first or his second administrative position before he earns this degree. This means that while he is serving as an administrator he will also be continuing his university work. Even if the doctor's degree does not become one of his goals, university graduate work should be a part of his continuing professional growth. Many workshops and seminars are planned particularly for the practicing administrator, and the insights gained on his job add value to any course he may take. Just as most salary policy statements in school districts require that the teacher return to a campus periodically for professional growth, it is important that the administrator consider this same requirement as it applies to him.

It should be noted also that the present trend in master's degree programs for educational administrators is to place less stress than formerly on specialization in administration and more stress on the broader areas of education in general. This means, in effect, that much of the course work in more advanced phases of administration is offered on the post-master's degree level and that such course work is planned for the person who has begun the practice of educational administration. In short, then, the master's degree represents minimum preparation for the educational administrator.

There are other possibilities for on-campus professional growth of the practicing administrator in addition to the course work we have stressed. Most universities hold conferences that offer opportunities for administrators to gain new understanding of their work. Many institutions have developed one- or two-day problem-centered clinics in which twenty or thirty administrators gather with university personnel and other consultants to deal with specific problems arising in the field. There are numerous opportunities for administrators to avail themselves of university services such as consultative service for local studies, co-operative research projects, or the development of local professional growth programs. The ideal situation is one in which the relationships between universities and administrators are continuous and mutually beneficial. Often, practicing administrators make themselves available to assist in a university's pre-service preparation program and serve in a variety of ways as co-operating university staff members. Only in this way can the two groups—the practitioners and those charged with the preparation of practitioners —provide each other with the unique and important advantages and aids which each has to offer the other.

GROWTH ON THE JOB

One of the best training grounds for the administrator is an administrative position. Every day presents him with opportunities not only to serve the schools of his school district but also to increase his own professional knowledge, skills, and competence. As we have stated much earlier here, if experience is to be educative, the educational values of experience must be actively sought. As the administrator works with teachers, with other administrators, with board members, with parents, or with community leaders, he should be increasing his qualifications as a top-level, competent administrator.

A number of activities in which administrators engage are aimed at professional growth. Included among these activities are planned programs of intervisitation, development by groups of administrators of handbooks and other materials for mutual use, and group studies of skills and techniques necessary for effective performance of various administrative tasks. Some of the most valuable activities available to administrators are sponsored by the various professional organizations to which they belong. By working with colleagues for professional growth, the administrator can help to insure that his competence for his present position and his qualifications for other, more advanced positons will continue to grow.

Almost every high school commencement speech includes the admonition that the end of one's high school experience must not mark the end of one's learning experiences. Too often, the prospective administrator assumes the attitude that he "has it made" when he reaches an administrative position. If educational administration is to grow as a profession, its practitioners must see themselves in a continual learning situation in which the aim is both their own growth and the growth of the profession.

SUGGESTED ACTIVITIES

1. Interview a number of principals and superintendents in your area and attempt to identify how they happened to get their first administrative position. From their perspective, what factors seemed to be important in their being appointed? What factors seemed unimportant?

2. Examine several university programs leading to certification as an educational administrator. What opportunities do these programs offer for connecting theory with practice and for obtaining familiarity with the world of practice?

3. Study the succession patterns of administrators in your area. When appointing people to their first administrative position, do the school districts tend to appoint insiders or outsiders? Were the administrators whom you studied insiders or outsiders when they were appointed to their first administrative position? Are there differences in the succession patterns of elementary school principals, junior high school principals, senior high school principals, and superintendents?

SELECTED READINGS

BRIDGES, EDWIN M., and BAEHR, MELANY E. "The Future of Administrator Selection Procedures," *Administrator's Notebook,* **XIX,** 5 (January, 1971).

BRINER, CONRAD. "The Superintendent and the Selection of Subordinate Administrators," *Administrator's Notebook,* **VIII,** 6 (February, 1960).

CLARK, JAMES V. *Education for the Use of Behavioral Science.* (Los Angeles, Calif.: Institute of Industrial Relations, 1962).

CULBERTSON, JACK, and HENCLEY, S. P. *Preparing Administrators: New Perspectives.* (Columbus, Ohio: University Council for Educational Administration, 1962).

GOLDHAMMER, KEITH. *The Social Sciences and the Preparation of Educational Administrators.* (Alberta, Canada: Division of Educational Administration, University of Alberta, and the University Council for Educational Administration, 1963).

HENCLEY, S. P., ed. *The Internship in Administrative Preparation.* (Columbus, Ohio: University Council for Educational Administration, 1963).

HOWSAM, ROBERT B., and MORPHET, EDGAR L. "Certification of Educational Administrators," *Journal of Teacher Education,* **IX,** 1 (March, 1958), 75–96 and **IX,** 2 (June, 1958), 187–203.

WOELLNER, ELIZABETH H., and WOOD, M. AURILLA. *Requirements for Certification of Teachers, Counselors, Librarians, Administrators for Elementary Schools, Secondary Schools, Junior Colleges.* (Chicago: The University of Chicago Press, revised annually).

14

Challenge Of Administration

As we reflect upon what we said about the job of administration and about the man who is to undertake such a job, we feel some need to present and amplify the challenge or challenges inherent in educational administration. This chapter, perhaps more than any other part of the book, is our credo.

We take the position that a particular kind of educative process open to all is necessary in a society that aspires to a democratic way of life. In like manner we see a public school system characterized by certain values and practices as an essential part of the educative process; and finally, we take the position that administrative leaders who meet certain requirements occupy critical roles in the public school. We shall now amplify each of these challenges.

THE DEMOCRATIC WAY OF LIFE

We believe that the democratic way of life offers the primary challenge to educational administration. To be sure, this is a challenge to all citizens of our nation, but we think that such a challenge holds unique meaning for the school administrator.

A GREAT EXPERIMENT

The democratic way of life was and is a great experiment. When, historically, America fell heir to movements that had begun to stir Europe, one of these was the Protestant Reformation, which challenged the authority of church and state. The movement placed great stress upon the responsibility of the individual for the salvation of his own soul. John Locke in England during the seventeenth century supplied some of the intellectual foundations for popular rule. Denying that kings had any divine right to rule, he placed sovereignty in the hands of the people. The founders of our government referred to him as "the great Mr. Locke" and utilized much of his thinking in formulating our federal constitution.

As Counts has so well described it, this intellectual leadership shifted later to France:

> In the eighteenth century the leadership in thought crossed the Channel to France. A galaxy of brilliant minds, with great gifts of expression, so dominated the age that it has come to be called after them and their work—the Age of Enlightenment. They proclaimed the coming victory of naturalism over supernaturalism, of science over theology, of human reason over established authority. Voltaire attacked the traditional dogmas of church and state as barriers to human advance. Montesquieu saw government, not as unchanging and sanctified by divine will, but as an expression of a people living in a particular time and place. Diderot and d'Alembert edited the great Encyclopedia which, they hoped, would bring the best of scientific and practical knowledge to many people and arouse enthusiasm for reform and improvement. Rousseau popularized the political ideas of Locke defending with the power of genius the doctrine that only the freely expressed will of the people can render any government legitimate. Condorcet, in his *Historical Sketch of the Progress of the Human Mind,* clothed with vast learning and philosophic grasp the idea of human progress and the perfectibility of man and his institutions. These men, and others like them, prepared the way for the French Revolution and other revolutions to follow in the nineteenth century.[1]

The movement to free the common man found fertile soil in America, where, in the first place, tradition was not such a binding force. Secondly, free land was available, for almost three hundred years, to any who would settle upon it and begin its cultivation. Economic opportunity appears to have had much to do with the development of social and political democracy.

But from its inception the idea of a democratic way of life was a radical one. The thought that all men could and should read and interpret the scriptures for themselves, as advocated by Luther, was in direct contradiction to the established order of the Catholic Church. Locke's ideas of the sovereignty of the people ran counter to centuries of governmental practice. Yet despite the novelty of these ideas, many of them have been put into practice in America. What success they will have one cannot yet say; the experiment goes on. The impact of the idea is still being determined, for the capacity of

---

[1] George S. Counts, *Education and American Civilization* (New York: Bureau of Publications, Teachers College, Columbia University, 1952), p. 52.

the common man to rise to such a role is fraught with difficulties. If one is both a common man and a black, the difficulties appear to be somewhat greater. But the excitement of participating in a great experiment can be experienced by any who will.

OUR HISTORICAL DOCUMENTS

Despite the uneven course of the development of the democratic way of life in America, and despite times when there has been downright despair regarding the status of the movement, our historic documents attest that, in the long view, there has been steady growth in this direction. Let us make brief reference to some of those documents.

As early as 1620 the Englishmen who had set out to plant a colony in the northern "Parts of Virginia" signed what has now become famous as the Mayflower Compact. Among other things they stated that they

> Do by these Presents, solemnly and mutually in the Presence of God and one another, covenant and combine ourselves together into a civil Body Politick, for our better Ordering and Preservation, and further-ance of the Ends aforesaid. . . .

This is a clear expression of the need to work together for the common good. Despite the conviction these people had that they must leave their own country and go to a new land where they could worship God according to their own conscience, they recognized that there must also be group action for the common good. This concern for the common good became one of the values of the new society.

More than a hundred and fifty years later, in 1776, when the Colonists felt it necessary to explain to the world their resistance to the British Crown, the Declaration of Independence was enunciated. In that document, well known to most of us, is language relevant to our purpose here:

> We hold these truths to be self evident, that all men are created equal, that they are endowed by their Creator with certain unalienable Rights, that among these are Life, Liberty, and the pursuit of Happiness. That to secure these rights, Governments are instituted among Men, deriving their just powers from the consent of the governed. That, whenever any Form of Government becomes destructive of these ends, it is the Right of the People to alter or abolish it, . . .

Let us look at two of the ideas in the above excerpt. "That all men are created equal" is a powerful concept. Men, to be sure, are not equal, physically or intellectually. But before God and the law our founders contended that they are equal. With all of our fumbling regarding civil rights, this aspect of the democratic faith has persisted—persisted until the franchise was widened, until the Emancipation Proclamation was issued, until the school desegregation decision of the United States Supreme Court was handed down in 1954, and until the voting law of 1965 was passed. While general acceptance of the idea in practice has been distressingly slow, the idea itself has conquered the armies of kings and dictators and continues to be more than a match for bigotry and sophistry.

Another concept from the Declaration of Independence is that government should serve the people who create it. And when it no longer serves the purposes which the people intended in creating it, it is to be altered or abolished. Here is legal approval for revolution. Here also is the enunciation of the idea that man is of prime importance and his institutions secondary. Man's institutions, being instrumental, are to be shaped to his needs and not his needs to the institutions, as has been attempted in totalitarian regimes.

As the various states debated the federal Constitution from 1787 to 1790, it became clear that a bill of rights would have to be appended. Thus, the first ten amendments to our Constitution became effective as of 1791. The first amendment includes these significant words:

> Congress shall make no law respecting the establishment of religion, or prohibiting the free exercise thereof; or abridging the freedom of speech or of the press; or the right of the people peaceably to assemble . . .

A reading of the McCollum,[2] Zorach,[3] and Schempp[4] cases will convince one that the injunction on religion is still a very live issue. And in hundreds of instances, our courts have affirmed freedom of speech, of press, and of assembly. These freedoms, despite their abridgment at times, have become part of the democratic doctrine.

Following the Civil War more specific language was necessary to insure the application of some of these freedoms to blacks. Thus, in

[2] *McCollum v. Board of Education,* 333 U.S. 203.

[3] *Zorach v. Clauson,* 343 U.S. 306.

[4] *School District of Abington Township v. Schempp,* 374 U.S. 203.

1868, the fourteenth amendment to the Constitution, part of which reads as follows, became effective:

> No State shall make or enforce any law which shall abridge the privileges or immunities of citizens of the United States. . . .

These words definitely strengthened the hand of the federal government in protecting the rights of minorities from what had been discriminatory legislation in some of the states. More important, our national values were now to be policed by our *national* government.

In considering the extension of voting privileges, it seems rather shocking that it was not until 1920, with the addition of the nineteenth amendment to the Constitution, that women in all states of our nation were granted the franchise. Tardy as such action now seems, the event is further evidence that early pronouncements on the democratic way of life must receive later implementation.

Space does not permit us to continue this survey of our historical documents. We would, however, like to make reference to the now famous Brown case of 1954.[5] After suggesting the central place of public education in a nation such as ours, the U.S. Supreme Court said:

> We conclude that in the field of public education the doctrine of "separate but equal" has no place. Separate educational facilities are inherently unequal. Therefore, we hold that the plaintiffs and others similiarly situated for whom the actions have been brought are, by reason of the segregation complained of, deprived of the equal protection of the laws guaranteed by the Fourteenth Amendment. . . .

This decision by the Court and subsequent action again appear to represent movement toward full realization of democratic values.

One can quarrel with the above presentation. One could say our words as Americans are better than our deeds. They are. But we keep at it, and our deeds seem to improve. One could say that ours is essentially political democracy, and that our social democracy has not kept pace with it. Again, one might be right, but we submit that political democracy is essential if social democracy is to be achieved. Or one could say the right to vote assumes that accurate information is available to the voter, a condition which many now attempt to subvert. To be sure, this is one of our difficulties, but this very

---

[5] *Brown, et al., v. Board of Education of Topeka,* 347 U.S. 483.

condition constitutes part of the challenge with which we are faced. In other words, what has been done and what remains to be done constitute two parts of the great experiment.

OPERATIONAL AGREEMENTS

Although our culture, as we shall note later, is far from expressing unanimity on many value questions, we do seem to have reached certain operational agreements. Some of those agreements were reflected in the words of President Johnson when he convened the White House Conference on Education in 1965. He said,

> . . . I want you to bring all the tools of modern knowledge—from physics to psychology—to bear on the increase of learning. And if these tools are still inadequate, then it's our job to fashion new ones and better ones.
>
> To guide discussion in this conference we are formulating a series of questions, and I hope you'll give these questions your most careful thought and your boldest imagination . . . [at] the conference. They include:
>
> How can we bring first-class education to the city slum and to the impoverished rural areas? Today the children of five million families are denied it.
>
> How can we stimulate every child to catch the love of learning so that he wants to stay in school? One million children now drop out of schools each year.
>
> How do we guarantee that new funds will bring new ideas and techniques to our school system—not just simply expand the old and the outmoded?
>
> How can local and state and federal government best cooperate to make education . . . the first among all the nation's goals?[6]

Reference to *Goals for Americans,*[7] the work of the President's Commission on National Goals, at an earlier time, is also illuminating. This commission emphasized that opportunity for individual development must remain a primary concern; that discrimination on the basis of religion, sex, or race was morally wrong; that the degree of effective liberty available to the people is the ultimate test; and that the development of the individual and the nation demands that education at every level be improved.

---

[6] Subcommittee on Education of the Committee on Labor and Public Welfare, United States Senate, *White House Conference on Education.* (Washington, D.C.: U.S. Government Printing Office, 1965), p. 17.

[7] Report of the President's Commission on National Goals, *Goals for Americans* (Englewood Cliffs, N.J.: Prentice-Hall, 1960), pp. 3–6.

It seems possible to arrive at the value positions noted above from different philosophical orientations. For that reason we are stressing here our *operational* agreements rather than our philosophical differences. This we must do, in any culture as diversified as that in America, if there is to be a common ground for action.

In light of such a position, we wish to set forth a set of values which we think gives meaning to what we have been calling a democratic way of life. First, there is implied a *belief in people*. This, as we have already indicated, is much harder to live than to say. Nevertheless, our history and our action, even though the latter has at times been tardy, suggest that most of us place people above institutions. For most of us this means all people, without regard to race, color, religion, economic circumstance, or national background. In particular, we believe that educational opportunity should not be denied any person.

A second value characteristic of the democratic way of life is a belief in *co-operation for the common good*. True, some cry out against the welfare state, but when the nation has been threatened, even as early as the Mayflower Compact, we have been willing to join together, to submerge individual desires when necessary, to foster the welfare of the group. This tendency received special impetus during the era of the New Deal, but it is noteworthy that Republican administrations have repealed little of the New Deal legislation. Actually, both political parties act this way because we as people adhere to this principle.

Three, our nation believes in *freedom of the press, of speech, and of religious expression*. This was the substance of the first amendment to our federal Constitution. Again, we have abridgment and abuses of these rights, but in the end our courts and the public stand up for these freedoms. To be sure, we have had to learn that freedom is a relative matter and that it must be accompanied by responsibility. The relative nature of freedom does not mean that any one of us is free to pursue his own interests to the detriment of the group. This balance between personal freedom and the social good is the thing we are working to achieve.

Finally, our people accept *the method of intelligence* as an approach to problem-solving. In this process, some of us may exhibit a blind faith in scientism[8] or accept the intelligence of others as a substitute for utilizing our own intellectual abilities. Yet there seems to be a conviction on the part of most Americans that we can, by

[8] See William H. Whyte, Jr., *The Organization Man* (New York: Simon and Schuster, 1956), Chap. 3.

giving thought, solve the many problems with which we are faced. Moreover, we have a conviction that this ability to think is not the possession of just the few, but the heritage of the many.

CHALLENGES TO THE DEMOCRATIC WAY

There are both challenges *to* and challenges *of* the democratic way of life. Let us deal with the first of these. Briefly, the challenges to the democratic way might be categorized as outside and inside challenges. The chief outside challenge, as is now clear to most of us, is world communism. Communism in its Russian or Chinese expression is a far cry from what Karl Marx, its founder, visualized. To be sure, Marx advocated a militant movement, but the ends he sought seem to many to be in keeping with the Hebraic-Christian ethic to which we ourselves subscribe. He wanted an abundant life for the individual, the elimination of the exploitation of man, and the establishment of a world-wide regime of peace and brotherhood.

It has now become clear that communism in practice exalts the state above the individual, that the ruling hierarchy is straining to perpetuate autocracy, and that any challenge to the system will be quelled by force. It may have taken such events as the Hungarian rebellion of 1956 and the invasion of Czechoslovakia in 1968 to convince many people, but most of us now see world communism for what it is. Clearly, we do not wish to be dominated by such a system.

There is also a challenge to democracy from within. In spite of our optimism about what we believe to be long-term gains in the achievement of the democratic way, there are definite schizophrenic symptoms in our culture. Brameld has listed them as follows:

Self-interest versus social-interest.

Inequality versus equality.

Planlessness versus planning.

Nationalism versus internationalism.

Absolutism versus experimentalism.

Man-against-himself versus man-for-himself.[9]

An examination of each of these issues will convince one that at both the verbal and the operational levels of American life there are

---

[9] Theodore Brameld, *Philosophies of Education in Cultural Perspective* (New York: Dryden Press, 1955), pp. 53–62.

adherents of each of the contrasting approaches. Unfortunately, the perpetuation of these dichotomies obscures the point that, in many cases, it is not an either-or proposition. There may be, for instance, an enlightened self-interest that is consistent with social interest.

Seeman has also dealt with our cultural conflicts.[10] We have summarized his descriptions of these conflicts as follows:

1. The status dimension—conflict between success ideology and equality ideology.
2. The authority dimension—conflict between values of dependence and independence.
3. The institutional dimension—choice of universalist as against particular criterion for social action.
4. The means-ends dimension—conflict of getting the job done against emphasis on the process.

While these two analyses of our cultural conflicts do not correspond entirely, they have many points in common. An examination of them should make it quite clear that our society is a dynamic one, that its direction may not always be clear, and that in the arena of ideas a good many battles are still ahead of us. This struggle is the inside challenge to the democratic way.

CHALLENGE OF THE DEMOCRATIC WAY

There is also the challenge *of* the democratic way of life. Let us examine briefly a few aspects of this part of the problem. The first of these is perhaps the challenge of accurate information. If the average citizen is to participate in his economic, social, or political destiny, he must be informed. This has always been a difficult expectation. In our early history it was a question of teaching people to read and to understand, and then of making written documents widely available.

In recent decades the process has been complicated by the tremendous development of the mass media, notably radio and television, and by the great competition for the mind of man that has evolved. As a matter of fact, the money spent annually on advertising in this country approximates that spent for the operation of all the schools and colleges in the nation. In advertising, of course, the motive is not primarily to inform but rather to sell.

---

[10] Melvin Seeman, "Role Conflict and Ambivalence in Leadership," *American Sociological Review*, **18** (August, 1953), 373–380.

The appeal of advertising to the conscious man seems serious enough, but recently, with the rise of motivation research (M-R), there is also planned, large-scale appeal to man's subconscious.[11] The application of M-R to the selling of automobiles may seem somewhat amusing, but when the same techniques are applied to presidential elections, as they were in recent campaigns, one can become cynical about the "information" made available to the average elector.

A second challenge *of* the democratic way is that of concern about public affairs. A number of studies suggest that in most communities, about 50 percent of the people are uninformed and apathetic about public questions.[12] This condition represents two potential dangers. There is first the possibility that the leadership group of a community will go unchecked. Such a course of action may mean that the leaders cease in time to represent the values and programs of their constituents. The second danger inherent in apathy is found in the possibility that citizens with no facts at hand may become prey to those who seek personal advantage and who do not hesitate to use emotional and biased approaches. In both of these dangers the challenge of how to create concern in people is clearly exemplified.

Along with the challenges of providing information and of creating concern, there is the challenge of action. How Americans exercise their voting privileges may serve to illustrate our point. In recent presidential elections only about two-thirds of the persons of voting age in the nation cast their ballots. In some states between 70 and 80 percent of the potential voters cast their ballots, while in other states only 30 to 50 percent voted.

This problem, particularly in the Southern states, is not merely a question of apathy, but also represents the results of a social tradition in action. One wonders why even in seemingly progressive states like California and New York only two of every three persons of voting age actually vote. If voting is indicative of other action on the part of citizens concerning the common good, and we fear it is, there is little wonder that organized efforts to thwart projects designed to foster the general welfare do succeed.

---

[11] See Vance Packard, *The Hidden Persuaders* (New York: David McKay Company, 1957) See also Joe McGinniss, *The Selling of the President, 1968.* (New York: Trident Press, 1969).

[12] See *Supplementary Papers—Cincinnati School Survey.* (Chicago: Midwest Administration Center, University of Chicago, 1968), pp. 9–24–9–54.

THE EDUCATIVE PROCESS

The second challenge to educational administration is the educative process. We contend, moreover, that without an educative process of the kind we shall describe, the democratic way of life is an impossibility. In other words, if the great experiment to which we have alluded is to succeed, a genuine opportunity for learning must be available to all.

MEANING OF THE EDUCATIVE PROCESS

The educative process of which we speak is much broader than schooling. Actually, much of what we have learned was not acquired in school. Our schooling seems to have relatively little to do, perhaps unfortunately, with how we vote, how we spend our leisure, and the ways by which many of us make our living. Without in any sense deprecating the school, it sharpens our discussion to recognize that education and schooling are not synonymous.

Upon reflection one soon decides that the total culture is involved in teaching and learning. Perhaps we can see this point more easily in cultures other than our own, described in the writings of the anthropologists.[13] For instance, Benedict speaks of the Zuñi Indians as a ceremonious people. She says that grown men spent most of their waking hours in ceremonial observance, for which a staggering amount of word-perfect ritual has to be memorized.

The teaching-learning potential of our own culture has been dealt with in dramatic terms by Bloom.[14] After a comprehensive synthesis of the research in human development, he concludes that, with the exception of school achievement, the most rapid period of development is in the first five years of life. Thus, physical growth, intelligence, language development, and other characteristics are more than 50 percent determined by the home and its surrounding culture by the time the child enters the school.

[13] For example, see Margaret Mead, *Coming of Age in Samoa* (New York: W. Morrow & Company, 1928) and Ruth Benedict, *Patterns of Culture* (Boston: Houghton Mifflin, 1934).

[14] Benjamin S. Bloom, *Stability and Change in Human Characteristics* (New York: Wiley, 1964).

In this educative process, or cultural adaptation, what are the important steps? As we see it, they are three in number: (1) acquiring of a feeling of being at home in one's culture, (2) learning about one's culture, and (3) contributing to one's culture. Let us look at each of these.

The first step of coming to feel at home in one's culture appears to be largely emotional in character. The affection extended to the new baby by the parents and other members of the family are part of it. The trial and error of age-mates as they learn to play together, whether in a nursery school or on the street, represent an important potential in the process. The great need for peer approval found in most adolescents and the need which all of us have for recognition on the part of other adults are also involved. Somehow we must feel that we belong.

But we must feel that we belong to the larger culture, not merely to some minority group within it. This point has particular relevance today for those who grow up in the slums of our central cities. The feelings of hopelessness and alienation of youth in slum neighborhoods has been depicted by Conant.[15]

His observation that social dynamite was building up in our large cities in the form of unemployed out-of-school youth, particularly in the black slums, has been well borne out by recent developments. But alienation is found not only in the slums. Increasingly, today we see manifestations of alienation among privileged youth in our high schools and on our college campuses. Keniston has argued that alienation from American society is fostered by stresses flowing from the unquestioned primacy of technology in our society.[16] According to his analysis the supremacy of technology de-emphasizes human values and needs and creates conditions such as chronic social change, fragmentation in society, discontinuities between childhood and adulthood, and value conflicts, which alienate us all to some extent and totally alienate certain especially sensitized individuals. We cannot pass from this topic without noting that, in addition to the adverse effects of technology, another source of alienation among our youth in recent years has been the increasingly obvious contradictions between our society's ideals and its practices, especially with respect to racial equality.

But the educative process cannot stop with belonging; there is also

---

[15] James B. Conant, *Slums and Suburbs* (New York: McGraw Hill, 1961).

[16] Kenneth Keniston, *The Uncommitted: Alienated Youth in American Society* (New York: Dell Publishing, 1965).

the necessity for understanding. This places great demands upon all of us. How can we learn about the social and physical world in which we live? Much can be gained from observation, but we soon find a need for trained observation, and observation, without reference to some conceptual scheme, may be relatively pointless. Regardless of the field of study, we soon learn that we need to consider the observations, the feelings, and the reflections of others. This process would seem to constitute the beginning of scholarship, whether in or out of an organized school.

But there is still another aspect of the educative process. Feeling at home in and knowing about one's culture ought to lead one to contribute to that culture. Contributions, to be sure, will vary greatly in nature and in quality; and ways of improving the culture will be apparent only to those who have the capacity to examine critically the cultural practices now extant.

The challenge of the educative process to equip people to reflect critically about the conditions of life around them and to project possible improvements is, we believe, the aspect of the educative process most important to the survival of the democratic idea. Unfortunately, those who attempt to examine our way of life critically, in an attempt to make improvements, are often misunderstood and sometimes even called subversive. Many people fail to recognize the value and importance of this critical examination, and ignorantly use words of abuse to describe people who, through their criticisms, are contributing toward the improvement of our way of life.

MANY INSTITUTIONS CONTRIBUTE

Many institutions make contributions to the educative process. The home, despite the suggestion of some that it has reached a point of declining influence, still seems to be the most important educative agency we have. Our basic personality characteristics, including such simple matters as friendliness or distrust, are in large part a product of the home. Our attitudes toward religion, government, sex, and learning itself reflect the home environment. To be sure, the home also tends to reflect the biases of the culture of which it is a part. In other words, a middle-class home has different standards with respect to cleanliness and schooling, for instance, than a lower-class home has. The home, as any social worker or psychiatrist can testify, is a significant influence in whatever a person learns.

For most people the church, too, is an important agency in the educative process. That segment of our population that affiliates with a church and participates in church activities is subject to an educative influence of considerable magnitude. For instance, the attitudes of these people toward marriage, toward childbearing, toward authority, and toward social behavior are greatly influenced by the church. For those people who belong to no church, the influence of the church may be less direct, but it is nonetheless significant. The nonchurchgoer as well as the churchgoer is affected by the Hebraic-Christian tradition as it has found expression in our ethics and in our law.

Also important is the street corner or the play group of one's peers. Beginning at about age eight or ten and continuing through adolescence, most young people feel great need for acceptance by their peers. Often it takes expression in the clothes that are worn. If bell-bottom pants are the thing, then bell-bottom pants there must be. Woe to any parent who has the temerity to suggest that there is a satisfactory substitute. Many times status with one's fellows is acquired by doing those things which the gang has decided to do. Drag-racing with souped-up cars, for instance, in some communities among certain youngsters has become a prestige activity. Anyone not joining in the activity is labeled "chicken." Clearly, then, these peer groups have great influence with young people and are thus potent educative influences.

Nor should we stop with young people. Riesman has made the point that our culture is becoming more and more other-directed.[17] In other words, the sanctions one feels, which influence one's behavior, have their origins in the group to which one belongs rather than in one's upbringing as reflected in one's conscience. Whyte makes a similar point when he speaks of the organization man.[18] For all of us, the group or groups with which we affiliate, particularly in our work, seem to be decisive forces in determining our family life, our goals for educating our children, our dress, our leisure, and our values in general.

All of this has caused Hart to point out that "education goes on whether school keeps or not."[19] Having made this point, however, we should not overlook the fact that the school has a unique role in

---

[17] David Riesman, *et al., The Lonely Crowd* (New Haven: Yale University Press, 1950).

[18] William H. Whyte, Jr., *op. cit.*

[19] Joseph K. Hart, *Education in the Humane Community* (New York: Harper & Brothers, 1951), p. 4.

the educative process, as we shall soon see. May we conclude this section by emphasizing the point that an educative process that is comprehensive, understanding, and permissive within limits is essential to the democratic way of life. This means that the educative role of many institutions in our society should be recognized. It means, too, that each institution should exercise its role with some recognition that other influences and agencies are and must be at work in our kind of society. Finally, it means that class barriers should be sufficiently flexible so that one's place and position in society can be altered through the educative process.

THE PUBLIC SCHOOL

The third challenge to education administration is found in the public school itself. Despite the breadth of the educative process, as suggested above, we hold that the public school has a unique, indeed an indispensable, part to play in that process. Let us examine such an idea.

CHARACTERISTICS

Most of the children and youth in this country attend public schools. Indeed, recent reports indicate that 87 percent of the elementary school pupils and 90 percent of the high school pupils of the nation attend such schools.[20] Without deprecating the role of the private school in American education, it seems clear that a great part of the task of providing formal schooling is placed squarely upon the public school.

The significance of the percentage of total school enrollment found in the public school is not entirely a matter of numbers. The pupil populations of the public schools tend, by and large, to be more heterogeneous than the pupil populations of the private schools. Although this circumstance has its problems, it is just here that the public schools find one of the real opportunities, for the public school becomes a prototype of our society itself. The diversity of our nation socially, economically, politically, religiously, racially, and academically is well reflected in the public school.

[20] *Statistical Abstract of the United States, 1969* (Washington, D.C.: U.S. Government Printing Office, 1969).

We do not wish to overdo this matter. We are well aware of the fact that many individual public schools, particularly in urban and suburban areas, have pupil populations with relatively less diversity than suggested above. Indeed, some suburban communities have segregated exclusive schools and central cities tend to have segregated slum schools. Programs of slum clearance, urban redevelopment, and enlargement of small school districts may alleviate segregation of both social class and race. It now seems clear, however, that there must be deliberate social planning of both housing and school attendance areas if most youngsters in the public schools are going to have the opportunity to find out how the other half lives.

In this diversity, once common and now harder to attain, the public school pupil has an opportunity to acquire a sense of realism as to what people are like; he can note the variety of contributions that its various members make to the group; and he can learn much about relating himself to many kinds of people. These skills are essential in our kind of culture.

The public school has still another opportunity. More than any other nonschool community agency, and possibly more than most private schools, the public school can be the most impartial institution in our culture. Business, labor, and farm organizations have great difficulty in viewing all sides of a controversial issue, particularly if the issue affects them in any way. Most churches must approach problems within a particular framework. Thus, useful as these organizations are for some purposes, they alone cannot nurture adequately the person with an inquiring mind who wishes to weigh the evidence on all sides of a tough problem and come to his own decision.

We recognize that some teachers in the public schools are not adequately prepared to guide objective inquiry, but we still maintain that the opportunity for objective inquiry is present in the public school and that it is being admirably exploited in some instances. Moreover, we have found that thoughtful members of special interest groups such as business, labor, and agriculture are expecting the public school to exercise its role of impartiality.

THE SCHOOL'S UNIQUE ROLE

With this brief consideration of what the public school is like, actually and potentially, we shall next turn to the unique role of the public school. This is a difficult task, for over the years public schools have gradually taken on more and more functions, usually as a result of public demand. Moral education on one hand, and driver training on the other, are two cases in point. Sometimes it seems that relatively little examination of the appropriateness of the new functions being placed in the public school has been made either by the public or by the school people. Perhaps, in some cases, other agencies in society are better equipped to meet these new demands than is the school. We believe that the transfer of certain child-rearing functions from the home to the school is a case in point.

Another reason it is difficult to delimit the public school's role is the concomitant character of learning. As a child learns to read and write he is also learning many other things. He may be learning to like or dislike school. He may be learning to like or dislike teachers. He may find in his acquiring of skill with words that the doors to ideas have been unlocked, or he may find reading a wearisome task, never to be pursued except under duress. We cannot ignore or be unconcerned about these concomitants.

Despite the difficulties inherent in depicting the unique role of the school, we shall attempt such a task. Our concern is that the public school recognize some sort of priority in what it does, so that those things which are essential to the democratic way of life· and to the educative process shall not be left undone. We are not offering objection to the fact that other functions can and in many cases should be performed. Moreover, we recognize that the school shares with other institutions responsibility for helping the young acquire constructive beliefs and attitudes. We do hope, however, that as the demands placed upon the public school increase, the financial resources to meet such demands will be proportionately increased.

The first task we would place upon the public school is teaching for literacy. To read, to write, and to figure are old, old expectations of what the school is to do. We recognize that with the advent of mass media reading has come to seem relatively unimportant to some people. Moreover, literacy alone may simply make people prey to those who control what is to be read. However, this is an unlikely result of literacy in a free country, and it is clear that all citizens of a nation such as ours need skills in reading, writing, and numbers.

The fact that literacy is a matter of acquiring certain skills—skills that are helpful in developing certain understandings and appreciations—might cause some to suggest that those understandings and appreciations were the *sine qua non* of education, and that the skills were only instrumental to their achievement. Much as we recognize the logic of this position, we still think there are practical reasons for the public school to consider its first indispensable task to be that of teaching for literacy.

If the public school does not do the job of teaching for literacy, it will not be done. For most people the private school cannot do it. Relatively few parents are equipped to do it. Other agencies in society are even less able to step into such a role. Literacy on the part of most citizens is indispensable to our way of life, and the public school is indispensable to providing this literacy.

The teaching of critical thinking is, we think, the second unique task of the public school. This is really the purpose that the founders of our public schools had in mind when they spoke of the need of intelligence on the part of all people. Note a part of what Caleb Mills had to say to the legislature of Indiana in 1846:

> The true glory of a people consists in the intelligence and virtue of its individual members, and no more important duty can devolve upon its representatives in their legislative capacity than the devising and perfecting of a wise, liberal, and efficient system of popular education. . . . It is, indeed, a favorable circumstance that appropriate and efficient action on this subject will awaken no sectional jealousies, alarm no religious prejudices, subserve the interests of no political party. It is emphatically a topic which, ably discussed and wisely disposed of, will benefit every part of the State, improve every class in the community, give permanence to our civil and religious institutions, increase the social and literary capital of our citizens, and add materially to the real and substantial happiness of everyone. Such a system of improvement ought surely to require no logrolling to secure its adoption by the representatives of an intelligent people, nor will the burden its operation may occasion be reluctantly borne by a community that scorns the repudiation of a debt incurred for the construction of railroads and canals.[21]

Mills and others may not have appreciated fully what it takes to get people to behave intelligently, but there was no question in their minds about the need for such behavior. Nor did those early champions of the public school foresee the age of propaganda, the rise of mass media, and the intensity of the struggle for the mind of man. Yet the objective they had for public education still stands, even though its achievement has been beset with new difficulties.

What do we mean by critical thinking? We mean simply the ability to define a problem, to seek the relevant facts having to do with it, to weigh the evidence, and to make decisions based upon the evidence.

---

[21] Quoted in Ellwood P. Cubberley, *Readings in Public Education in the United States* (Boston: Houghton Mifflin, 1934), 192.

In short, we are talking of problem-solving or the scientific method. Literacy, as we have discussed it above, is a necessary tool to most problem-solving, but literacy alone is not enough. Also necessary are the ability to suspend judgment until the evidence is in, and the ability to analyze the evidence so as to detect when personal bias or privileged position has obscured, slanted, or selected the facts. There is, finally, the courage to accept the position supported by the evidence even in face of preconceived notions.

This is a big order. The capacity of people to learn critical thinking, even with the best of tutelage, varies just as it does with other kinds of learning. The public school must provide opportunity and encouragement for such learning. We have already indicated that the public school can be the most objective institution in our society. Such objectivity must be exploited by teachers if children are to learn critical thinking.

Perhaps Thelen has given us a cue as to how critical thinking is to be fostered when he says:

> . . . inquiry involves firsthand activity in real situations. In most cases, the inquiring student is aided by working close to some adult with whom he can identify—some adult he would like to be like, perhaps, but at the least an adult he can easily trust. This adult must be without ulterior motives in dealing with the students. He has a job to do; he helps define the role of the student on the job, and the demands the student has to meet come either from the nature of the task or from the nature of the social conditions obviously required to get the work done. In other words, I want the student to transact his business directly with the work and the work environment; I want him to discover that there are realities outside of his own personal desire or those of "authorities," for it is only within such a stable framework of action that his own behavior can be assessed unequivocally by himself. It is only thus that he can discover and learn to depend on his abilities and that he can face up to weaknesses, because they cannot be blamed on other persons.[22]

The White House Conference on Education in 1956 highlighted the third unique task we shall suggest for the public school, the facilitation of social mobility. A part of the Report reads:

> The schools have become a major tool for creating a Nation without rigid class barriers. *It is primarily the schools which allow no man's failure to prevent the success of his son.* [italics in original][23]

[22] Herbert A. Thelen, *Education and the Human Quest* (New York: Harper & Brothers, 1960), p. 107.

[23] The Committee for the White House Conference on Education, *A Report to the President* (Washington: U.S. Government Printing Office, 1956), p. 9.

To be sure, other institutions in our society contribute to social mobility. For some the ladder is supplied by business, for others by the military, and for others by the church. But the schools seem to be the chief agency in society that can and should accept as one of its prime tasks the providing of opportunity for the upward (or downward) mobility of its students. Again, the relative inclusiveness of public school enrollments is a pertinent matter. For most of our people the public school can discover and encourage ability. When the school accepts this as one of its major functions, those who live "across the tracks" have an opportunity to rise in the world.

To suggest that the school should contribute to social mobility opens up a larger question. While we believe that the primary purpose of the school is educative in nature, the school is also an instrument of social policy. Havighurst[24] maintained that the program of the school was the most powerful factor contributing to the decision of middle-income people to live in the central city or the suburbs, or to live in one section of the city or another. In a very real sense one can say that as go the schools so goes the city. Boards of education and school workers fail, at times, to recognize the social import of their decisions; indeed, they occasionally rebel at the social role they are required to play. We see no alternative. Education has become a powerful social factor and those who are charged with its governance cannot escape their social role.

This whole matter of the need for social mobility and the part the public school might play in such a process takes on a new urgency in a technological society. In practically every skilled and professional occupation the shortage of workers is serious. Overall, the only source of supply to meet this deficit is to be found in the unskilled workers and the children of unskilled workers. If these children are to enter new jobs and acquire new social status, they must have more schooling. For most people the extent of upward mobility in a single generation is probably limited, but the need for such mobility and the role of the school in the process should be clear.

To summarize, if the public school is to fulfill its unique role in the educative process necessary to our way of life, it must teach literacy, stimulate critical thinking, and provide opportunity for those with ability to rise occupationally and socially. We need to recognize that as the school performs these functions it also serves as a powerful instrument of social policy.

---

[24] Robert J. Havighurst, *The Public Schools of Chicago* (Chicago: Board of Education, 1964), p. 28.

ADMINISTRATIVE LEADERSHIP

The fourth challenge that we see, perhaps the pivotal one as far as this book is concerned, is the challenge confronting administrative leaders in the public schools. Or, to put it differently, an indispensable condition necessary for the public school to perform adequately its unique role is the type of administrative leadership we shall now describe. When we speak of administrative leaders, we refer to appointed or official leaders in the school system, such as principals, supervisors, directors, and superintendents. It is the challenge confronting them as official or status leaders with which we are concerned.

We do not wish to minimize the roles played by classroom teachers as the public schools attempt to meet their obligations. Teaching and learning go on only through the teachers. At the same time, teachers and researchers alike have repeatedly indicated that a good part of what any school does is dependent upon the administrative leadership given to that school. The principal, for instance, has a key role in setting the tone, establishing the conditions, and providing stimulation for the kind of living and learning in his school. It is the challenge inherent in such a role that we wish to discuss here.

As suggested in Chapter 8, each administrator finds himself related to certain major reference groups. In each of these relationships there is a challenge to administrative leadership. We shall, therefore, examine the nature of that challenge with respect to the community, the board of education, the teaching staff, and the pupils.

THE COMMUNITY CHALLENGE

Since we are speaking of administration in the public schools, obviously the public or the community is a major reference group with which any school administrator must work. Most people see this clearly as it applies to the superintendent of schools. For the school principal, however, such recognition is not as general. As a matter of fact, some of the studies suggest that principals have almost no relationships with the citizens of their respective attendance areas or school communities.[25] This condition seems most undesirable to us. We think

---

[25] For example see Odean L. Hess, "Critical Areas of Administrative Behavior of Elementary School Principals" (Unpublished doctoral dissertation, The Ohio State University, 1955).

every superintendent and every principal in the public schools must deal extensively with the public. While supervisors and directors may deal somewhat less with the public, we are convinced that they, too, must be involved in some public relationships.

The public, as we indicated in Chapter 8, is not monolithic in nature. Actually, there are many publics. The school administrator may stand alone among other administrators in the great number of publics to whom he feels responsible. Moreover, let us point out that these publics are more than local in nature. Often decisions affecting local school districts are made at county, state, and national levels. This very condition suggests one aspect of the challenge. It is necessary that the administrator ascertain for his school or school district who these publics are and how they believe and act with respect to school matters.

Thus it is necessary that communication with the many publics of a school community be a two-way process. The old business of selling, or telling, or interpreting the schools just will not suffice. Just as the problems, the achievements, and the shortcomings of the public schools must be explained, the feelings, the beliefs, and the aspirations of the people who make up the various publics must also be ascertained. There is, then, the need for listening as well as telling; the need for assessment as well as projection. Hearing what people say in our pluralistic society is no simple task. There are many conflicting voices particularly in our large urban centers. Moreover, some of the voices once submerged are now loud and vociferous. Blacks and other minorities are insisting upon participation in educational matters whether they be related to the curriculum or to the organization and control of the schools. In many places these new demands are caught up in the term "community control."

The real challenge to the administrative leader in dealing with the many publics of the school community comes in what he does with the feelings, beliefs, and aspirations of the people. Ordinarily, he cannot accept these data alone as providing the basis for charting courses of action, any more than he can impose his own professional values on a community without consideration of the factors existing in the particular situation. In other words, the administrator finds out what people think, what they value, and what they want in order to determine where to begin or to determine what are the reasonable limits beyond which action cannot go.

The excitement comes in finding and helping arrange ways by which people get new ideas, gradually come to accept new values, and come to have more realistic expectations of the public school. Or it may be that in the diversity of ideas and aspirations among the publics of a school community, ways can be found by which a greater degree of agreement can be reached so that the course of school operation can go forward at a higher level.

We are not suggesting that the administrator can be all-wise in this situation, nor that his task is simply one of ingenious manipulation. Actually, the administrator may be no wiser than other leaders in his school community. He would do well to relate himself to people in such a way that he might learn from them as well as influence them. We do suggest, however, that the administrator needs professional knowledge, and values that include a conviction that the democratic way of life is important and that the public school has a significant role to play in the realization of that way of life. With that as his prime motivation, he can keep a focus without offending by insisting upon patterned behavior.

In the end the community must take action for public education. This may involve the selection of wise school board members, the passing of bond issues, and the approval of operating levies. Important and necessary as these separate acts are, the continuous voice of the community as it gives expression to what schools ought to be, and as it reacts both favorably and unfavorably to what schools are, may be even more indicative as to how well the community challenge is being met.

THE BOARD CHALLENGE

Public schools in America are controlled through legally constituted boards of education. These boards have been given broad grants of power by the respective state legislatures. In most states the board members are publicly elected to their offices, and while they are assumed to be representative of the people of the school district, the courts have actually declared them to be state officers.

School board members are usually selected from the professional and managerial groups of society, though in rural areas they are often farm owners. This fact has caused some to conclude that boards would be strong defenders of the status quo. Studies of board performance indicate that that interpretation is too simple an explanation and in many cases not warranted. Actually, most board members are seriously concerned with their responsibility and welcome professional help in interpreting and implementing this responsibility.

Clearly, the board of education is the major reference group with which the superintendent must deal. In most school districts the superintendent of schools, as the chief school administrator, will be most directly concerned with the board of education. On occasions, however, superintendents will ordinarily involve other administrators in the board relationship, and board opinions, board action, and board policies are always significant to administrators.

The superintendent of schools has two major roles to play if he is to meet the challenge of working with the board of education. First, he is the chief executive of the board. This may involve helping a board decide what its legislative and judicial functions are, and what the executive functions of the superintendent are. Even after such definition there may be the continuing necessity of clarifying the board-superintendent relationship. This clarification may be even more necessary as new members come on the board.

Assuming that reasonable agreement concerning the board-superintendent relationship can be reached, the superintendent still has the challenge of the executive function. Can he and his staff develop an adequate instructional program? Can he and his staff secure competent personnel? Can he and his staff develop a satisfactory building program? Can he and his staff project accurately the financial needs of the district? Can he and his staff expend efficiently the available funds, and account accurately for them? These represent some of the major expectations most boards of education hold for their superintendents.

In addition to being the chief executive officer of the board of education, the superintendent has a second role as chief educational adviser to the board. In this role the superintendent helps the board form basic policy for school district operation. It is in this role that he brings professional knowledge to board deliberation, and that he broadens the understanding of board members so that they function with greater intelligence as the chief policy-makers for a school district. Allison,[26] as noted earlier, found that most board members not only expect their superintendents to implement board decisions, they also rely heavily on them to help in establishing policy.

For the superintendent to serve as chief educational adviser to the board, certain conditions are necessary. As in the case of the

---

[26] Howard C. Allison, "Professional and Lay Influences on School Board Decision-Making" (Unpublished doctoral dissertation, Department of Education, University of Chicago, 1965).

community, the superintendent must bring to his task professional understanding and convictions. Moreover, he will find it necessary to work closely with his staff so as to reflect the best possible insights to the board of education at a particular time and place. Meeting these conditions may help the superintendent become, in a very real sense, the teacher of the board of education. In few places is teaching a more critical occupation.

THE STAFF CHALLENGE

Another major reference group for any school administrator is the school staff. We use the word "staff," at this point, to designate all certificated personnel within a school system, including teachers, pupil personnel workers, and administrators. Much of what we shall say about the certificated personnel also applies, of course, to the non-certificated personnel of a school system. The staff represents another challenge to administrative leadership, the nature of which we need to examine.

The first challenge is that of building and maintaining a staff that is thoroughly equipped to do the job of the public schools. If the district is a sizable one, there must be a staff for the central office. For any school district there is the problem of building the staff for each school building, whether there is one or a hundred. These circumstances make it clear that building a staff is the obligation of the chief administrator assisted by his entire administrative staff, including each of the building principals.

There are also other aspects to the staff challenge. While the overall shortage of teachers characteristic of recent decades seems to be at an end, there remains a shortage in certain fields and for certain types of schools. The appropriate involvement of staff members already in a school or school system in the selection of new staff members is also a part of the challenge being suggested here. For instance, some superintendents have not yet learned how to use their building principals in getting teachers well suited for the positions that are open.

There is also the challenge of evaluating the work of staff members. Ascertaining the competence of teachers or administrators is a very difficult matter. Establishing criteria of competence is essentially a valuing procedure and may vary from district to district. The collection of evidence on teaching or administrative performance is difficult when criteria are clear and practically useless when criteria are nonexistent or confusing. Thus, it is understandable that superintendents and principals are, at times, a little hazy on the matter, and no wonder at all that the problem is even more dimly perceived by the lay mind. Despite these difficulties, there are ways of checking the performance of any prospective teacher and administrator in order to get at least a rough measure of how well he fits the job description. By employing these ways and keeping a record of his batting average, any practicing administrator can increase his power of discrimination regarding personnel selection.

May we emphasize the critical nature of each staff selection! The school system may actually work years with a relatively incompetent teacher in order to help him reach a better level of performance. A better selection in the first place would have saved hundreds of hours of effort on the part of the principal and the supervisors. Or the selection of an inadequate principal may mean that for years the program and atmosphere of an entire building, often with hundreds of youngsters involved, may be seriously handicapped. To secure for each position the most competent available person is a continuing challenge to administrative leadership.

Assuming the administrators of a school system have been able to build a competent staff, there is still the challenge of keeping the staff productive. In too many school systems one can find teachers and even administrators and supervisory personnel who, once vigorous, stimulating, and effective people, have now settled into a dull routine of doing what has to be done but with no zest for the task as it now exists or as it might be altered. The factors contributing to such a situation are undoubtedly complex. They may include low salaries, which force many teachers to take a second job and thus become part-time teachers. They may include a seeming lack of opportunities for promotion, particularly within the teaching ranks. But we suspect that other factors of importance lie within the control of administrators and thus constitute a part of the challenge to their leadership.

As further challenge to administrators, teachers and other staff members have become increasingly militant in recent years. Teachers' organizations, whether union or association, are no longer willing to be treated paternalistically by the superintendent or the board of education, no matter how benevolent such action might be. More and more, school managers are faced with annual negotiating sessions with teachers in which the procedures developed in private industry are being adapted to the school situation.

At least a partial understanding of this situation may be found in some of the studies on administrative behavior. Halpin found that staff members preferred their superintendents to be strong both in consideration and in the initiating of structure in group interaction.[27] Research clearly supports the concept that organizations have both a normative and a personal dimension, and that both of these must be taken into account to explain organization behavior.[28] In fact, no proposition in administration has been as well documented as the one that effective administrators perform above the mean in *two* major areas of behavior. The first is consideration or adequate human relations. The second is the initiation of structure or the development of understanding concerning roles and responsibilities of people within an organization.

The evidence suggests clearly that it is not enough for an administrator to be concerned with human relations only. Personal concern on the part of the administrator for each member of his staff is necessary and appropriate. In addition, the administrator must be able to help a staff develop goals and a plan of action, he must be able to help each staff member see where he can make his particular contribution to the total effort, and he must stimulate each staff member to make his contribution the best of which he is capable. Thus, with staff as with the board of education, the administrator is required to become a teacher of high order.

THE PUPIL CHALLENGE

Another major reference group with which administrators must deal is composed of the pupils—the children and youth who are enrolled in school. In a sense all challenges to administrative leadership have their focus here, because the pupils are the immediate consumers of the school program. School–community agreements, school board action, and staff efforts culminate in what happens to youngsters. These more remote and instrumental programs, no matter how pretty they appear on paper, are of no avail unless they make a difference in the programs of instruction and services to pupils. This is the whole purpose of educational administration, as was suggested in Chapter 4.

Of all administrators and supervisors within a school system, the building principal is nearest to the teaching–learning situation. His

[27] Andrew W. Halpin, *The Leadership Behavior of School Superintendents,* 2nd ed. (Chicago: Midwest Administration Center, University of Chicago, 1959).

[28] Jacob W. Getzels, James M. Lipham, and Roald F. Campbell, *Educational Administration as a Social Process* (New York: Harper & Row, 1968).

influence in that situation is a strategic one. As a matter of fact, what central office people can do to influence instruction must, for the most part, be expressed through the building principal. In better schools the principal, more than any other person, can see that teacher assignments are appropriate, that necessary pupil personnel services are made available, and that extra-class activities are made significant experiences for youngsters.

The principals of most school buildings will wish some direct contact with pupils, but research is tending to suggest that there are appropriate limitations to such activity. Effective principals recognize that their chief work group is the faculty and that most of their influence with pupils will be expressed through the faculty and through the programs of the school.

In working with his staff to build and to implement a school program the principal must recognize three aspects of such a program: the classroom instruction, the pupil personnel services, and the extra-class activities. There is always the question of how each of these parts should fit into the total offering. Continually, there is the need to keep classroom instruction stimulating and challenging. Often with the extra-class activities, particularly at the secondary level, there is the problem of keeping them educative and not exploitative or simply commercial. With respect to pupil services, there is the need of providing those services, whether in health, guidance, or some other area, which will contribute to the total development of each youngster or permit his learning to go on more effectively. Trying to provide the best possible program for each pupil enrolled is the tremendous challenge to public education. As the principal deals with instruction, with services, and with extra-class activities, he, like other school workers, needs to be aware of the social role the school is playing.

As noted earlier, increasing numbers of students today are showing signs of alienation in our high schools as well as on our college campuses. This development, plus a more general and widespread sense of discontentment among youth regarding the nature and relevance of conventional high school education, constitutes a very serious and important new dimension to the pupil challenge. Students today are not reluctant to tell us when they believe we have not achieved the goals we discussed in the foregoing paragraph. Indeed, a growing number of young people are contending that the social climate of most high schools today is impersonal, dehumanizing, and authoritarian and that the educational programs are sterile, irrelevant, and deadening. Some critics also add that the social role of the schools in fact seems to be to produce unreflective passive consumers who fit narrow slots in a mechanistic and exploitive society. Moreover, students today not infrequently back up or accompany their complaints or "demands" with strikes or other kinds of protests. The great challenge for administrators here is to try to create open and responsive communication channels among students, themselves, and the faculty and also vehicles for the collective reformation of those aspects of the social climate or educational programs which, upon examination, prove to be in need of change.[29]

A FINAL WORD

We began this chapter by presenting challenges to educational administration. We said that our first challenge, the democratic way of life, is dependent upon an educative process open to all, in which the contributions of many agencies are recognized. While we noted that the educative process is much broader than that provided by the public schools, we maintained that the public schools of this nation perform a role that is an indispensable part of that process. Finally, we took the position that the public schools cannot perform adequately except as administrative leaders in those schools give appropriate direction to the enterprise.

Now let us reverse the process. If the administrative leaders of the public schools of this nation can visualize the crucial place of the public schools, and if they can bring adequate understanding and skill to their task, the public schools can contribute substantially to the development of the people's capacity to do critical thinking. People with such capacity can, and we think will, take steps to preserve that which should be preserved in our culture and to change that which needs to be improved. These people will function through numerous community agencies, and thus the programs of those agencies will reinforce and complement the efforts of the public schools. This effort will perpetuate and extend the democratic way of life. To the educational administrator is given the privilege of participating significantly in this whole endeavor.

[29] For a succinct analysis and set of proposals on this topic, see Edwin M. Bridges, "Student Unrest and Crisis Decision-Making," *Administrator's Notebook,* **XVIII,** 4, December, 1969.

Index